NOTIONS OF THE AMERICANS

NOTIONS
OF THE AMERICANS

Picked Up by a Travelling Bachelor

James Fenimore
COOPER

Volume II

Introduction By
ROBERT E. SPILLER

FREDERICK UNGAR PUBLISHING CO.
NEW YORK

CONTENTS *

Volume II

**Letter numbers and titles have been
supplied by the Editor*

LETTERS,

&c. &c.

TO THE COUNT JULES DE BETHIZY,

COLONEL EN RETRAITE OF THE IMPERIAL GUARD.

Washington, ——

I WRITE you from the little capital of this great republic. After lingering at Baltimore until reasons for all further delay were exhausted, we reluctantly turned our faces westward. Cadwallader had pointed out to me sundry busy-looking travellers, who were strolling through the streets of the town, with more gravity of mien (assumed or natural) than is common to meet in a city, and whispered in my ears that they were members of Congress, on their way to the seat of government. This was a hint not to be disregarded. Tearing ourselves from the attraction of bright eyes and soft voices, we gallantly entered a coach, and broke the chain of attraction which, like the fabled magnet of Mahomet's coffin, had so long kept me suspended between heaven and earth. Heigho! dear Jules, I confess to twenty-four hours, when a treacherous intention of resigning, to some less inexorable successor, the stall which I so unworthily fill in our self-denying chapter, was insidiously floating before my imagination. But a resolution which has borne me through so many similar dangers in triumph, (aided by the members of Congress), was victorious. By-the-bye, I am grieved to the heart to hear of the sad accident that has befallen the professor, and most sincerely do I pray that the time may be long averted when it shall become necessary to supply a vacancy in our numbers, from a cause so fatal as a marriage. The grave might be wept over, and time would soften grief for the death of even a bosom friend, but what could time do towards mitigating a penance performed at the *confessional* of Hymen? The more sincere, and the more frequent the acknowledgments, the more keen and helpless would the bitterness of a spirit so thoroughly bruised become. If you pass through the queen of cities this winter, order a new cushion to my chair; I intend that the sittings of 1827 shall wear well into the mornings!

The road between Baltimore and Washington is neither particularly bad nor particularly good.* It passes through a comparatively barren, and a little inhabited country. It was here that I first observed the great difference between the aspect of the slave-holding and the non-slave-holding States. In Pennsylvania, at the distance of sixty miles north of our present route, we should have seen a landscape, over

---

* It may be well to state, once for all, the following facts concerning the American roads. In all the northern and eastern States, for nine months in the year, they are, as a rule, tolerably good in those parts of the country where the establishments are old enough to admit of it. In the spring, and in the autumn, there are periods when most of the roads are bad. There are many roads, however, as good as the ordinary turnpike roads of England, and which vary very little in quality throughout the year. A traveller in an American stage-coach cannot well compare the roads of the United States with those of England, for the coaches of the former are not suspended on springs, though the seats are sometimes supplied with them. As one quits the older parts of the country, the roads gradually grow worse, until, in the very newest settlements, they are often no more than trees that are marked, or *blazed*, to indicate the courses of the route.

which farm-houses, barns, and all the ordinary objects of a prosperous husbandry, were profusely sprinkled, while here the houses began to be distant from each other, or were grouped in little clusters apart from the highways. This portion of America bears a greater resemblance to continental Europe, than the States we have quitted. The dwelling of the planter is the château; and the huts of the slaves form the contiguous village. A difference in the moral condition of the ages in which the two have been constructed, has induced some very sensible alterations in the plans of the buildings; but, still the outline is the same.

I was surprised at the sterility and nakedness of the country through which we journeyed, though I was given to understand that a great deal of the State of Maryland is land of the richest quality. There were one or two small villages on the route, but which, after those we had seen further north, wore a miserable air. I am not certain, however, that they are not quite as good in every particular as the ordinary villages of Europe. Here I first saw fields for the tobacco plant. It grows in hills, not unlike the maize, and is rarely, or never, fenced, no animal but man having a relish for the unsavoury weed.

At the distance of six or seven miles from Washington, we stopped at the village of Bladensburgh, a place notorious for two circumstances. It lies just without the territory of the district of Columbia, and is the spot usually chosen for the decision of private combats ; and it is the place where the affair between the English and the Americans was fought a few hours before the former entered the city.

I confess I had thought it surprising that so small a force (about 5000 men) could have taken possession of the capital of so powerful a nation ; but a nearer view has entirely dissipated the wonder. It was a point where the Americans, having nothing of military importance to defend, had assembled no force, and there is not probably on the whole line of their coast, a more deserted and tenantless region than the country traversed by the invaders. The troops rallied to resist the English, as their intention became known, were merely the citizens of the adjoining country, who assembled in a very imperfect state of preparation, and who were very little, if at all, superior in numbers to their antagonists. They had not even the ordinary inducements to risk their lives against those of hireling troops; for, even to this hour, it is difficult to find what object General Ross could have had in hazarding his army in an expedition that might have been attended with destruction. A man like Jackson to oppose him would have insured it.

I alighted at Bladensburgh, and, accompanied by my friend, walked in advance of the carriage over the ground, attended by a sufficiently intelligent man who had witnessed the whole affair. As it is a little in your way, the details I gleaned shall be rendered as an offering to your military *goût*. Should they fail of the interest which has so often been thrown over the entrances of Moscow and Paris, you know how to make allowances for an inferiority in dramatic effect, which is no more than a natural consequence of the difference between the conquest of a city of half a million of inhabitants, and of a town of eight or nine thousand.

The country around Bladensburgh is gently undulating and moderately wooded. A small stream lies near the village, and between it and the capital. It is crossed by a wooden bridge. So much hurry and indecision appear to have existed among the defenders, that even this bridge was not destroyed, though it might have been rendered impassable in ten minutes. It would seem, however, that many of their troops, such as they were, only reached the ground at the critical moment when they were wanted in

the combat. The dispositions for resistance were made along the crest of a gentle acclivity, at the distance of rather more than a mile from this bridge. The centre of their position was on the highway, and its defence was intrusted to a few seamen and two or three hundred marines, the only disciplined forces on the ground. A few light troops (all militia) were pushed in front to the banks of the stream, and two pieces of artillery were placed at a point to command the passage of the bridge. There was a little skirmishing here; and it seems, by the English accounts, that they suffered severely from the artillery in crossing the bridge. The ground in front of the seamen and marines was a gentle acclivity, and perfectly open. Here there was some sharp fighting. The British columns were obliged to open, and General Ross began to manœuvre. But the militia did not wait to be turned, for they retired to a man (the skirmishers excepted), without firing a gun. The seamen and marines stood well, and were necessarily brought off to prevent capture. The artillery was all, or nearly all, taken. This is, in substance, what is called the Battle of Bladensburgh. The American loss was trifling, less than two hundred, and that of the English perhaps three or four hundred.

It is easy to criticise the disposition of the American commander. This gentleman was an able lawyer of the adjoining State of Maryland, who had listened to the whisperings of that uneasy ambition which sometimes makes men heroes. He had quitted the gown for the sword a short time before, and probably knew as little about his new profession as you know of the one he had deserted. Lawyer or not, had this gentleman placed his fellow-citizens (for soldiers they cannot be called) in and about the Capitol, and had they only fought as well as they did, he taking care not to give them any particularly favourable opportunity of dispersing, I think General Ross would have been spared the very equivocal glory of burning all that then existed of that edifice; viz. the two wings. He listened to other counsels.

As we approached the capital, we saw before us an extent of open country that did not appear to be used for any agricultural purposes. It lay, without fences, neglected, and waste. This appearance is common just here, and is owing to the circumstance that tobacco exhausts the soil so much, that, in a country where land and its products are still so cheap, it is not worth the cost of restoring it. We soon got a view of the dome of the Capitol, and the whole of the facade of that noble edifice came into view, as we mounted a slight eminence which had partly concealed it. As my eye first wandered eagerly around, at this point, to gather together the scattered particles of the city, I will take the present occasion to convey a general impression of its appearance.

The seat of government was removed from Philadelphia to this place, in order that it might be more central. So far as a line drawn north and south is in question, this object is sufficiently answered. But Washington stands so very far east of a central meridian as to render it probable that other considerations influenced the change. I have never heard it so said, but nothing is more probable than that the slave-holding States required some such concession to their physical inferiority. At all events, every body appears perfectly satisfied with the present position of the capital. Perhaps, notwithstanding the difference on the map, the place is practically nearer the centre than if it stood farther west. The member from Alabama, or Louisiana, or Missouri, arrives by sea, or by means of the great rivers of the west, with about the same expense of money and of labour as the member from Vermont, Maine, or New-Hampshire. Some one must always have the benefit of being nearest the political centre, and it is of no

great moment whether he be a Virginian or an Ohiese. As the capital is now placed, it is more convenient for quick communication with Europe than if farther inland, and it is certainly nearer the centre of interests where it stands, than it would be in almost any other spot in the confederation.

Had the plan of the city been as well conceived as its locality, there would be less ground of complaint. The perspective of American character was certainly exhibited to great advantage in the conceptions of the individual who laid out the site of this town. It is scarcely possible to imagine a more unfortunate theory than the one he assumed for the occasion. He appears to have egregiously mistaken the relative connexion between streets and houses, since it is fair to infer he would not have been so lavish of the one without the aid of the other, did he not believe the latter to be made use of as accessories to the former, instead of the reverse, as is every where else found to be the case. And, yet I think, both nature and art had united to point out the true plan for this city, as I shall endeavour to convince you without delay.

The ground occupied by the city of Washington, may be described as forming a tolerably regular triangle. Two of its sides are washed by the two branches of the Potomac, which diverge towards the north-east and north-west, while on its third, there are no limits to its extent, the land being a somewhat gentle acclivity, gradual on the whole, though undulating, and often broken in its minute parts. The river below the point is a noble stream, stretching for many miles to the southward, in full view of the town. Both of its branches are navigable for near a league. At the distance of about two miles from the point, the main river (west branch), which had hitherto washed a champaign country, enters a range of low mountains, and makes a still more decided inclination to the west. Here is the head of tide and of navigation. The latter circumstance had early pointed out the place for the site of a town, and accordingly a little city grew on the spot, whence tobacco and lumber were shipped for other ports, long before the neighbourhood was thought of, as the capital of a great nation. This place is called Georgetown. It is rather well built than otherwise, and the heights, in its rear, for it lies against an acclivity, are not only beautiful in themselves, but they are occupied by many pretty villas. It contains in itself, perhaps 9000 inhabitants. It has a college and five churches, two of which are Episcopal.

Georgetown is divided, from what is termed Washington City, by a rapid little stream called Rock Creek.* The land, for a considerable distance after the creek is crossed, is well adapted for a town. It is sufficiently unequal to carry off the water, and yet sufficiently level for convenient streets. Here is the spot, I think, where the buildings should have been collected for the new city. But at the distance of about a mile and a quarter from the bridge, a vast square is laid out. On one of its sides is the President's House,† flanked by the public offices. A few houses and a church are on two more of its sides, though the one opposite to the 'White House' is as yet entirely naked. From this square, sundry great avenues diverge, as do others from another centre, distant a mile and a half still further east. The latter square is adorned by the Capitol. Across all

---

* The Americans often call a small river a creek, and brooks of a large size are oftener called creeks than any thing else. Schoharie Creek is as large as the Seine, at Paris. It is, to all intents, a rapid river; but the size of many of their rivers is so great as to produce a sort of impression that the smaller streams should be of a different class.

† The Americans familiarly call the exceedingly pretty little palace in which their chief magistrate resides, the " White House," but the true appellation is the President's House.

these avenues, which are parallel to nothing, there is a sort of net-work of streets, running at right angles with each other. Such is Washington on the map.

In point of fact, but few of the avenues or streets are opened, and fewer still are built on. There is one of the former running from the bridge at George-town to the first square, and another leads from the President's House to the capitol. There are two or three more which connect important points, though only the two named are sufficiently built on to have the least of the character of a town. There are rather more streets open, though not one of them all is absolutely built up from one end to the other.

In consequence of the gigantic scale on which Washington is planned, and the different interests which influence the population, its inhabitants (including Georgetown) are separated into four distinct little towns, distant from each other about a mile. Thus we have Georgetown in the west, containing 9000 souls; the town immediately around the President's House, (extending towards the Capitol,) with perhaps 10,000; that around the Capitol, of some two or three thousand souls; and the buildings at the Navy-Yard, which lies on the east branch, still a mile further. The whole *city*,* including its three divisions, with here and there a few scattered buildings, may now contain about 16,000 souls.

When the people of the United States determined to have a more central capital, it was thought best to give the general government absolute jurisdiction over it. In order to effect this object, it was necessary to extinguish the State rights. This was done

---

* Georgetown, it will be remembered, is not properly a part of the *city* of Washington, though in the district of Columbia; but, in point of fact, it is as nigh the President's House, as is the Capitol. There is also a little group of houses at the junction of the two branches of the Potomac.

by Virginia and Maryland ceding sufficient territory to make a district of ten miles square at the point I have described. In this little territory the President exercises the authority which a governor commonly exercises in a State, or rather, there is no intermediate or concurrent executive authority between him and the people, as in the several States; and Congress, though in fact elected by the citizens of the States, does all the legislation. Thus the inhabitants of this territory have no representation whatever; neither voting for members of Congress, nor for members of any State legislature. But their voices are often heard in the way of petitions and demands. It is probable that when they shall become as numerous as the smallest State, they will receive the right of electing representatives.*

---

* The writer will take this opportunity of introducing a short account of the formation of the government of the United States, since it will assist to explain a good deal of that which is to follow.

The executive power is in the *President*. He nominates to office; pardons all offences, except convictions under impeachments; conducts negotiations; sees that the laws are administered, and is the military chief of the army and navy, subject to the laws. He makes treaties with the consent of the Senate, and gives his assent to all laws, though a law can be passed without him, if two-thirds of both houses vote in its favour. The *Senate* is the representation of the sovereignty of the States, each State sending two members, who are chosen by their respective legislatures. They serve for six years, one-third vacating their seats every new Congress. They have a concurrent power with the lower house in enacting laws; they ratify treaties; they approve of nominations to office, and they constitute a High Court of Impeachment. The *Representatives* are elected directly by the people, one member being sent from a regulated number of electors. They serve for one Congress, which exists two years, commencing on the 4th of March of one year, and ending on the 3d of March of the year but one that follows. The official term of the President is for two of these Congresses, and that of a Senator for three. The Representatives, or members of the lower house, have concurrent power in the enactment of the laws, and being the grand inquest of the nation, they can impeach any officer of the government.

I think you must be enabled to understand the anomaly of the district of Columbia. It has been necessarily fostered by the nation, for as it has been entirely called into existence, as a separate commu-

---

Every citizen of the United States, who is twenty-one years of age, and who possesses certain trifling qualifications, can vote for a member of the House of Representatives, provided he himself be a resident of a State. The *confederation* is only of the *States;* but there are vast regions belonging to them as common property, which do not lie within the boundaries of any State. This country is subdivided for the purposes of convenience, and is governed entirely by the authority of the President and Congress, or according to laws enacted for that purpose. With the exception of one (the *District of Columbia*) they are called *territories.* Thus, besides the twenty-four States, there are the North-western, Michigan, Arkansas, and Florida territories. Certain legislative rights are granted to all the territories that have a sufficient population, but none is yet granted to the *District of Columbia.* Some of the territories even send *delegates* to Congress. These *delegates* can speak, but they cannot vote. As the territories reach an established rate of population, they are uniformly admitted into the confederation, as *States.* It is probable that Michigan, Florida, and Arkansas will be admitted as *States* soon after the next census, after which a long period will be likely to elapse without any farther increase of the number of the *States.* The great difficulty in making a foreigner comprehend the institutions of the United States, exists in the double form of its government. Neither the President, nor Congress, nor both, have authority to interfere with government beyond the power which has been conceded to them by the States. They can make war, raise armies, lay taxes, send fleets to sea, and do many other things, but they cannot punish a theft, unless committed on the high seas, to which their jurisdiction of course extends, or in some other place where they have the exclusive or a concurrent power. Thus, the President of the United States, may pardon a man convicted of robbing the United States' mail, though the act should have been done in the most crowded street of the city of New-York, because the regulation of the mail, being a matter of public convenience, is vested in the government of the confederation, with all power necessary to its safety and despatch; but, if the same coach should be robbed in a forest, and it did not contain a mail, or something else over which the United States have jurisdiction, the robber would be punished by the laws of the State where the offence was committed. In order that these laws may be executed, each government has its own agents. Thus, there are judges of the State courts, and judges of the courts of the United States. The former have jurisdiction in cases that are strictly municipal, or rather which

nity, for their use, it owes most of all it possesses to the public grants and to the presence of the ministers of the government. With a view to *force a town*, establishments have been formed which will probably linger in a doubtful state of existence for a long time to come, if, indeed, they ever prosper. Among others is that of the Navy-Yard.

The village around the Navy-Yard is the least important of the three which properly constitute the community assembled at Washington Proper. You will remember that I now exclude Georgetown from this enumeration. It possesses a different city government, though it is, in point of fact, quite as near the centre, or the President's House, as the Capitol. Alexandria, a little city, also, of about 9000 inhabit-

---

are confined to their respective States, and the latter in cases which arise under the laws of the United States, or in cases in which the citizens of *different* States are parties. This latter power of the courts of the general government is one of the most important features of the confederation. It has a tendency to equalize the State laws, by rendering them all subject to the great principles of the constitution, as well as to those of natural justice. It will be seen at once, that this confederation differs from all that we have hitherto known by the complicated nature of the action and re-action between the people and their general government. It is much the same, in fact, as if charters were given to certain towns, in a constitutional government, whether monarchical or not, under favour of which the inhabitants of those towns were authorized to enact certain laws for their own private convenience, while they continued subject at the same time to the general laws of the empire. The theory is certainly different; for here the power which belongs to the general government, is a concession from the particular States, whereas, in the other case, the power exercised by the corporations would be a concession from the principal government. Still the cases bear so strong a resemblance, that one can readily understand the nature of the two authorities which exist in this country. But we in Europe, while we are accustomed to see cities and universities, and even parts of empires, exercising this species of divided sovereignty, have not been accustomed to see them exercising it to the extent that is practised in America. The difference arises from the common circumstance, that the conceding party has, in both cases, seen fit to retain the most of the power in its own hands.

ants, is equally within the limits of the District, but it lies on the opposite side of the Potomac, and at a distance of six miles. There are not many good houses in the quarter of the Navy-Yard, and I should think that a great portion of its inhabitants are people dependent on the establishment for support. Notwithstanding there is a long river to navigate before a ship can get into the bays below, a very considerable number of the public vessels are built and repaired at this spot. Seamen, there are none at Washington, for the simple reason that there is no commerce. A few ships are, indeed, seen at the wharfs of Georgetown and Alexandria, but the navigation of the two places united is far less than that of most of the fourth-rate commercial towns of the Union.

As the department of the navy, and the board of naval commissioners, are both established at Washington, this yard may be of some service in the way of modelling, and for the superintendence of inventions. A ship built here is said to cost more than one built in any of the more northern ports, and it is therefore plain, that when the size of their marine shall compel the Americans to observe a rigid economy in its construction, the relative importance of this yard must cease. It may long continue a school for experiments, but it can never become what was once anticipated for it, a large and flourishing building establishment.

I saw, in the Navy-Yard at Washington, the only public monument in commemoration of the dead that I could find in the city, unless a few simple stones, erected around the graves of members of Congress, who have died while here in the discharge of their official duties, can be so termed. This little monument was erected to commemorate the deaths of the officers who fell in the war with Tripoli; a war to which the United States' marine owes its present high and merited character. It is a simple column, wrought in Italy at the expense of the survivors, and erected on this spot under the impulse of that stubborn feeling of independence which distinguishes this people.   The high-spirited contributors to the little work, thought the Congress did not pay a suitable respect to their petition for a site in a more public situation.   They were masters of the Navy-Yard, and in disgust they caused their modest memorial to be put up in the centre of its area.   It may be doubted, after all, if any other situation so appropriate, or so touching, could have been found.   This monument has received some injury, by having one or two of its ornamental figures broken.   On one of its sides I read the following inscription : "Mutilated by Britons, August, 1814."   This was the date of the inroad of the English.

Now it struck me that this inscription was in singularly bad taste.   The incursion of General Ross was not an affair in which either party should exult. It was no extraordinary military achievement for four or five thousand highly disciplined troops, to land under the protection of an overwhelming naval force,* and to make a forced march, for a few days, through a perfectly defenceless, and nearly uninhabited country ; to attack and disperse a hastily assembled body of armed citizens, who were but little, if any, superior to them in numbers ; to enter a line of straggling villages ; to remain one night, and then to retreat at a rate that was quite as precipitate as their advance. Perhaps it was not bad policy, in the abstract, for a people who possessed the advantages of the British, to take this means of harassing their enemy.   But I doubt the policy, in a nation situated precisely as England was and is, of proving so practically to a nation with the spirit, the resources, maritime char-

---

* The frigates ascended the river to Alexandria.

acter, and prospects of this, that a powerful navy is so absolutely necessary to defend their coast. The use that was made of the success, too, might admit of some cavilling. But, on the other hand, the Americans fell so far short in their defence of what even the case admitted, and so very far short of what, even under less propitious circumstances, they themselves effected at New-Orleans, that wisdom would prescribe silence as the better course. It is permitted for the defenders of Bunker's hill to allude to their defeat, but the chisel of the Americans should have been industriously employed to erase every vestige of, and not to commemorate, even thus indirectly, the occupation of their capital by an enemy. But, even admitting that the defence of the town had been quite equal to the means at hand, what was the immediate offence that called for this particular punishment? The English occupied the Navy-Yard, and, although a little hurried, they certainly had time to have *destroyed* this small monument, instead of *mutilating* it, by knocking the heads off one or two small marble angels. The very nature of the injury proves it was the act of an individual, and not of the authority, which alone should be considered responsible for any grave national accusation. Cadwallader is of my opinion, as, indeed, were half-a-dozen naval officers who showed us through the yard. The latter said that the inscription was by order of an officer of rank, who had reasons for a special degree of antipathy against their late enemy. No man, especially in a country like this, should be permitted, however, thus to interpose his personal resentments between a nation and its dignity.

It is more than a mile from the quarter of the Navy-Yard to that of the Capitol. I have read accounts of this place, which convey an idea that it was lately a forest, and that the wood had been felled in order to make a space to receive the town. There is some error in this impression. Most of the country, for miles around Washington, was early devoted to the growth of tobacco. It is a baneful consequence of the cultivation of this weed, that, for a long time, it destroys the fertility of the soil. Thus, one sees vast fields here, which wear the appearance of neglected heaths. A growth of low, stunted, dwarfish trees succeeds in time, and bushes must, of course, first make their appearance. I could see no traces of wood in any part of this city, nor for some distance around it, though it is not improbable that some copses of a second growth did exist at the time the plan was formed. All I mean to say is, that the vicinity of the Capitol has rather the appearance of an old and an exhausted, than of what is here called a new country. A great deal of the land in and about the town is not fenced, and the whole appearance of the place is that produced by the separate villages I have described, lying on a great heath, which is beginning to be cultivated, and whose surface is irregularly waving. The avenues in those parts which are not built, consequently, cross these open fields, and the view is perfectly unobstructed on every side.

The quarter of the Capitol stands on elevated ground, and is certainly the most picturesque portion of the city proper. The Capitol itself is placed on the brow of a considerable declivity, and commands a noble view. There is something exceedingly imposing in the aspect of this building, with its powerful accessories of scenery and of moral association. I shall beg your patience while I attempt an imperfect description.

The edifice is of a light greyish freestone. It has been found necessary to paint it white, in order to conceal the marks of the smoke left by the conflagration of 1814. This is in better taste than the inscription on the monument. The effect of a clear, brilliant white, under so fine a sun, is in itself exceedingly striking. The antiquarian may riot in the rust, but every plain-viewing man sees that the coin is never so beautiful as when it is new from the mint. This freshness of air is rather a peculiarity throughout mos* of the United States, and it is exactly the appearance the country should wear in order to be in keeping with its recollections.

The Capitol is composed of a centre and two wings. The former is something more than 150 feet square. or nearly square, and the latter are each just 100. The several parts are in a line on the eastern front, and consequently the wings are thrown back on the western. This irregularity of the western fa-cade is a great defect: it impairs the unity, and con-sequently the majesty, of the edifice. There are too many angles, those fatal blots on the beauty of archi-tecture. There is another serious defect in the build-ing as seen from the west: the centre is not only a story higher, but it is also a story lower than the wings. On this side the edifice stands on the brow of the hill. In order to profit by the formation of the ground, a basement, which is below the level of the earth to the east, but not to the west, has been constructed beneath the centre. But this basement necessarily comes into the view ; and the fact of its being painted white, coupled with its airy situation, gives the whole construction the air of a mighty ostrich which is just extending its little wings from the centre of a clumsy body, not to fly, but to scud across the plain beneath. The effect of a fine colonnade is much weakened by this substructure of the edifice. But you, who have so often seen the Louvre, can understand how easy it is to give the basement too much importance in a building ; and you, too, who know the Garde Meuble so well, must be sensible of the fine effect of a judi-cious observance of the proper proportions. Some plan is in agitation to conceal this superabundance of foundation ; but it is rare indeed that a capital defect in a building is successfully repaired by any second-hand expedients.

The eastern front of the Capitol promises to be beautiful : it possesses unity of design, perfect simplicity of outline, and a noble colonnade. As it is not, however, yet completed, it would be premature to pronounce with confidence on its final appearance. The building stands in a spacious inclosure, which is itself nearly surrounded by houses. These dwellings are of bricks, three stories high, and decent, without being in the least elegant. Much the greater part of them are occupied as lodging-houses for the members during the session. There are also a few short streets built about the Capitol.

You will have understood that the plan of the city is that of an infinite number of wide streets intersecting each other at right angles, and which, in their turn, are obliquely intersected by sundry great avenues, which are intended to shorten the distances between the more important points, and, I presume, to beautify the city. Several of these avenues diverge from the Capitol square, like radii from a common centre. They are called after the different States. One, the Pennsylvania Avenue, is the principal street of Washington. Standing at the Capitol, the view along this avenue is somewhat striking. It is built on more than one-half of its whole length, and it is terminated by an oblique view of the President's House. You will bear in mind, that as very few of the dwellings on this avenue approach the Capitol, they form part of another quarter. Still, paved walks and a few scattered buildings, serve to give them something of the air of *beginning* to belong to the same town.

The quarter of the President's House is less compact and more populous than either of the four. It forms, properly, the heart of the city. It approaches towards Georgetown on one side, and the Capitol on

the other, without absolutely joining either. A few
of the streets have the air of a town, though there is
in every part of this place a striking disproportion in
magnitude between the streets and the houses. In
order to produce the effect intended, the buildings on
the Pennsylvania Avenue, for example, should be of six
or seven stories, whereas in fact they are some such
houses as one sees in an English country town. Another striking defect in the plan is also made manifest
by the waste of room on this avenue. As the avenues
cross the streets obliquely, it is plain the points of
intersection must make a vast number of acute angles.
There is always on one side of each street, between
that street and the avenue, a gore of land that is so narrow that it will never be built on until real estate shall
get to be far more valuable than it is likely soon to
become here. Consequently the distances are unnecessarily increased, and by this means, and its four
different quarters, Washington has all the inconvenience of an immense town, without any, or scarcely
any, of its counterbalancing conveniences.

It is unnecessary to say any thing more of Georgetown, which is a well-built, clean, and rather pretty
town. The avenues between this place and the Navy-
Yard, a distance of near five miles, are like so much
grande route which runs through a little cultivated,
but open country, on which stands one straggling town,
and a village, and which terminates in a cluster of
houses. The buildings of the towns, or villages, on
the route, are much like those of other small towns,
with the exception of the public edifices, which are
like those one sees in a city. If you can reconcile all
these contradictions, you may get a tolerably accurate
notion of the capital of the United States of America.
You will recollect that the whole population of the
place, or places, (Georgetown included,) is about
25,000 souls. The whole district, Alexandria included, contains 40,000.

The President's House is a neat, chaste building, of the Ionic order, built of the same material, and painted like the Capitol. It stands on a public square, and in a considerable garden, and is one hundred and seventy feet in length, by eighty-five in breadth. In a parallel line with one of its fronts, though a little in advance, stand the offices of the four great departments. They are large buildings of brick, and are placed in pairs, on each side of the "white house," one in front of the other, having open courts between them. The two most in advance have plain colonnades, but the other two are as naked as can be. Besides these buildings there are one or two more in a distant part of this straggling quarter, which merit no particular description.

TO THE ABBATE GIROMACHI.

&c. &c.

Washington, ——

My attention, after our arrival at this place, was early called to the great body, which was about to assemble. We had taken a little suite of rooms in a lodging-house, or rather tavern, which soon began to fill with members of Congress from all quarters of the country. Perhaps of the whole legislative corps of the country, there is not a single individual who is the proprietor of a dwelling at the seat of government. Those who are of sufficient estate to main tain two houses, have their town residences in the capitals of their own particular States, though a very large majority of the members are far from being men of large fortunes at all.* There are a few individuals who appear at the capital with their wives and families, but by far the greater part of those who have them, leave them at home. The common practice is, for a certain number of the members who are acquainted with each other, to make what is called a "mess," at some chosen boarding-house. Here they reside together, during the session, like the members of one large family. Even ladies are often included in these arrangements. Others again choose to live entirely secluded : and, in some few instances, families keep their regular winter establishments, in such narrow accommodations as the place affords. The fact that a member is so completely dependent on the public will, for his election, is enough in itself to prevent any one but a man of very large estate from incurring the expense of building on so uncertain a tenure.

A member of the Congress of the United States is, in fact, what the office professes to be, a representative of the people. It is not pretended that he should be, as a matter of course, a gentleman, in the ordinary acceptation of the term. On the contrary, he is very commonly a plain, though always a respectable yeoman, and not unfrequently a mechanic. I remember to have passed a night, in one of the northern States, in a very good, cleanly, cheap and comfortable inn, whose master was a member of the lower house. In the southern States, where the white men of smaller fortunes are by no means of so elevated a character as their brethren of the north, a choice from the middling classes rarely happens ; but from the more northern, eastern, and north-western States, such selections are by no means uncommon.

---

* Does not this fact go to confirm the opinion of Cadwallader, that frugality in the public expenditure of a country, is by no means a necessary consequence of power resting in the hands of the comparatively poor ?

When Cadwallader first directed my attention to this fact, I confess a little surprise entered into my view of the composition of the American legislature. Perhaps the circumstance of so material a difference between the Congress and the British Parliament was at the bottom of my wonder; for we in Europe are perhaps a little too apt to try all experiments in liberty, by those which England has so long practised with such comparative success. I alluded, a little freely, to the circumstance of their having so far departed from the practice of the mother country, with a view of extracting an opinion on the subject from my companion. The plan was successful.

"If departure from the policy of our ancestors is to create your wonder, the feeling should be neither new nor trifling. What we do now, in this particular, we have practised, not only without inconvenience, but with signal success, for near seven generations. The representation under the crown differed but little from that of the present day. It is, in truth, a representation; and the surprise should be, not that the people choose so many men of a situation in life closely resembling that of the majority, but rather that they choose so few. There is a practical good sense in the mass of the community, here, that tells them a certain degree of intelligence and of respectability of character is needed in a representative of the nation. No one will deny that they sometimes deceive themselves, but, on the whole, they are sufficiently critical. For native talent, practical intelligence, moral character, and political honesty, the Congress of the United States need not dread a comparison with the legislature of any other country. I do not mean to say that they are perfect, but I am quite certain, from tolerably close observation, that they do as much good and as little harm as any other similar body in the world.

"He who enters the halls of Congress, expecting

to find the same conventional finish of personal deportment, or the same degree of education, as he will find in the British Parliament, or in the French Chambers, enters it under a gross misconception of the nature of its organization. But he who enters either of the two foreign legislative bodies I have named, expecting to meet with the same useful and practical knowledge of life, in those details on which a legislator is called every hour to act, the same degree of native capacity, or even the same aptitude of applying the great principles of government to their direct and desirable uses, will fall into an error quite as gross. We have men, and very many men, in our legislature, that may be safely placed at the side of the most eminent politicians of Europe ; and perhaps no people in the world could more easily fill every chair on the floors of the two houses with representatives who, by their intelligence, practical knowledge, independence, and honesty, would do high credit to a nation, than ourselves. But there are many reasons why we do not. The first, and the most important of all, is, that we have happily got the country into that onward movement, that there is little or no occasion for legislative impulses. As a rule, besides the ordinary grants of money, and the usual watchfulness over the proceedings of the executive, the less they do the better. We find it useful to place the check of plain men, with moderated views of life, on the speculations of educated theorists. Besides, every class of society has its interests, and it is proper that they should have their representation. It is certainly true, that many members of Congress sometimes believe it necessary to yield to the mistaken prejudices of a majority of their constituents ; but it may be well questioned, whether as much evil to the community results from this pliancy, as from that which obeys the beck of a minister. In America, we have some of the former and none of the latter ;

in Europe, you have a great deal of the latter, and none of the former. Now, in the United States, if the mistake of the people entails inconvenience on themselves, they are sure to get rid of it; but I am yet to learn in what manner you dispose of a blunder, or of an intentional innovation, of a minister. You must always remember that we claim no perfection; it is not a quality of earth. All we wish to maintain is, that our system is the best known, and perhaps the best practicable; but if you will show us a better, we will adopt it. Nothing can be more absurd, than to accuse almost the only nation on the earth that is constantly endeavouring to amend its institutions, of a besotted opinion of its own immaculate wisdom. I know you will say, that changes are frequently dangerous, and that they too often lead to evil. Now, I am not at all disposed to deny that you are partially right as respects yourselves; but we know that we can improve, or even afford to deteriorate a little, without much danger; and therein we think we have no small advantage over all the rest of the world. If you doubt the fact, compare our actual situation, the past, and what we have done and are doing, with what other governments have done and are about, and let the result speak for itself.

"You will see on the floors of Congress men belonging to every condition of society known to our community, with the exception of that which necessarily infers great ignorance and vulgarity. All the members are respectable, and very many of them are gentlemen. There are some who are scholars, and not a few have been improved by travel and by observation of other countries. A remote frontier district, however, must send such men as it possesses, or trust its peculiar interests to those who have but little concern in its welfare. The Senate is, in some respects, rather more select than the lower house, because their constituents have a State instead of a district to choose from, and because that body is expected to temper the proceedings of legislation with a peculiar degree of moderation and dignity.

" In the British Parliament there is some show of this universality of representation. Certain corporations send men of their own stamp ; but in England every thing has a tendency to aristocracy, while, in this country, every thing which pertains to the government must seek its support in the democracy. The " worthy alderman," who may have commenced life behind a counter, endeavours to forget his apron when he takes his seat on the opposition benches. Instead of returning to his shop when the session is ended, he becomes a deserter to aristocracy, the moment he has received the seal of office from the people. How far he may contribute to the boasted refinement of the higher classes, I cannot pretend to say ; but it is certain that he does not, like his American prototype, assist to give respectability and elevation to that of which he was originally a member. It is this elevation of character among the middling, and even among the more inferior classes of our community, which chiefly distinguishes us from all other nations. Europe must show a population as much accustomed to political power, as moderate in its exercise, as practised in all that controls the general interests of life, and as shrewd in their estimate of character, as this of ours, before she should pretend to infer the results of democratic institutions by any facts drawn from her own experience. We do not deny the universality of human impulses, we only insist that governments have not the habit of giving them fair play. The two houses of Congress are, and ever have been, living proofs that the majority of men are not disposed to abuse power when it is once fairly intrusted to them. There is not a doubt that the comparatively poor and ignorant might fill all our legislative chairs with men of their own class, and yet they rather take pride in seeing the representation respectable for information. Some part of this seeming generosity is, no doubt, owing to the superior influence of intelligence; but you must allow there is a prospect of quiet and durability under a system in which the majority find no reason to complain, and in which the minority must see the folly of usurpation. But as the two houses are by this time organized, we will go to the Capitol, and hear the message. When on the spot, I will endeavour to direct your attention to such individuals as may serve to elucidate what you have just heard."

We proceeded to the Capitol in a coach. Alighting at the foot of the hill, we mounted it to a door on the western façade, and entered the edifice through its *substratum*. Passing among a multitude of eating rooms, &c. &c., we ascended, by a noble flight of massive steps, to the true basement, or to that story which runs through the whole building. Directly under the dome is a gloomy vaulted hall, that I have heard called the " caucus ;" more, I believe, from its fancied fitness for the political meetings that are thus termed, than from the fact that it has ever actually been appropriated to such an use. It has the air, however, of being admirably adapted to the purposes of a secret conclave, though, in truth, it is a common thoroughfare of the building. Immediately above the " caucus " is the principal hall. It is circular, large, high, and covered with a fine dome. There is not much richness in the ornaments of this hall, though it is sufficiently wrought to prevent the appearance of nakedness. It contains, among other things, four bas-reliefs in stone, which are intended to illustrate as many of the most striking incidents in the original settlement of the country.*   I have no

* The writer is himself but a traveller, and he should, therefore, speak reverently of the craft. But he will seize this occa-

·hsposition to criticise their execution. Historical pictures are to be placed in the panels beneath.

From the great hall we passed into that of the House of Representatives. My friend was formerly a member, and by an usage he is permitted to enter the body of the chamber, or rather to occupy a seat that is only separated from those of the actual members by a slight division. Under his auspices, and by the aid of a little interest, I was permitted to be his companion.

The hall of the House of Representatives, without being particularly rich, or highly wrought, is one of the most beautiful apartments I have ever entered. The form is semicircular. It is lighted from above, and from windows on its straight side. Between these windows and the body of the hall, is a sort of lobby or gallery, which is separated from the other parts by a colonnade. Here the members and privileged persons promenade, converse, stand, listen, or repose, without, in fact, quitting the room. It is

---

sion to express his surprise at the very different view which he has taken of visible objects from those of some others of the class, who, like himself, have been pleased to put their observations before the world. In the " Personal Narrative of Lieutenant the Honourable Frederic de Roos," p. 15, is the following sentence, while speaking of the apartment just named: "The walls are destitute of ornament, if we except some pieces of sculpture, representing various wars and treaties with the Indians. The artist might have selected subjects more creditable to his country." Now, if the writer has not been greatly deceived, these four bas-reliefs are on the following subjects: the landing of the pilgrims on the Rock of Plymouth; the Treaty of William Penn with the natives for the possession of their soil; the beautiful and touching story of Pocahontas saving the life of Captain Smith, and a personal rencontre of Colonel Boon, the patriarch of Kentucky, with the savages. These are four distinct historical events, which are connected with the settlement of the four principal parts of the Union. More illustrious incidents might have been chosen, beyond a doubt: but there is certainly nothing discreditable to the American character in those they have selected for this purpose.

sufficiently withdrawn to prevent the appearance of disorder, and yet near enough to render the debates audible.

In the centre of the diameter which cuts the circle is the Speaker's chair. It is, in fact, a little sofa, sufficiently large to hold, on occasion, the President of the United States, the President of the Senate, and the Speaker. Immediately in front, and four or five feet lower, is a chair for the presiding member, when the house acts as a committee. On a line with the Speaker the clerks have their places. In front of the chair there is a vacant semicircular space of perhaps five-and-twenty feet in diameter. Then the seats of the members commence. They are arranged in semicircular rows, preserving the form of the exterior walls, and are separated by a great number of little openings, to admit of a passage between them. Each member has an arm-chair and a low desk, in mahogany. In the first row, they sit in pairs, or there is a vacant space between every two, and each successive row increases its number by one member. Thus, in the last row, some six or seven are placed side by side, as on a bench (though actually on chairs), while those in front are in pairs. The practice is for those who arrive first to choose their seats, and the choice is invariably respected.

There is no such thing known as a political division of seats. Members of the same politics certainly often choose to be placed near to each other, and sometimes the entire representation of a particular State is to be seen as near together as possible. But there is no rule in the matter.

The seats of the members are separated from the semicircular passage in which Cadwallader and myself were placed, by no other division than a low railing. Sofas lined the whole of the exterior wall : and as the floor rises a little from the centre, or the area in front of the Speaker, we had the best possible opportunity for seeing and hearing. A spacious and commodious gallery, of the same form as the hall, completed the outline of the apartment. It was raised several feet above the level of the chamber, and is intended for the use of spectators.

The house was organized when we entered, and was engaged in some business of form. Nearly all the seats were occupied; and, as the message was expected, the gallery was crowded with ladies and well-dressed men. The privileged places around the floor of the hall were nearly all filled. The Speaker was uncovered, but most of the members wore their hats. No one appeared in costume, nor is there any official dress prescribed to the members of Congress for any ceremony whatever.

After what Cadwallader had told me of the true character of the representation of his country, I confess I was rather surprised with the appearance of the individuals who composed this assembly. It was to be expected that they should all be well attired, but, on the whole, with some very few exceptions, they had quite as much the air of the world about them as those who compose the chambers of the two first nations of Europe. No one is allowed to sit in the lower house who has not attained the age of five-and-twenty; but, in point of fact, there is not, probably, a single member of Congress who has seen less than thirty years. The greater number seemed to be men between the ages of thirty-five and fifty-five. There were but very few who could be termed old. All, or very nearly all, were natives of the country.

I was struck with the simple but imposing aspect of this assembly. Though so totally destitute of any personal decorations, the beauty of the hall, with its magnificent row of massive columns,* the great neat-

---

* The roof of the hall of the House of Representatives is supported by a noble semicircle of columns of pudding-stone. They

ness of the fautëuil and desks, the beautifully carpeted floors, and the long range of sofas, serve to relieve a scene that might otherwise have been too naked. It appeared as if the members had said, thus much may you do for the benefit of comfort, for the encouragement of the arts, and, perhaps, as a testimonial of the respect due to the sacred uses of the place, but man must be left in the fullest force of his simplicity. None of the attendants even wore any badges of their offices. There were neither swords, chains, collars, stars, bayonets, nor maces, seen about the place, though a quiet, and order, and decency, reigned in the hall that bespoke the despotic dominion of that mighty, though invisible, monarch—the Law.

A discussion on some question of order was getting to be a little general, and one member was addressing the chair [they speak from their places, as in the British Parliament] with some earnestness, when the principal door was thrown open, and an officer proclaimed aloud, "A message from the President." The members all rose in their places, the Speaker included, when a young gentleman entered, and passed through the body of the house to the chair. He was attired in a neat morning-dress, and having placed his document in the hand of the Speaker, he bowed and withdrew. It was then decided that the communication should be read.* There was much interest

---

are highly polished, and have a pleasing no less than a striking effect.

* The instances of a propensity in Europeans to misconstrue the political and moral condition of the United States are numberless. One may be quoted here with propriety. Since the return of the writer to Europe, he has, on more than one occasion, heard the fact that the President of the United States sends a message to Congress, commented on in a significant manner, as if the circumstance were portentous of some great political change! "Parliament would scarcely brook a *message*," said an Englishman, with emphasis, when the subject was alluded to. The writer saw nothing, at the time, in the thing itself, but the

to hear this document, which always contains a great outline of the state of the republic. It was a clear, succinct narrative of what had been done in the course of the past year, of the condition of the

---

most perfect simplicity; but, determined to sift the matter to the bottom, he mentioned the subject in a letter to his American friend, and extracts a part of his reply: "I am not at all surprised," said Cadwallader, "that thousands in Europe should easily pervert every possible circumstance into an evidence of a state of things which they rather desire than seriously expect. There has not been a single change, however, in all our usages, which goes less to prove the justness of their anticipations, than the fact you have mentioned. When the government, as it now exists, was first organized, Washington met the two houses and made his annual communication in a speech. The practice had prevailed in the colonial legislatures. We have never been in a hurry to make unnecessary innovations. Reform marches with a dignified pace—it is revolution that is violent. The States continued the practice of the colonies. It was quite natural that the first Presidents should conform to existing usages for a time. We have never been great sticklers for shadows, though no principle is ever listened to that is likely to entail a disadvantage. In the course of a few years, men began to ask themselves, why does the President make a *speech* at the opening of a session? He sends messages at all other times, and why not on this occasion? The substance of what he has to communicate, can be told by a message quite as well as by a speech. The amount of it all then is, that the parade of a speech is a mere matter of state and show, and although some little ceremony is, perhaps, necessary, we ought to have as little as possible, since common sense, which is our palladium, is always a sufferer in ceremonies. You will understand me; a state of society may exist, in which it is good sense to adopt ceremony, but such is not the case in the year 1827, in the United States of America. Every sage physician adapts his remedy to the disease. Mr. Jefferson dispensed with speeches, because they did no good, and might do harm by drawing us nearer to the usages of Europe, when it is so often our business to recede from them. For my own part, I think it rather better as it is, though it cannot be a matter of much moment. It is, however, odd enough, that the very usage which has been adopted for its simplicity and republicanism, should be tortured into a proof of a directly contrary tendency. It may be a sufficient answer to the remark of your English friend, 'that the British Parliament would be apt to grumble at receiving a message from the king,' to say that should Congress not

finances, of the several negotiations, and concluded with a statement of what the people had a right to anticipate for the future.

When the message was ended, Cadwallader introduced me to several of the members to whom he was personally known. Most of them were men of good manners, and of education, though one or two were certainly individuals who had paid far more attention to the substance of things than to forms. The former were of course of that class of society which, in Europe, would be termed the gentry, and the others were probably farmers, if not mechanics. There was an air of great self-possession and decorum in the latter; nor could the slightest visible difference be traced between the respect which they received, and that which their more polished confederates bestowed on each other. A simple, quiet courtesy is certainly the tone of manners in Congress. While we stood together in the lobby, a grave-looking, middle-aged man, of a slightly rustic air, approached, and addressed my companion. His manner was manly and independent, but at the same time decent, and I think it was to be distinguished by a shade of respect. They shook hands, and conversed a little concerning some questions of local politics. Promises were made of exchanging visits. "This is my friend, the ―――――," said Cadwallader; "a gentleman who is travelling in our country." The stranger saluted me, offering his hand with the utmost simplicity. "If this gentleman comes into our part of the country, I hope to see him," he said, and soon after took his leave. When he was gone, I learned that this individual was a member of Congress from the county in which the pater-

---

receive one from the President at a pretty early day in the session, they would be very apt to appoint a committee to inquire why he had forgotten to lay the state of the nation before them. I am no quarreller about terms, and I leave you to decide where the substance of things is to be found."

nal estates of my friend lie; that he was a farmer of moderate means and good character, whom his fellow-citizens had sent to represent them. His constituents might very possibly have made a better choice, and yet this man was not useless, since he served as a check on the schemes of those who would be legislating for effect. A gentleman-like man of sixty came next, and he and my friend met as equals in all respects, except that the latter paid a slight deference to the years of his acquaintance. I was introduced. We touched our hats, and exchanged a few words. The next day, I received this gentleman's card, and as soon as his visit was returned, an invitation to dine in his private lodgings followed. This was Mr. ——, a man of immense hereditary landed estate. His alliances, fortune, and habits, (though tempered by the institutions of his country,) are, to all intents and purposes, the same as those of a gentleman or nobleman in Europe. His character is excellent, and, in consequence, he is now, and may be to the day of his death, the representative of his native district. Here you have the two extremes of the representation of this country—a yeoman, and a great proprietor whose income would put him on a level with most of the great men of our hemisphere. They represent no particular interests, for all interests unite to send them here. They happen to please their constituents, and the fact that the one is a yeoman, and the other a species of lord of the manor, produces no effect whatever. These men meet in Congress on terms of perfect equality. It often happens, that a yeoman, possessed of a vigorous native mind, has vast influence.

While quitting the Capitol, two more members of Congress spoke to Cadwallader. They walked with us the whole length of the avenue. One of them was a man of a fashionable air, and of exceedingly good manners. He spoke French, and we conversed to-

gether for some time in that tongue. I found him
agreeable and intelligent, and was glad to perceive
he was disposed to renew the interview. But the
other individual puzzled me not a little. In dress
and externals, he differed but little from his more
agreeable companion. His air, however, was not
that of a man of the world, and his language was sufficiently provincial to be remarked. I should not
have taken him for one of a station in life to be found
in such company, did I not know his official rank,
and were I not prepared for the great admixture of
ordinary American society. But if I was a little per-
plexed by the provincialisms of this individual, I was
not less surprised at his shrewdness and intelligence.
He used his words with great discrimination, and
with perfect grammatical accuracy; and he spoke
not only with good sense, but frequently with power,
and always with prodigious clearness. When we
parted, I again expressed surprise at the manifest
difference in manners that existed between the two
members.

"You will begin to know us in time," returned
Cadwallader. "Those men are both lawyers. He
whose air and language are so unexceptionable, is a
member of a family long known in this country for
its importance. You see he has not lost, nor will he
be likely to let his posterity lose, the manners of the
world. He is far from being rich, nor is he remarkable for talent, though rather clever. You find he
has a seat in Congress. The other is the child of an
affluent tradesman, who has given his son an education for the bar, but who could not give him what he
had not himself,—a polished exterior. But he is
gleaning, and, before he dies, he will be in the way
of imparting a better air to his descendants. In this
manner is the whole of our community slowly rising
in the scale of mere manners. As to talent, this provincial lawyer, for he is provincial in practice as

well as by birth, has, as you must have observed, enough of it. He is a good man in Congress, whatever he may be in the saloons. He has got the intelligence, and no small part of the feelings, of a gentleman; he may never get the air, for he began too late for that, and, like most men, he probably affects to despise an unattainable advantage. But as it is in nature to wish for distinction, rely on it, he is secretly determined to amend. Perhaps one of these parties loses a little by the intimate association which is a necessary consequence of their common situation; but the gradual approximation is, on the whole, produced by the improvement of the other. In the great essentials of soundness of feeling, morals, and common sense, they are quite on an equality."

TO THE ABBATE GIROMACHI,

&c. &c.

FLORENCE.

Washington, ——

I HAVE been a daily visiter at the Capitol. The proceedings of the two houses are never without interest, since they control the entire foreign policy of this growing republic, which is daily becoming of more importance in the eyes of Christendom. Some of the peculiar practice of American legislation may be of interest, and before I write of individuals, I will attempt a brief outline of their forms.

You probably know already that the President of the United States is assisted by a cabinet. It is composed of four Secretaries, (state, treasury, war, and navy,) and of the Attorney-General. As the President is alone answerable for his proper acts, these ministers have no further responsibility than as their own individual agency is concerned. They have no seats in Congress, since the constitution forbids that any officer of the general government should be a representative either of a State (a Senator), or of the people (a member of the House of Representatives). Thus, the judges and generals, and colonels, of which one reads in Congress, are not officers of the United States, but of the States themselves. The difference is material, since the authorities by whom they are commissioned have no power over the measures on which they are called to legislate. You will understand me better if I go a little into detail.

The President of the United States has no voice in the appointment of any officer whatever, under the government of a State. The government of a State has no voice whatever in the enactment of the laws, or in the appointment of the officers, of the United States. There may be, and unquestionably there sometimes is, a reciprocal influence exerted between them; but the instances are rare, and liable to a good deal of explanation. It is not probable that the government of the United States ever interests itself at all in the appointments of a State; but, as the appointments of the United States are often of a nature to produce a direct effect on the interests of a particular State, it is not uncommon for the members of its government to lend their influence to such applicants as they believe the most likely to be of benefit to its community. Still, it is no more than influence; no two governments in the world being more perfectly distinct from each other, than that of the United States and that of an individual member of the confederation, if we make the single exception, that both are bound to respect the great principles of the constitution.

It is an unsettled point whether Congress has a right to admit the ministers to possess consultative voices in the two houses. I think the better opinion is, that they have; but the practice has never yet been adopted. Indeed, there is a sort of fastidious delicacy observed on this subject, which, in effect, prevents the Secretaries from attending the debates even as auditors. I have never yet seen any member of the cabinet in the chamber of either body. On the last day of the session, it is the practice of the President to come to the Capitol, and to occupy an apartment which is fitted expressly for his use. The object of this visit is to be near the legislative bodies, in order that he may give his assent to, or rejection of, the bills that always accumulate at that time. He is, of course, attended by his cabinet, the members of which, I am told, are then in the habit of sometimes entering the halls. This is the only occasion on which the President appears in the Capitol, unless it be at his inauguration, or at some ceremony not at all connected with government.

The exclusion of the ministers from the debates is thought, by many people, to be a defect, since, instead of the verbal explanations which they might give, if present, it is now necessary to make formal demands on the different departments for information. On the other hand, it is contended that the existing practice compels members to make themselves familiar with details, and that they are none the worse legislators for their labour. In no case could the minister be allowed to vote, or even to propose a law, directly.

For the introduction of the laws, there are two courses in practice, though only one in theory. Each Secretary makes a formal report of the state of his particular department at the commencement of every session. In this report, he takes care to recommend those measures that he deems needful for his immediate branch of the public service. The substance of these reports is embodied in the message of the President; and it is the duty of that high officer to invite the attention of the legislature to such subjects as he may consider of national importance. The matter of the message is necessarily divided into a certain number of leading topics. Regular, or, as they are here called, standing committees, are appointed at the commencement of every Congress.* To these committees all the usual matter of the message is referred. Thus, whatever relates to the finances is referred to " the committee of ways and means;" to the army, to " the military committee," &c. &c. If the message should include any extraordinary matter, as is usually the case, a special committee is appointed to attend to it. At the head of each committee, (they exist in both houses), there is placed some member who is supposed to be more than commonly acquainted with its business. As Congress is so completely composed of practical men, these duties are generally discharged with a good deal of dexterity, and often with rare ability. These committees have rooms of their own, where they assemble and get through with all the drudgery of their duties. They communicate with the departments ; and when there is an agreement of opinion, the necessary bills are framed between them. The chairman is the usual organ of communication with the house. We will, however, assume a case, and follow it through its legislative forms, in order to render the usage as clear as possible.

The President and his cabinet believe the public good requires that a dozen regiments should be added to the army. The fact is communicated to Congress, in the annual message, accompanied by a statement of the political events which have induced the necessity. Then comes the report of the Secretary, with a detailed view of the present force, and a general comparative statement of that which it is thought will

---

* Once in two years.

be needed. The military committees enter into a minute examination of the circumstances and estimates, and make such reports to the two houses as they deem prudent. If it be in favour of an increase, they recommend a bill. In order to get rid of certain forms, and with a view to render legislation deliberate, the whole house sit as a *committee*. This, you know, is a practice derived from the English Parliament. The bill, amended or not, is first passed by the committee of the whole house; but its opponents have still a chance to dispute its passage in the house itself. When it has passed one of the houses, it is sent to the other, where it goes through the same forms. It is hardly necessary to say that the committees of the two houses commonly consult together, and make their reports as nearly alike as possible. In general they are the same, though the fate of a bill is by no means sure because it has been approved by the committees. All these forms do not prevent individual members from offering bills of their own; it is merely a practice, adopted to favour examination, and to expedite business.

When a bill has passed the two houses, it is signed by the Speaker of the House of Representatives and the President of the Senate, and sent to the President for his approbation. That officer submits it to his cabinet, as a matter of prudence and of courtesy, though not of right. Should he choose it, however, he can demand the written opinion of any of his ministers, and then the individual who gives it may be supposed to become responsible for the honesty of his views. The President decides as he sees fit; there remaining no alternative to the minister but submission, or separation from an administration of whose policy he disapproves. If the President sign the bill, it is a law; but if he does not sign it, he is obliged to send it back to Congress with his reasons. Should he neglect to do either, for ten days, it be-

comes a law without his agency; and should he then
refuse to sign it, he may be impeached and punished,
as, probably, might such of his ministers who, it could
be proved, had been accessary to his obstinacy. If
Congress be not satisfied with the objections of the
President, they put the bill to the question again;
and should two-thirds of both houses support it, it
becomes a law, without his agency.

The Congress of the United States is not remarkable for the despatch of public business, nor is it
desirable that it should be. One of the greatest
merits of the peculiar government of the country, is
to be found in the fact, that the people are left, as
much as possible, to be the agents of their own prosperity. The object of the laws is protection rather
than patronage. Haste is rarely necessary, where
such a state of society exists; and though there may
be, and, undoubtedly, frequently is, inconvenience in
the delays that sometimes occur, more good than evil
is thought to follow the practice. The cause of delay
most complained of, is the habit of making set
speeches, which is, perhaps, too common.

You are not, however, to suppose that a member
actually talks seventy-two hours without stopping, because he is said to have occupied the house three days.
Though Æolus himself does not seem to be longer
winded than some of the American legislators, none
of them are quite equal to such a blast. If we say
nine hours, perhaps, we get the maximum of their
breath; and even this period is to be divided into
three several and distinct divisions. The houses
meet at twelve o'clock. They are commonly occupied in the order of the day until two, when they go
into committees of the whole, or take up the deferred
business. This leaves the Demosthenes of the occasion but three hours each day for the exercise of his
oratory. But bottom enough for three days, on the
same subject, is not the fortunate quality of many

men : so, after all, very few members ever occupy
the house more than an hour or two. The evil does
not so much exist in the extraordinary length of the
speeches, as in the number of those who can arrange
words enough to fill an hour of time.

The Americans are fond of argument. They discuss in society, a thing which is done nowhere else,
I believe. The habit is often disagreeable, since
their opinions are not unfrequently coarsely urged ;
but the truth is profusely shaken from its husks, in
these sharp, intellectual encounters. It is not surprising, that men, who have been accustomed all their
lives to have a word in what is passing, should carry
the desire to speak into a body which is professedly
deliberative. Still, if the trifling inconvenience of
these delays shall be put in contrast with the cold
and uncalculating injury, the prodigal expenditure,
and the quiet corruption with which legislation so
often flows on in its silent course, elsewhere, the advantage will be found immensely on the side of these
talkers.

In point of manner, the debates in both houses of
Congress are conducted with decorum. Those in the
Senate are particularly dignified ; that body maintaining, at all times, rather more of gravity than the
other. In the Senate, the members are all uncovered ;
in the lower house, they wear their hats, if they please.
The arrangements of the two halls are very much the
same ; but the Senate chamber is, of course, much
the smallest. The members of the Senate may be,
on the whole, rather older than the representatives ;
though there are several between the ages of thirty
and five-and-forty. It is necessary to be thirty, in
order to sit.

The forms of the two houses are the same. They
meet at a stated hour (12 o'clock), and, after listening to prayers, the regular business of the day is commenced. You would probably suppose that, in a

country where there is no established religion, it might be difficult for an indiscriminately collected assembly to agree on the form in which these petitions should be offered up to the Deity. Nothing is, however, more untrue. Each house chooses its own chaplain, or chaplains, who are sometimes of one denomination, and sometimes of another. Prayers are vastly better attended than in England, on such occasions. I remember once to have asked the member from Cadwallader's county, how he reconciled it to his conscience, to listen to the petitions offered up by a clergyman of a sect entirely different from his own. The simple answer was, that he believed the Almighty understood all languages.*

Although instances of want of temper and of violent expressions have certainly occurred in Congress, they are rare, and always strongly condemned. Each new speaker is patiently heard, and there is no other manner of manifesting indifference to his logic practised, than those of writing letters, reading newspapers, and sometimes of quitting the hall. There is far greater silence than in the French Chambers, though more moving about than in the House of Commons, for the simple reason that there is more room to do it in. There is sometimes a low laugh; but systematic coughing is never heard. Cries of approbation or of disapprobation, interruptions, unless to demand order, or any other similar indecencies, are unknown. These people appear to me to have no fear of themselves, or of any body else, in matters

---

* The writer was afterwards present when a Roman Catholic preached to both houses of Congress in the hall of the House of Representatives, although it is not probable that more than one or two of the members were of his religious persuasion, if, indeed, there was one. Nearly all of the higher officers of government were present, though they were Protestants to a man. Nor was there any show of liberality in the affair at all, but every thing appeared natural, and quite as a matter of course.

that relate to government. They go on boldly, systematically, and orderly, without any visible restraint. It appears as if they knew that use and education had implanted such general principles in every man, that they know where to find him, on all grave occasions. If they scatter firebrands freely in debate, and in their journals, it is because they are sure there are no combustibles into which they can fall. The gallery of Congress is very capacious, and any one may enter it, who pleases. If there could be a hazardous experiment tried on the government, I think it would be in attempting to browbeat Congress. It would be quite as safe to attempt to assassinate a sovereign, in the midst of his guards. The members, the army, the navy, the community, and even the women, would rise in support of its privileges. The perfect security of its rights might render the effort of an individual too ridiculous for resentment; but any serious plot of the sort would be sure to draw down the indignation of the whole republic.—Adieu.

TO THE COUNT JULES DE BÉTHIZY,

&c. &c.

Washington, ——

To you, who so stoutly maintain that the regulations of etiquette are necessary to order, it may be surprising to learn with how little of preparation the functionaries of this government get through the ceremonials of their offices. Just so far as etiquette is of use in facilitating intercourse, is it rational; but these people very rightly believe, that their institutions enable them to move on with far less than is practised in Europe. We will seize a moment to discuss the matter in some of its general bearings.

In point of style, there is none whatever practised in addressing any one officer of the government. The naked appellation of the office is used in conversation sometimes, and commonly, though not always, in notes and letters. The tone can be taken best from the incumbents themselves. An invitation to dine at the "White House," always runs, "The President requests the pleasure," &c. A secretary commonly says, "Mr. ———— requests," &c. Now, the best style, and that which is expected, is to reply in the same form. Thus a note should be addressed "To Mr. ——," to "the President," "To Mr. Adams, (the secretary of state)," or "To Mr. Southard (the secretary of the navy)." The use of honourable to either, or indeed to any one else, is not deemed *bon ton.* It is done, however, quite frequently by those who are ignorant of the tone of the place. The use of the terms "excellency" and "honourable," came in with the colonial practices. I have more than once had occasion to say that these people have never been violent in their innovations. The changes in things not deemed material, have always been gradual, and the work of time. Washington, at the head of the army, was called "his excellency," as a matter of course, and he carried the title with him to the chair of state. The colonial governors had the same title, and one of the States (Massachusetts) continued it in its constitution. But, though often observed, even now, it is a practice gradually falling into disuse. It is not seriously pretended there is any thing anti-republican in giving a title to a public officer; indeed many contend it should be done, as a way of imparting more consideration to the rank; but, as near as I can learn, the taste of the nation is silently receding from the custom. Cadwallader tells me that, twenty years ago, it would have been thought rather a breach of politeness to address a letter to a member of Congress, without prefixing 'honourable' to the name, though the better practice now is to omit it.   When I asked him if he saw any reason for the change, he answered, none, but the fact that the thing grew contemptible from its frequency.

" Twenty years ago," he continued, " an officer of the militia, above the rank of captain, was sure of bearing his title; but now, among men of a certain class, it is getting into disuse, unless one has reached the rank perhaps of general.   There is no general rule, however, as the people of the country are fond of calling a man by the title of an office which they may have had an agency in conferring. I think there is a quiet waggery in the nation, that takes pleasure in giving quaint names.   Thus, dwarfs are often called ' major'*—heaven knows why! but I have met three who all bore this title. I have a gardener, who is universally styled judge, and an old black family servant is never known by any other name than that of governor.   Nicknames are rather too much in use with us.   The liberty is not often taken, of course, with men of the better orders.   They are much disposed to dispense with all sorts of titles.   We call a gentleman an esquire, by courtesy, according to a practice imported from England; though some one-sided masters of ceremonies deny that any but magistrates, counsellors, &c. have a right to the title; just

---

* The writer has just seen an American play-bill, in which Major Stevens, a dwarf, is advertised to enact the part of Tom Thumb.   There is also a strange effect, in the way of names, produced by reading.   The writer met several men, who were called *Don* Sebastian, *Don* Alonzo, &c. &c. In one instance, he knew a person who was called Lord George Gordon.   The latter proceeded from waggery, but the mothers of the former had found names in books that captivated their fancy. Women of a similar rank of life in Europe, would know but little of titles beyond the limits of their own parishes.

as if even they could find better authority for their
claims than any body else.   The truth is, the courts
continue a few of the colonial forms, which may be
well enough, and their officers sometimes think that
use has grown into a law.   In New-England the
custom goes so far as to call a deacon of a church by
his title ; and I have even seen ' serjeant' placed be
fore the name of a respectable yeoman. The practice
as it confines the appellation to the office, is rather
republican than otherwise ; but, as I have just said,
it is getting into disuse, because it is no longer a distinction."

In conversation, the actual President, I find, is
called Colonel Monroe.   I am told his predecessors
were addressed as Mr. Madison, Mr. Jefferson, Mr.
Adams, and General Washington.*   The Secretaries
and the members of Congress are addressed as other
gentlemen.   In the two houses, the etiquette is to
speak of another member as " the gentleman from
Virginia," " the gentleman from Connecticut, who
spoke last," and, sometimes, as " the honourable gentleman," &c.   The President is commonly alluded
to, in debate, as " the executive."   Other indirect
means of indicating the members meant, are sometimes adopted ; but, as in the British Parliament,
names are always avoided.

No civil officer of the government has a costume,
except the judges of the supreme court.   The latter
wear, in court, plain black silk gowns.   They com
menced with wigs and scarlet robes, but soon dis-
carded them as inconvenient.   The President might,
on occasion, appear attired either as a general or an
admiral ; and, in some instances, Washington did as
the former ; but it is the usage for the President to

---

* The present President (1828) is called Mr. Adams. The
writer never heard the term " excellency " used, in speaking to
him or to his predecessor.

dress like any other gentleman, consulting his own taste and appearance. The same is true of the Vice-President, of the Speaker of the House of Representatives, and of all other officers and members. You know there is no order of knighthood in the country. At the close of the war of the revolution, the officers of the army formed themselves into a society called the society of Cincinnati. They adopted a little enamelled badge, which bears some resemblance to a simple European cross. Even this immaterial distinction gave offence, and some of the State societies were abolished many years ago. The plan was to perpetuate the feeling which had united them as a corps, through their descendants, it being intended that the eldest male heir should succeed to the father. You may trace, in this little circumstance, the lingering of ancient prejudices. Still, had not Washington been at the head of this society, and had not the services of its members been so undeniable, and so pitifully rewarded, this trifling consolation to their pride would not have been endured even at that time. The society is daily getting of less importance, though possibly of more interest, and there is no doubt but it will disappear entirely, with the individuals who were personal actors in the scenes which called it into existence. It is probable there will be no more members of the Cincinnati a dozen years hence.

The constitution has shown a marked jealousy of the introduction of any distinctions that are not solely attached to office, which, as you know, are fluctuating, and entirely dependent on popular favour. Thus, no American can receive a title, or a decoration, from a foreign court, without losing his citizenship; nor can any officer of the government receive even a trifling present from another power. There are a good many people here whose fathers bore titles. In all cases, where use had not become too strong, they

were dropped.   In short, I think the tone in all such
matters in America, is to follow the natural course
of things.   It is not natural for a community, like
this, to cherish hereditary titles, and yet it would be
doing violence to usage by attempting to change the
appellation of an individual, who had been known by
a title for perhaps half a century.   The Dutch in
New-York had a sort of lords of the manor, who
were known by the title of patroons (paterons).   Cadwallader tells me that, in his youth, he knew several
of these patroons.   But they have all disappeared,
except one.   The exception is a gentleman resident
at Albany, who is perhaps the greatest landed proprietor in the United States.   Every body, who is
familiar with the habits of that part of the country,
calls this gentleman " the patroon."   His father, and
several of his ancestors, bore the same appellation.
There is not the slightest jealousy or feeling on the
subject.   He is a member of Congress ; and though
persons from other parts of the Union address him
by his real name, my friend always calls him " patroon."   The immense estate of this gentleman was
entailed, and he came into possession about the time
of the revolution.   But there are no more entails in
any of the States ; and although the possessions of the
patroon will undoubtedly go to his children, it is more
than probable that the appellation will cease with
his own life.

The etiquette of the American government is as
simple as possible.   Some attention to forms is found
convenient, and as so many foreign ministers reside
here, perhaps it is necessary.   The practice of all
American society, in respect to precedency, is very
much like your own, always excepting the great officers of the two governments.   Age, talent, and character, exercise a great and a natural influence, and
there, I think, the matter is permitted to rest.   A
governor of a State, or even a Senator of the United

States, would be expected to lead the mistress of the house to the table, perhaps, just as a stranger, or a man of particular personal claims, would be permitted to do the same thing. But the deference paid to official rank would be very apt to end there. A mere member of the lower house may receive certain distinctions in public ceremonies, but scarcely in society. It would be intolerable for a son of the President to presume on his birth in any situation. He might, and certainly would be more caressed, on account of the circumstance; but he must always content himself with precisely the degree of attention that is offered. The son of any other gentleman is, in every respect, his equal in society, and the son of any other man his equal before the world. You will understand me to speak now with direct reference to practice, for in theory there is no difference at all.*

---

* The writer, since his return to Europe, has had an opportunity of ascertaining how far the question of precedency is sometimes pushed in England. At an entertainment given not long since in London, there were present, besides many Englishmen of rank, a Russian and a Roman Prince. The high-bred English peers could not hesitate to give the *pas* to the strangers; but these gentlemen were delicate in respect of each other. The question was one far too awful for the mistress of the house to attempt to decide. After the whole party had stood in reverential silence for a sufficiently awkward minute, the ladies moved to the banquet in a body, followed by the gentlemen in the same solitary order. Within a fortnight of that memorable *coup d'étiquette*, the writer was present at a similar entertainment at Paris. Here there were also men of distinction from different countries, without any graduated scale to determine their corelative rank. There was, however, one gentleman whose claims, though a countryman of the hostess, might, in all fairness, be considered to be pre-eminent, since, to personal rank, he united the highest talents, and the utmost private merit. The lady of the house, in order to anticipate any doubts, took his arm, and then, with exquisite grace and tact, she saw each of the other claimants accommodated with a proper companion, and every one advanced towards the *salle à manger* in less than a minute.

The present Secretary of State* undertook, in great
simplicity, to give his opinions lately on some questions of etiquette connected with the subject of official intercourse.   There was probably a great deal
of good sense in what he published, and no doubt the
practices he recommended were not without convenience.   But it is generally thought he committed an
error in writing about them at all.   Now, it is just in
this fact that I think the common sense of the Americans is to be traced.   Whatever is convenient, in the
way of ceremony, they are very apt to adopt; but
they are not disposed to make trifles matters of serious discussion.   The Secretary was a good deal
quizzed for his essay, though I dare say most people
practised the very thing they laughed at.

At Washington official rank is certainly more attended to than elsewhere.   I cannot give you an insight
into the whole table of precedency, but some of its
secrets have been practically divulged in my presence.
The day after our arrival, Cadwallader and myself
left cards at the President's House; at the houses of
the heads of departments; at those of the foreign
ministers; and at the lodgings of a dozen Senators.
We met sundry members of Congress, but my friend
did not appear to think it necessary to treat them as
personages entitled to particular deference.   Their
claims form a disputed point, I find; but Cadwallader
knows his own foothold in society too well to trouble
himself with a disputed point.   We called on a few,
as "good fellows," but on none officially.

Our cards were all returned, except by the President.   During the session this functionary never visits,
though he receives twice a week.   Between the
sessions, when the society of Washington is reduced
to a very few families, I understand he consults his
own pleasure.   In the course of the week we received

* The actual President,

notes to attend the "evenings" of those who opened their houses; and invitations to dine with the Secretaries soon followed. The dinner of the President came last; but as it contains the essence of all the etiquette of this simple court, I shall select it for a short description.

Cadwallader was personally known to Mr. Monroe (the President), and we took an opportunity to repeat our call between the time of leaving our cards and the day of the dinner. The principal entrance of the "White House" communicates with a spacious vestibule, or rather a hall. From this we passed into an apartment, where those who visit the President, in the mornings, are to wait their turns for the interview. Our names had been given in at the door, and after two or three, who preceded us, had been admitted, we were desired to follow the domestic. Our reception was in a cabinet, and the visit of course quite short. Colonel Monroe received us politely, but with an American gravity, which perhaps was not mis placed in such an officer. He offered his hand to me, though an entire stranger, and asked the commonplace questions concerning my visit to the country. We took our leave in less than ten minutes.

I found the President a man of a gentlemanlike, but of a grave and simple deportment. He expressed his hope of seeing us soon again, in a way to make me suspect we had rather been invited to his dinner, as a matter of course, than by any express commands. Let that be as it might, we went on the appointed day, with as much confidence as if the banquet were expressly spread in our behalf.

On this occasion we were honoured with the presence of Mrs. Monroe, and of two or three of her female relatives. Crossing the hall, we were admitted to a drawing-room, in which most of the company was already assembled. The hour was six. By far the greater part of the guests were men, and perhaps two-thirds were members of Congress. It is unnecessary to describe a company that was composed of a very fair representation of Congress, which, as you already know, is composed of a very fair representation of the whole country, the very lowest classes always excepted. There was great gravity of mien in most of the company, and neither any very marked exhibition, nor any positively striking want, of grace of manner. The conversation was commonplace, and a little sombre, though two or three men of the world got around the ladies, where the battle of words was maintained with sufficient spirit. I do not know that it differed materially from a reunion any where else. To me the entertainment had rather a cold than a formal air. When dinner was announced, the oldest Senator present (there were two, and seniority of service is meant) took Mrs. Monroe and led her to the table.* The rest of the party followed without much order. The President took a lady, as usual, and preceded the rest of the guests.

The drawing-room was an apartment of a good size, and of just proportions. It might have been about as large as a better sort of Paris *salon*, in a private hotel. It was furnished in a mixed style, partly English and partly French, a custom that prevails a good deal in all the fashions of this country. It was neat, sufficiently rich, without being at all magnificent, and, on the whole, was very much like a similar apartment in the house of a man of rank and fortune in Europe. The dining-room was in a better taste than is common here, being quite simple, and but little furnished. The table was large and rather handsome. The service was in china, as is uniformly the case, plate being exceedingly rare, if at all used. There was, however, a rich plateau, and a great abundance

---

* The wife of the President is always styled the same as any other lady.

of the smaller articles of table plate. The cloth, nap-
kins, &c. &c., were fine and beautiful.

The dinner was served in the French style, a little
Americanized. The dishes were handed round, though
some of the guests, appearing to prefer their own customs, very coolly helped themselves, to what they
found at hand. Of attendants there were a good
many. They were neatly dressed, out of livery, and
sufficient. To conclude, the whole entertainment
might have passed for a better sort of European dinner party, at which the guests were too numerous
for general, or very agreeable discourse, and some of
them too *new* to be entirely at their ease. Mrs. Monroe arose at the end of the dessert, and withdrew,
attended by two or three of the most gallant of the
company. Being a stranger, Jules, I forgot the credit
of the club, and remained to see it out. No sooner
was his wife's back turned, than the President of the
United States reseated himself, inviting his guests to
imitate the action, with a wave of the hand, that
seemed to say, "Now have we a matrimonial fourth
of July." Has it never struck you, Comte de Béthizy,
that these domestic subjects feel a species of momentary triumph, as they figure at the head of their tables
without any rival in authority near? Your Englishman, and his cis-atlantic kinsman, are the only real
slaves in their own households. Most other husbands
consider matrimony, more or less, a convenience;
but these downright moralists talk of its obligations
and duties, Obligations! There is our triumph. It
is when they feel the man within them waxing bold,
as they imbibe courage with their wine, that the wife
prudently retires, rather than remain to dispute a
sway that she knows is about to weaken itself, by
libations to victory. I never feel so thoroughly independent as when I see one of your immoderately
henpecked heroes, bristling up and chuckling with
glee as he looks around on the domestic throne which

has just been momentarily abandoned by her who is seated there all the rest of the twenty-four hours. No one need seek deeper into the history of customs, than the date of this triumph, to find the origin of drunkenness after dinner.

I cannot say that Colonel Monroe abused his opportunity. After allowing all his guests sufficient time to renew, in a few glasses, the recollections of similar enjoyments of their own, he arose himself, giving the hint to his company, that it was time to join the ladies. In the drawing-room coffee was served, and every body left the house before nine.

On the succeeding Wednesday, Mrs. Monroe opened her doors to all the world. No invitation was necessary, it being the usage for the wife of the President to receive once a fortnight during the session, without distinction of persons. I waited for this evening with more curiosity than any that I remember ever to have sighed for. I could not imagine what would be the result. To my fancy, a more hazardous experiment could not be attempted. "How dare she risk the chance of insult—of degradation? or how can she tolerate the vulgarity and coarseness to which she must be exposed?" was the question I put to Cadwallader. "*Nous verrons*," was the phlegmatic answer.

We reached the White House at nine. The court (or rather the grounds) was filled with carriages, and the company was arriving in great numbers. On this occasion two or three additional drawing-rooms were opened, though the frugality of Congress has prevented them from finishing the principal reception-room of the building.* I will acknowledge the same sort of surprise that I felt at the Castle Garden fête, at find-

---

* The people furnish the entire house. It is the practice to make a moderate appropriation for that purpose, at the accession of each new President.

ing the assemblage so respectable, in air, dress, and
deportment. Determined to know exactly in what
view to consider this ceremony, I gave my companion
no peace until every thing was explained.

The " evening" at the White House, or the drawing-room, as it is sometimes pleasantly called, is in
fact a collection of all classes of people who choose
to go to the trouble and expense of appearing in
dresses suited to an ordinary evening party. I am not
sure that even dress is much regarded; for I certainly
saw a good many men there in boots. The females
were all neatly and properly attired, though few were
ornamented with jewelry. Of course the poorer and
labouring classes of the community would find little
or no pleasure in such a scene. They consequently
stay away. The infamous, if known, would not be
admitted : for it is a peculiar consequence of the high
tone of morals in this country, that grave and notorious offenders rarely presume to violate the public
feeling by invading society. Perhaps if Washington
were a large town, the "evenings" could not exist ;
but as it is, no inconvenience is experienced.

Squeezing through the crowd, we achieved a passage to a part of the room where Mrs. Monroe was
standing, surrounded by a bevy of female friends.
After making our bows here, we sought the President.
The latter had posted himself at the top of the room,
where he remained most of the evening, shaking
hands with all who approached.* Near him stood
all the Secretaries, and a great number of the most

---

* It is a mistaken opinion, however, that shaking hands is a
custom not to be dispensed with in America. Most people practise it certainly, for it is thought to be a frank, manly, and, if
you will, a republican usage. But in a certain class, it is not
considered a mark of breeding to be too free with the hand, in
casual introductions, Two gentlemen meeting would be apt to
touch their hats (unless intimates) just as in Europe, though
either of them would offer his hand to any one who he thought

distinguished men of the nation. Cadwallader pointed
out the different judges, and several members of both
houses of Congress, whose reputations were quite
familiar to me. Individuals of importance from all
parts of the Union were also here, and were employed in the manner usual to such scenes. Thus
far the "evening" would have been like any other
excessively crowded assembly; but while my eyes
were roving over the different faces, they accidentally
fell on one they knew. It was the master of an inn,
in one of the larger towns. My friend and myself
had passed a fortnight in his house. I pointed him
out to Cadwallader, and I am afraid there was something like an European sneer in my manner as I
did so.

"Yes, I have just shaken hands with him," returned my friend, coolly. "He keeps an excellent
tavern, you must allow; and, what is more, had not
that circumstance been the means of your making
his acquaintance, you might have mistaken him for
one of the magnates of the land. I understand your
look, Count de ———, better than you understand
the subject at which you are smiling. Fancy, for a
moment, that this assembly were confined to a hundred or two, like those eminent men you see collected
in that corner, and to these beautiful and remarkably
delicate women you see standing near us; in what,
except name, would it be inferior to the best collec-
tions of your side of the ocean? You need not
apologize, for we understand one another perfectly.
I know Europe rather better than you know America,
for the simple reason, that one part of Europe is so
much like another, that it is by no means an abstruse

expected it. When an European, therefore, offers to shake hand;
with an American of breeding, unless on familiar terms, he mistakes the manners of the country. The natural feeling of gentlemanly reserve is the guide there, as it is with us.

study, so far as mere manners are concerned; whereas, in America, there exists a state of things that is
entirely new.   We will make the comparison, not in
the way you are at this moment employed in doing,
but in the way common sense dictates.

"It is very true that you meet here a great variety
of people of very many conditions of life.   This
person you see on my left is a shopkeeper from New
York: no—not the one in black, but the genteel-
looking man in blue—I dare say you took him for an
attaché of one of the legations.   And this lovely creature, who demeans herself with so much elegance
and propriety, is the daughter of a mechanic of Baltimore.   In this manner we might dissect half the
company, perhaps; some being of better, and some
of worse, exteriors.   But what does it all prove ?
Not that the President of the United States is obliged
to throw open his doors to the rabble, as you might
be tempted to call it, for he is under no sort of obligation to open his doors to any body.   But he chooses
to see the world, and he must do one of two things.
He must make invidious and difficult selections,
which, in a public man, would excite just remarks
in a government like ours, or he must run the hazard
of remaining three or four hours in a room filled with
a promiscuous assembly.   He has wisely chosen the
latter.

"What is the consequence?   Your ears are not offended by improper discourse.   Your individuality is
not wounded by impertinence, nor even your taste
annoyed by any very striking coarseness of manner.
Now it appears to me, that every American should
exult in this very exhibition.   Not for the vulgar reason that it is a proof of the equality of our rights, for
it is a mistake to think that society is a necessary de-
pendant of government.   In this respect the 'evenings' are some such deception as that ceremony one
hears of in Europe, in which sovereigns wash the

feet of beggars. But he should exult that the house
of his first magistrate can be thrown open to the
world, and an assembly so well-behaved, so decent,
so reasonable, so free alike from sheepishness and
presumption, in short so completely creditable, in
every point of view, is collected by the liberty.
Open the doors of one of your palaces in this manner, and let us see what would be the character of
the company.

" There is a good sense in our community, which
removes all dangers of unpleasant consequences from
too much familiarity. It imposes the necessity on
him who would be thought a gentleman, of being cir-
cumspect and reasonable, but it leaves him sufficiently the master of all his movements and associations.
The seeming scarcity of high-bred men in this country, compared with the number one sees in Europe,
is much less owing to our form of government, than
the fact that they are so widely scattered. Quite
half, too, of what is called fastidious breeding, is purely conventional, and, to make conventions, men must
meet.

" I have known a cartman leave his horse in the
street, and go into a reception-room to shake hands
with the President. He offended the good sense of
all present, because it was not thought decent that a
labourer should come in a dirty dress on such an occasion ; but while he made a trifling mistake in this
particular, he proved how well he understood the
difference between government and society. He
knew the levee was a sort of homage paid to political equality in the person of the first magistrate, but
he would not have presumed to enter the house of
the same person as a private individual without being
invited, or without a reasonable excuse in the way
of business.

" There are, no doubt, individuals who mistake
the character of these assemblies, but the great ma-

jority do not. They are simply a periodical acknowledgment, that there is no legal barrier to the advancement of any one to the first association in the Union. You perceive there are no masters of ceremonies, no ushers, no announcing, nor indeed any let or hindrance to the ingress of all who please to come; and yet how few, in comparison to the whole number who might enter, do actually appear. If there is any man, in Washington, so dull as to suppose equality means a right to thrust himself into any company he pleases, it is probable he satisfies his vanity by boasting that he can go to the White House once a fortnight as well as a governor or any body else. You will confess his pride is appeased at a cheap rate. Any prince can collect a well-dressed and well-behaved crowd by calling his nobles around him; but I fancy the President of the United States is the only head of a nation who need feel no apprehension of throwing open his doors to every body. Until you can show an assembly composed of similar materials, which shall equal this, not only in decency, but in ease and in general manners, you ought in reason to be content to confess your inferiority."

You will perceive the utter impossibility of having an opinion of your own, dear Jules, when a man is obstinately bent on considering things always in reference to common sense, instead of consulting the reverend usages which have been established by the world, whether founded on prejudice or not. So far as mere appearance goes, I must confess, however, my friend was not very wrong, since the company at the White House, on this occasion, was certainly as well-behaved, all things considered, as could be wished.

TO THE BARON VON KEMPERFELT,

&c. &c.

Washington, ———

WASHINGTON, as it contains all the public offices, is the best place to ascertain the general statistical facts connected with the condition of this country. I have hitherto purposely avoided touching on the marine of the United States, until I should have an opportunity of getting the information necessary to do it justice. On no occasion, however, have I neglected to examine the ships and the navy-yards as I passed through the seaports, though I have reserved all my remarks until I had something material to communicate. It is my intention to dispose of the subject altogether in this letter.

Until the period of the war which separated the two countries, the American mariners performed most of their military service in the navy of Great Britain. The history of the colonies, however, is not altogether destitute of nautical incidents, that were rather remarkable for skill and enterprise. The privateers of this hemisphere were always conspicuous in the colonial contests; and they were then, as they have always been since, of a character for order and chivalry that ought not to be too confidently expected from a class of adventurers who professedly take up arms for an object so little justifiable, and perhaps so ignoble, as gain. But men of a stamp altogether superior to the privateersmen of Europe were induced, by the peculiar situation of their country, to embark in these doubtful military enterprises in America. There was no regular service in which to show their martial qualities; and those among them who felt a longing for the hazards and adventures of naval warfare, were obliged to hoist these semi-chivalrous flags, or to stay at home. Still, unless very wrongly informed, it was much the fashion for the gentry of the colonies to place their sons in the navy of the mother country; and many distinguished names, in the higher ranks of the British marine at this day, have been pointed out to me in corroboration of the circumstance. It is generally believed that Washington himself was destined to such a life, and that nothing but the unconquerable reluctance of a tender mother prevented him from figuring in a very different character from that which he was afterwards enabled to enact with so much usefulness and true glory.

The first evidences of a nautical enterprise, on an extended scale, that I can discover in the history of these people, are contained in the accounts of the expedition against Louisbourg. The States of New-England, or rather Massachusetts alone, undertook to reduce that important fortress during the war of 1745. A considerable naval armament accompanied the expedition, which was successful, though it contained no ship of a force sufficient to combat with the heavier vessels of their enemy. Still it manifested a disposition to the sort of warfare of which I am writing, more especially as the mother country not only possessed a squadron near, but actually employed it in the service. A people whose maritime propensities were less strong might have been content to have thrown the whole of this branch of the undertaking on an ally that was so well qualified to discharge the duty with credit.

At the commencement of the struggle for independence, notwithstanding the overwhelming force of their enemy, the Americans early showed the new flag on the ocean. Almost any other people of the world, under similar circumstances, would have re-

tired into their valleys and fastnesses; but the privateers and public cruisers of America, while the
divided and feeble population at home were struggling daily for their political existence, continued,
during the whole of that war, to carry hostilities
even to the shores of Great Britain. Had the government of the country even wished to husband its resources for domestic defence, it is more than probable
it would have been found that it did not possess sufficient authority to repress the nautical temper of the
country. It acted a wiser part. Although a more hopeless adventure could not apparently be conceived,
than for these infant States to contend against the
overwhelming power of England on the ocean, yet
the new government early directed a considerable portion of its scanty means to that object. Nor was the
desperate adventure without its benefits. It served to
make the nations of Europe more familiarly acquainted with the power that was struggling into existence,
and it afforded an additional pledge of its final success, by furnishing visible evidence of the possession
of an enterprise that merited confidence and support.
Though the marine of the United States, in the war
of the revolution, was imperfectly organized, and
exceedingly weak, the spirit of their seamen was
often exhibited in a manner to show that the nation
possessed an extraordinary aptitude to that particular
species of service. Their discipline was not, nor
could not well be, better than that ordinarily observed
on board of private vessels of war, since the ships
were of necessity officered by men taken from the
trading vessels of the country; still the battles of that
period were often bloody and severe, and were fre
quently attended with a signal and brilliant success.

At the peace of '83, the half-formed and imperfect
marine of the country disappeared. The confederation, as it then existed, did not admit, without an
important object, of the exercise of a power that

involved so serious an expense as its maintenance.
Each State, at that time, collected its own imposts,
and imposed its own taxes. A few schooners, for the
security of the revenue, were kept in some of the
larger seaports; but of a navy, either in officers or
ships, there was postively none.

When the constitution of the country, as it now
exists, was adopted (in 1789), Washington was placed
at the head of the country, filling, for the first time, its
highest civil station. He recommended the construction of a few frigates, in order to protect its commerce
against the depredations of the Barbary powers, who
were then in the fullest practice of those lawless
robberies which were so long the scourge and disgrace of the civilized world. This recommendation
was the foundation of the present navy of the United
States. Though, so far as the Algerines themselves
were concerned, a war actually existed, no cruizer
of this country took part in its operations. According
to the fashion of that day, peace was soon *purchased*.
But the capture of a few of their unarmed merchantmen had served to apprize the Americans of the
absolute necessity of a marine to protect their rights
as a commercial community.

This little affair was scarcely adjusted before a
misunderstanding occurred between the French and
American republics. A sort of armed neutrality was
attempted by the latter; but, though no declaration
of war was ever actually made, it soon terminated in
open hostilities. It was now thought prudent to extend a still greater protection to the commerce of the
country, and a sudden and considerable increase to
the navy was made. In order to effect this purpose,
it became necessary to build or to purchase ships,
and to procure officers. Vessels were both bought
and constructed, and seamen of various degrees of
character were induced to abandon the peaceful for
the more warlike pursuits of their profession. A small

corps of officers had been chosen to command the first half-dozen frigates from among the veterans who still survived the great struggle for independence ; but this was a body soon exhausted, especially as it was found necessary that a rigid selection should be observed. To supply the deficiencies, spirited and skilful young men were sought among the masters and the mates of the merchantmen. A mixed marine was by these means created, though it is scarcely possible not to believe that in ships and commanders there must have existed the utmost inequality of merit and of fitness for the duty required of both. Still, as the propensity of the nation is so decidedly maritime, the war proved creditable. Many battles were fought, and with a success that was invariable.

This maritime war occurred during the presidency of Mr. Adams. The creation of a navy was thought to be a favourite measure of his policy ; and as opposition grew warm, the wisdom of so early and so considerable an expenditure of the public money was much disputed. Men who admitted that nature and reason both pointed to the ocean as the place where the rights of the nation were to be maintained, still affirmed that the measure was premature. The country was involved in a heavy debt, and the very means that were resorted to, in order to protect the wealth of the country, might induce quarrels which would inevitably involve its loss. But this reasoning did not immediately prevail, as the administration contrived to keep its majorities in the two houses until near the close of its constitutional period of service.

In the midst of these disputes, the grave determination of the country is to be traced in its permanent legislative enactments. In 1798, a navy department was created, and its Secretary was admitted to a seat in the cabinet. Notwithstanding the clamour which had been raised by the opposition against the marine, when the power passed into their hands no very serious blow was meditated or practised against its positive existence. So much had been said on the subject of economy, that some reduction became necessary. Perhaps in the peculiar circumstances under which the officers and ships had been collected, it was prudent. The vessels, which had been purchased to meet the emergency, were therefore sold, and by far the greater part of the officers were discharged.

At one time, during the disturbance with France, near sixty public cruisers were employed on the American coast, or in the West Indies, under the flag of the republic. Most of them were merchantmen that had been purchased and altered to suit their new destination, and many that were expressly built, had been constructed in a hurry, and of course imperfectly. Of the officers it is unnecessary to say more than that they embraced, perhaps, the very best and the very worst men of their class. Most of these vessels were small, the largest only rating 44, and actually mounting 54 guns. The majority were clumsy sloops, carrying between 16 and 24 guns.

Now that the heat of opposition has passed away, the best-informed men candidly admit that there was but little inducement to retain officers or ships so promiscuously and so hurriedly assembled. Notwithstanding its apparent hostility, the new government, while reducing the service, was rather disposed to cherish a good and efficient marine than to destroy it.

In 1801, an act was passed, creating a naval peace establishment. This was the law which gave form and permanent existence to the present marine of the country.

By the act of 1801, the number of the ships was reduced to nine frigates, of various sizes, with a few smaller vessels. A sufficient number of officers was retained for their command. From that hour to this,

the corps has never been reduced in the slightest
manner, though the army has been the subject of
repeated increases and of as frequent reductions.
The boy who now enters the navy a midshipman,
enters it with a conviction that, should he behave
with prudence and spirit, he has a highly creditable
employment for life.

The partial reduction of 1801, gave the marine
department an opportunity of making a selection
among the officers, as well as among the ships. Personal interest, apart from personal merit, could have
no great influence on the movements of this government, especially in a case of so great notoriety as
that of a choice between officers of any rank. The
captains retained were men of character and experience; and it is probable that a finer corps of inferior
naval officers, than those who were retained on this
occasion, never had an existence.

In 1803, the bashaw of Tripoli commenced hostilities against the republic. Different squadrons were
sent into the Mediterranean to oppose the depredations. His corsairs were driven from the sea, and
his town was blockaded. From watchfulness, the
Americans soon proceeded to attacks, until the slumbers of the Africans were almost nightly broken by
the assaults of their weak but spirited foes. The
history of this war, in miniature, is remarkable for
its romantic incidents, and for the high daring of the
actors. A few light cruisers, with a dozen gun-boats,
and a couple of ketches, backed by a single frigate,
would often lie for hours under the batteries and
shipping of the town, throwing their shot even into
the palace of the barbarian. On several occasions
the conflicts were still more serious. Battles were
fought in closest personal collision; officers and men,
Christian and Turk, struggling fiercely for the victory, hand to hand. It was to commemorate the
names of the brave youths who fell in these sanguinary

struggles, that the little monument, already named, was erected in the Navy-Yard at Washington.

The war with Tripoli was also distinguished by an enterprise that was as remarkable for its conception, as for the spirit and skill with which it was conducted. The reigning bashaw of Tripoli was an usurper, having, some years before, expelled his brother from the throne. The banished prince had sought a refuge among the Arabs of the desert in Upper Egypt. The American consul to the regency of Algiers, was a person of the name of Eaton. This gentleman had once been a captain in the army of the Union. He was a man distinguished for his reckless courage and for a restless enterprise. During the time the squadron of his country was employed in harassing the town of their enemy, Mr. Eaton, accompanied by two or three officers of the navy, sought out the exiled bashaw in the desert, and induced him to lend himself to an attempt to recover his throne. A force, consisting of Arabs, Turks, Christians, and of adventurers from all countries, was soon assembled. It entered the territories of Tripoli by its eastern frontier, and advanced rapidly upon Derne, the second town of the principality. Here it was met and sustained by a few light cruizers from the American squadron. A sharp skirmish was fought in the vicinity of the town, and the place was carried. A crisis was evidently at hand. There was every prospect of complete success to this chivalrous undertaking, when the whole enterprise was defeated by an event as mortifying as it was unexpected. A negotiator had just before arrived from America; conceiving it to be his duty to terminate the war, he profited by the terror excited in the bosom of the reigning bashaw, by the success of his brother, and signed a treaty of peace. But for this premature occurrence, the world would probably have witnessed the singular spectacle of a power of the western hemisphere commencing

thus early the work of retaliation, by setting up and
pulling down dynasties of the eastern.

The navy of the United States owes most of its discipline, and of its high reputation for spirit and enterprise, aided by the ambitious natural character of
the people, to the experience it obtained in the war
with Tripoli. The young men (chiefly of the best families of the country), who had commenced their military career in the affair with France, received their commissions during, or at the close of this war; and they
brought with them into the higher ranks of the service, the feelings and habits so necessary to their
class. Officers were now first seen in the command
of vessels, who had regularly risen from the lowest
ranks of the service.

From the time of the peace with Tripoli to that of
the war of England, the navy was employed in guard-
ing the coast, and in aiding to enforce the restrictive
laws of the country. A few light vessels were built,
and a plan of defending the seaports, in the event of
need, by gun-boats, grew into favour. The American
naval officers say, that the latter scheme had nearly
proved fatal to the tone and discipline of their service.
It was, however, of short duration, and the subsequent hostilities completely proved its fallacy.*

---

* Many absurd statements, concerning the organization of the
American navy, have been circulated in Europe. There is none
more false or more foolish than the story that young mates of
merchantmen are, or ever have been, taken for the first steps in
the service. Boys, between the ages of twelve and eighteen,
receive the appointments of midshipmen, and after having served
a certain number of years, they are examined for lieutenants.
These examinations are very rigid, and they are conducted with
the greatest impartiality. While the writer was in America, he
formed an intimacy with the commander of a frigate. One day,
at Washington, he entered the room of the captain, just as a
naval officer of high rank was quitting it. " You met one of the
commissioners at the door," said the writer's acquaintance; " he
has been to beg I would make his son, who is just ordered to my

In 1812, the marine of the United States existed rather as the *nucleus* of a future service, than as a force to be directed to any of the more important objects of warfare. It was sufficient to keep alive the spirit, and to gratify the pride of the nation, but not to produce any serious result on the great objects of the struggle. So far as I can discover, the whole

---

ship, mind his books. They tell me the young fellow is clever enough, and a very good sailor, but he has been twice defeated in trying to get through with his mathematics, because he will not study." In what other navy would the son of a lord of the admiralty lose his commission, in two examinations, for want of a little mathematics?

The most severe system of examination, not only into professional qualifications, but into moral character, is now rigidly observed in the American army and navy. The lower ranks of both branches of their service, are admirably filled. Midshipmen, instead of being taken from the merchant service, have been often taken from the service, under furloughs, to command merchant-ships. No man in the world is more jealous of his rank, than the American navy or army officer. It would far exceed the power of the President to push his own son an inch beyond the steps he is entitled to by his age and service. The Senate would refuse to approve of such a nomination. The same impartiality is observed in respect to commands. A captain, or commander, is not only sure of getting a ship, when his turn comes, but he must have an excellent excuse or he will be made to take one. Both establishments are kept within reasonable bounds, and promotions are slow and wary. There is not a single officer necessarily on half-pay, either in the land or sea service. There is not now, nor has there been for twenty years, an officer in the American navy, in command of a ship, the four or five oldest excepted, who did not regularly enter the marine as a midshipman. Even the oldest entered as low as a lieutenant, quite thirty years ago. A Secretary of the Navy, during the war of 1812, is said to have wished to introduce a brother from the merchant service, by giving him the command of a cartel, but entirely without success. Some six or eight clever men, who entered as sailing-masters, a class generally taken from the merchant service, have been so successful as to get commissions, a favour a little out of course, though sometimes practised to reward merit. Several of these, even, were midshipmen who had resigned, and had re-entered as masters, in the war, because they thought themselves too old to begin anew as midshipmen.

navy of the country, at that time, consisted of the
following ships : three frigates, rating forty-four guns
each, and fighting fifty-four ; three, rating thirty-six,
and fighting fifty ; one, rating thirty-two, and fighting
forty-two, or forty-four ; two, rating twenty-four, and
fighting twenty-four or twenty-six ; and eight or ten
sloops and schooners carrying from ten to twenty
guns.   There were three or four more frigates of no
great force : but they were rotten, and never employed.   Perhaps the whole marine might have included
twenty cruizers of all sizes.   The events of that period are so recent as to be sufficiently known.   The
war has, however, given a new impulse to the marine
of this country, and one which will probably lead to
the introduction of its fleets into the future contests
of Christendom.

The English are said to have employed more than
a hundred sail of cruizers on the coast of the United
States, between the years 1813 and 1815.   Whatever
might have been the intentions of the British government, it is very certain that much useless annoyance
was given to peaceful people by the depredations of
some of these vessels.   Even the expeditions which
were attempted on a larger scale, argued a great
ignorance of the character of this nation, since they
exhibited a very mistaken application of force to
attain what the world has every reason to believe
was the object of the assailants.

It is fair to presume that the English commanders
had determined to harass the country, with a view to
bring the war as near as possible to each man's door.
Now, it so happens, that, notwithstanding the large
bays and deep rivers of this continent enabled those
who had command of the water, to do a great deal
of injury, their attacks did not, nor could not, produce
the least effect on the mass of the nation.   Harassing
expeditions, and burnings, and alarms, might serve to
exasperate, but in no degree did they serve to subdue

They often wounded the pride, and excited the indignation of the Americans, without in the slightest degree enfeebling their power. A government like this is weak, or strong, for all offensive purposes, exactly in the proportion that its efforts are popular. It is well known that a serious opposition to the war with England existed in the country from its commencement to its close. But it is just as well known, that these very acts of exasperating hostility had begun to shut the mouths of the friends of England, while they permitted her enemies to declaim the louder. Had the contest continued another year, it is probable it would have afforded a very different scene. The American government, strengthened by the blunder, and excited by the inroads of its enemy, was seriously turning its attention to the work of retaliation. When peace was unexpectedly announced, two squadrons of fast-sailing schooners, bought for the purpose, were about to sail with orders to burn, ravage, and destroy. The firebrand would have gleamed on the island of Great Britain itself; and God only knows what horrid character the war would have next assumed. All experience shows that this is a nation, however patient and enduring it may seem under contumely and aggression, which knows how to rise in its anger, and to make itself dreaded even by the strongest.

But the chief and the most lasting effect of the British policy, during the war of 1814, has been to bring a respectable American marine into a sudden existence. This truth is proved by the fact, that the Congress, which, in these matters, takes most of its impulses from the people, exhibited the extraordinary policy of increasing, instead of reducing, its armaments with the peace. The whole nation saw and felt the necessity of protecting their coast, and the friends of the navy have seized the happy moment to interweave the policy with their institutions, in such a manner as to render them henceforth inseparable. That they ought to be inseparable, every man, in the least familiar with the interests of this country, can see; but it was a great point gained to induce a people so wary of expenditure, to incur the cost of a marine, without an immediate demand for its use. *You* need not be told, that without a service in peace a service in war is next to useless, since experience, method, and even the high spirit necessary to continued military success, are all the fruits of time. But economical legislators, who count nothing but the present cost, are not always so sagacious.

While passing rapidly over this subject, it may be well to mention the little incident of the last war with Algiers, since it serves to show the spirit with which these people will enter on all similar enterprises, when a little more age shall give maturity and strength to their efforts. The barbarians had seized the opportunity of the British war to commit depredations on the American commerce. No sooner was the peace of 1815 ratified, than Congress issued a solemn declaration of war against the regency. A squadron immediately sailed for the Mediterranean. It crossed the Atlantic; passed the Straits; routed and destroyed the marine of their foe; carried the war to the mouth of his harbour; and, in six weeks from the day of sailing, it dictated an honourable and lasting peace, under the cannon of the city. Ten years before, it had sued for disgraceful terms from an inferior power of Barbary. This was the first treaty, I believe, in which the right to lead prisoners into slavery was formally disavowed by any of the African states.

During the war with England, several laws were passed, empowering the President to add to the marine. In 1813, four vessels of a force *not less* than seventy-four guns, and six frigates of a force *not less* than forty-four guns, were authorized. Squadrons were constructed on the lakes, and sloops of war, of various sizes, were built, from time to time. In 1816 the Act "for the gradual increase of the Navy of the United States" was passed. By the provisions of this law, eight additional ships of the line, of *not less* than seventy-four guns, and nine additional frigates of *not less** than forty-four guns, were commanded. The President was instructed to procure the timber of three more steam-batteries, which were to be put in such a state as to admit of their soonest possible construction in time of need. As the object of this force was to anticipate the emergency of any future war, a sum of one million of dollars was appropriated annually, in order to procure the timber, and to insure the best and most desirable construction. In 1822, this law was altered, so as to extend the time, and to reduce the annual appropriation one-half.

Various other laws were passed, affecting the interests of the navy. Some were for the improvement of the officers; others for the preservation of the live-oak, the inestimable material always employed in the construction of a valuable American ship. So minute and cautious was the interest taken in the service, that a law was even passed to regulate the manner in which the vessels were to be named. A ship of the line was to be called after a State; the frigates, after rivers; and the sloops, after the larger towns. The vessels authorized by the last law are now all on the stocks, or they have been already launched.†

---

* Congress often gives discretionary power to the President, limiting its exercise in this manner. From this practice has arisen the mistake that the Americans mean to call three-deckers seventy-fours.

† While the writer was in the country, a law was passed to build ten additional sloops of war, and a frigate was bought that had been constructed for the Greeks. Since he has left America, another law has been passed, appropriating half a mil

The actual naval force of this country afloat, or which might be put afloat in the course of a few weeks, is nearly as follows : one first-rate ; eight second ditto, first class, and three ditto of second class ; nine third-rates, first class, and three ditto of second class ; and sixteen corvettes and sloops of war.   To these must be added a few schooners and light vessels, whose number is constantly varying. The materials of one forty-four are also prepared, but, in consequence of the purchase of a frigate, her construction is temporarily delayed.   There appears to be no use in urging the building of these vessels, which are all the better for delay, and which are only launched as they are wanted for experiments, or for actual service.   Perhaps we may call the force at instant command, or which might be fitted before the crews could be assembled, at fifty sail, of all sizes.* This excludes the vessels on the lakes, the whole of which were sold by a law of 1825, except two ships of the line (on the stocks) on Lake Ontario.   I exclude all vessels that are not actually intended to go to sea.   If there is any error, it is in the very smallest vessels, whose number, as I have already said, is con-

lion of dollars annually, for six years, for the purpose of purchasing the materials for vessels of the different classes already known in the service.   By the report of the commissioners, it seems that contracts have actually been made for the frames of five sail of the line, five frigates, and five sloops, all of the first class.   Two dry docks are, also, now in the course of construction, and a third is much urged in Congress.   A new navy-yard has also been established in the Gulf of Mexico.   A naval academy is pressed by the government.   He believes these are tho principal measures taken since the year 1826.

* To these must shortly be added, the vessels whose frames and materials are now in the course of collection.   The rapid manner in which the Americans run up a ship at need, is well known.   It is clear, that when the materials shall be in readiness. their force could easily be increased to near or quite seventy sail, small vessels included.

stantly varying, by shipwrecks, sales, and re-constructions.

With what force the Americans would absolutely put to sea, in the event of an immediate war, that should call for all their energy, might be difficult to anticipate. This government is at once both the strongest and the weakest in the world. It is weak compared to its wealth and physical means, in all cases of ordinary offensive operations, precisely as other governments are weak or strong in proportion to the absolute nature of the power they wield. But in a popular war, when power shall be conceded freely to the executive, it is so much the stronger as the government is assured of a cordial and enthusiastic support. I think the power of the United States, in actual warfare, will always be found to be exactly in proportion to the greater or less degree of cordiality with which the mass of the people shall enter into the views of the administration. The present navy of the United States would be formidable under any circumstances, to all second-rate maritime powers, since the skill and enterprise of its officers, aided by such legal support as a majority could always command, would at all times enable them to act with sufficient energy out of the country. I think also, in the event of a war, clearly defensive, with any of the greater powers, it would be unwise to calculate on having less than the whole of the marine to oppose, and that instantly. But we may form a better opinion of these matters by going a little into detail.

It would require about 20,000 men, to man the whole of the present marine of this country. This may sound large to your ears, but it is necessary to remember how very large a proportion of the estimated fifty sail are vessels of great size. Of this number more than one thousand would be those officers, who are always retained as a regular and durable part of the service. The fifty sail will carry, as near as I can discover, about 2,500 guns. It is a rule to put one marine to each gun. This proportion, including officers, non-commissioned officers, music, &c., would make a corps of troops of, we will say, 2,500. For petty officers and seamen 10,000 would be a very liberal allowance, leaving a deficiency of 6,500 to be composed of ordinary seamen, landsmen and boys. These calculations may not be critically exact, but I think that they are near enough to the truth to answer the present object.

I think it can scarcely be doubted that the United States possess 30,000 men, sufficiently skilful to be rated as seamen, on board a vessel of war. If this be admitted, the question is reduced to the inquiry, of whether she can induce one-third of her seamen to serve in her navy.

The plenty or scarcity of mariners in the United States, is altogether a matter of demand and supply. There is clearly no surplus population to beg employment; and there is also a general aptitude among the natives, that enables them to gain their living in more ways than one. A seaman is a sort of artisan; and he requires rather higher wages than the labourer on shore, as a reward for his peculiar skill, and a compensation for his greater privation. It is a peculiarity of this country, that sailors, especially in New-York, and in all the Eastern States, are often found on land; not begging their bread, or sweeping the streets, but engaged in some creditable employment that gives them support. To meet any extraordinary demand, these men commonly return to the sea. Such of them as are impatient of a monotonous life, and who are unwilling to serve for reduced wages, as is at present the case, seek employment elsewhere. The public and private cruizers of the South American States, abound with such adventurers.

Now, it is rather a striking feature in the character

of the lower orders of the Americans, that they rarely lose their native attachments. They have a great and fixed contempt for all monarchies. It is necessary to overcome a principle that has settled into a prejudice, in order to make them respect any sort of government but a republic. Money will buy them, no doubt, but they require to be bought. They are not accidents on the surface of society that are willing to float, like most other mariners, whither the current shall carry them, but they are men who can only find the opinions which lie at the root of all their habits, in their native land. Unlike the subject of any other system on earth, the American, who is unfortunate, can lay no part of his calamity to his country. He was not born in a region where climate, or monopoly, or excessive population, or any other adverse cause, presses him of necessity to the earth. He retains in all situations a respect, a love, and frequently a longing, for the place of his birth. With money and opportunity, America might procure thousands of every nation in Europe to serve in any cause; but it may be questioned if this whole country furnishes one hundred men base enough to enlist in positive warfare against its institutions or rights. It is a consequence of this feeling, that the United States are more sure than other powers of retaining to themselves that portion of their population, which has taken to the sea for a livelihood.

These feelings would recall, and have recalled, the American sailor home, in the moment of hostilities; a time when the mariners of other nations seek opportunities of going abroad. He is not afraid to stand, at any time, on his native soil, for he knows that there is a law for him as well as for other men. Though he may be the perfect master of his own movements, a sailor is eminently a social creature. He is ever inclined, as you know by experience, to follow a general impulse. I am of opinion that in a popu-

lar war, the naval rendezvous of this country would
be thronged; though it is certainly easy to conceive
circumstances in which it would be difficult to procure men.

In the war of 1798–9, crews were often got for
frigates in a single day. There were two reasons for
this abundance of men. Privateers were not profitable against the trade of France, and the conflict
was particularly in unison with the feelings of all
nautical men. In the war with England, there was
sometimes a momentary difficulty in filling a crew;
but then privateers abounded. There was also another reason why seamen were reluctant to enter
the national cruizers, during the war with England:
crews were often transferred, in gross, from the sea-
board to the lakes. The latter was a service in bad
odour. There was no prize-money, nor did it at
all accord with the prejudices of a tar, to be running
in and out of a port on a great fresh-water pond.
Still, near the close of that war, though the services
of a great number of men were lost to the country,
by being captured in privateers, I am told, that such
crews were rarely known in the marine of any nation,
as then began freely to offer themselves.

These are familiar reasons that must have a greater
or less bearing on the facility of procuring seamen
for the public service in the United States. The influence of a popular impulse can scarcely be estimated; though it is quite within the reach of probability that it should be exceedingly great. There are
also other influences, which might be very powerful
in producing a ready supply of men. A war would
be declared, either when many merchant-ships were
at sea, or when they were not. In the former case
the whole mercantile community would feel a direct
and powerful interest in manning their fleets; and in
the latter, seamen would be out of employ. Then,
the government could at all times create a monopoly

in its own favour, by refusing to grant private commissions, or even by imposing an embargo.   The
former has never yet been done, because it was the
policy of the country to encourage privateers, since,
heretofore, they have had no other very efficient
means of annoying their enemy.

On the whole, I incline to the opinion, that the
fifty sail, which this country now possesses, could be
manned, in a reasonable time, without resorting to
any extraordinary means of inducing the men to enter.
Still, in a country like this, so much depends on the
particular impulses of the day, that it is a question
which will admit of dispute.   A situation of things
might be imagined in which a ship of the line would
readily get a crew in a day, and then, again, circumstances might easily occur that would render enlistments tardy and reluctant.   This is always supposing
the supply to be left to the ordinary operations of trade,
or to the influences of popular excitement.   For the
purpose of any long-continued and serious naval service, the government has in reserve most of the ordinary resources of other nations.

Although impressment is not, ought not to be, nor
probably ever will be tolerated in the United States,
a naval draft would be perfectly just; and if it be not
now, it might easily be made constitutional.   As the
law stands, a seaman is exempted from all military duty, because it is the policy of the country to
encourage its commerce.   But there is clearly no
reason in natural justice why a sailor should not risk
his life in defence of the rights of his fellow-citizens
as well as a landsman.   This point being admitted, it
is both more politic and more humane that he should
perform the duty on an element to which he is accustomed, and in a service that he understands, than
by doing violence to his habits by becoming a soldier.
There are a variety of ways in which the government of the United States might even now, with per-

fect legality, place most of the seamen, which actually exist in the country, more or less at its own disposal. I have already mentioned an embargo as one powerful means of manning a fleet.

It is not an exaggerated estimate to suppose that, shortly after the commencement of the war with England, 10,000 men were serving in the American privateers. This number alone, added to the crews in the regular service at the same period, would more than man the whole of the present force of the country. There can be no doubt that what the nation did with a population of 8,000,000, and a tonnage of 1,200,000, it could now do, with far greater facility, with a population of 12,000,000, and a tonnage of near 1,600,000.

In almost every war into which the United States can enter, their operations must, of necessity be conducted on the water. Canada and Mexico excepted, they have no immediate neighbours on the land. But a war with Canada would be a war with England, and the experience of the contest of 1812, has taught the Americans, that neither their commerce nor their shores are safe in such a war without a marine. Their growing fleet owes its existence solely to this conviction. The present naval force of the country, compared to that which it possessed in 1812, is already as twenty to one : not in the actual number of the vessels, certainly, but in their size, and in their consequent ability to resist, or to attack. In 1812, the Americans could show but seven frigates, only three of which were of any magnitude, while now they might show a line of twenty-seven sail, the smallest vessel in which should be the largest vessel they possessed in 1812, and the largest a ship of six times the force of the latter. This change denotes, to say the least, a serious intention to protect themselves.

The situation of the United States calls for no very hasty, or over-jealous vigour, in military preparation. The people of the country know their unrivalled advantages. A war like that which England lately waged with France, a war of twenty years, would, if America were a party, be commenced with a nation of 12,000,000, and be ended with one of 20,000,000 of souls! In the security of their remote position, and of their rapidly increasing strength, the people of this country are in no hurry to spend their money Their actual fleet, instead of being a forced and premature establishment, is rather the result of inevitable circumstances. What nation before this was ever known to have 1,200,000 tons of shipping, with seven frigates and eight or ten small cruizers for its protection? It appears to me, that so far from considering the present maritime force of the United States as the utmost they can do, it ought to be considered rather as the result of what they cannot help doing. Money, skill, materials, pride, interest, and even necessity, unite to give birth to their fleets. The surprise should not be, that they are now creating a marine, but that they have so long neglected the duty. I am of opinion, that the past will be a guide for the future, in this respect. The United States may be driven to an exercise of their energies; but, if left to themselves, it will be found that all their military establishments will rather follow than lead the country. The natural order of things will accumulate the power of the republic quite fast enough for its own happiness, or for the peace of the world.

Until now the Americans have been tracing the outline of their great national picture. The work of filling up has just seriously commenced. The Gulf of Mexico, the Lakes of Canada, the Prairies, and the Atlantic, form the setting. They are now, in substance, à vast island, and the tide of emigration, which has so long been flowing westward, must have its reflux. Adventurers in the arts, in manufactures, in commerce, and in short, in every thing else, are already beginning to return from the western to the eastern borders. It is true that the force of the current is still toward the newer countries, but the time is near for those regions to give back some of their increase. Thousands of single men already find their way from Vermont, from the western counties of New-York and Pennsylvania, and from even Ohio, to the sea-shores, as labourers and traders. Population is becoming dense, and as it accumulates it will acquire the energy of a concentrated force.

Although ages must elapse before necessity shall drive man to beggary, or to abject dependence, in the United States, the time for a more regular increase of the people over the whole surface has commenced. It is true, that large districts still remain empty; but a variety of causes has, in the first place, a tendency to retard their settlement, and, in the second place, it must be remembered how much sooner 12,000,000 can fill a vacuum than 4,000,000.

The people of the older States are getting a taste for the arts and comforts of life, that disinclines vast numbers to encounter the privations of the forest. New-England, the great hive of emigrants, was a comparatively sterile and unfavoured region; and, twenty years ago, it possessed few other employments than those of husbandry. But climate, richness of soil, and moral considerations included, the more eligible parts of the country are now occupied. The emigrant (of 1790, and of 1800) to New-York or to Ohio, returned with accounts of advantages to which the inhabitant of Massachusetts or Connecticut was a stranger; but the emigrant to Illinois, to Indiana, to Kentucky, or to Missouri, is apt to pine for things that he has left behind him. Manufactures, and the thousand additional pursuits of a growing wealth, are beginning to chain men to their birth-places. The effects are already to be traced in the returns of the population.

New-York has been what is termed an emigrating State, these twenty years, and yet her population has increased near 18 per cent. within the last five.*

Although the supply of seamen must, for many years, be limited to the demand, since men can find support in other employments, the government can at any time create a demand of its own, in order to keep up the number necessary for the two services—viz. the navy and that of commerce. Hitherto no artificial means of creating seamen have been adopted. The government has as yet had no motive for such extraordinary care. They employ, in point of fact, only about twenty sail.† These vessels are manned by a very simple system, and with little or no difficulty. Rendezvous are opened in the different ports when men are needed; and, as they enter, they are placed on board of receiving vessels, where they continue until a draft is made for a crew. They pay no bounty, nor do the wages ever vary to meet the fluctuations in the price of seamen's wages in the merchantmen. The wages of a seaman are, however, something higher than those paid by any other nation to men in the public service.‡ When the ships are

---

* The births exceeded the deaths, in New-York, (1825) 38,840 souls; or at a rate that, notwithstanding emigration, would double its population once in forty years.

† The actual force of cruizers in commission (1828) is one ship of the line, six frigates, two corvettes, ten sloops, and four schooners. These vessels, including the ordinary, are manned by five thousand three hundred and eighteen men.

‡ A captain, commanding a ship of any force, receives 100 dollars a month, and eight rations a day; if he command a small ship, his pay is 75 dollars, and six rations. The pay of the other classes is as follows:—master commandant, 60 dollars, five rations; lieutenant commandant, 50 dollars and four rations; lieutenant, 40 dollars and three rations; master, 40 dollars and two rations; past-midshipman, 25 dollars and two rations; midshipman, 19 dollars and one ration; boatswain, gunner, sailmaker, and carpenter, 20 dollars and two rations; petty officers, 19 dollars and one ration; seaman, 12 dollars and one ration;

manned, orders are given to stop the enlistments. The supply varies, of course, a crew being sometimes obtained in a few days, and sometimes not in many weeks.

As the Americans add to the number of vessels employed in their service, they will, certainly, facilitate the means of a supply by increasing the demand. The great outlet to the rest of the world, the path of adventure, and the only, at least the principal, theatre for military achievements open to the people of this country, is on the ocean. It is only necessary to invite adventurers, to attract to their flag all, whom restlessness, ambition, misfortune, enterprise, or necessity, shall induce to wander.

The progress of the physical force of this country is not to be calculated by that of other nations. Independently of the gross amount of numbers, and the rate at which the population increases, there is another important fact to be considered in making all our estimates of the future power of this nation. When we say that America, with so many millions of people, has done this or that much, has furnished so many soldiers, or so many seamen, it is necessary to remark how very large a proportion of the population are of an age to be dependants, instead of actors. In 1820, 17.11 of the whole population were boys under ten years of age. Including girls, rather more than one-third of the population had not yet reached that tender

---

ordinary ditto, 10 dollars and one ration; boys, 6 dollars and one ration; chaplain and purser, 40 dollars and two rations; surgeon, 50 dollars and two rations; surgeon's mate, 30 dollars and two rations; captain of marines, 40 dollars and two rations; first lieutenant ditto, 30 dollars and two rations; second ditto, 25 dollars and three rations, &c. &c. The rations of all the officers are paid in money, if required, at the rate of 25 cents a day for each, except the marines, who receive army pay and allowances. An army ration is worth 20 cents a day. It is, however, intended to increase the pay of most of the officers. See note B. at the end of the volume.

period of life. So far, therefore, from being assistants, they had been clogs to the exertions of their parents. Of 7,856,269 whites in the country at the census of 1820, 3,840,899 were under sixteen years of age. It is a natural fact that the commerce of the country should grow with its population; but it is evident that the ability to furnish a supply of men, for all purposes, must increase in an augmenting ratio. The proportion between whole numbers and active agents has not yet reached the level of Europe, and the American is, therefore, entitled to so much greater credit for what his country has done, since, even supposing other things equal, it has certainly been done, in consequence of this peculiarity, with a comparatively diminished force.

The United States would certainly take a new position in the event of another general war. So far from being again the prey of the belligerents, she would (unless an actor) be a neutral, whose weight, thrown into either scale, might make her a power to be dreaded on the ocean. England herself would find the fifty, or a hundred sail, which these people could, and, no doubt, would employ, highly embarrassing. The country, without precccious, or unnatural efforts, has reached the point when it has become an important ally. The West India seas would even now lie greatly at her mercy, especially if England, or France, had enemies nearer home. In a very few years this republic will not be very wary as to its choice of a foe, and in yet a few more, it will be able to meet fearlessly the greatest power of the earth in any way that man can elect for the gratification of his lawless propensities.

Still I think that the government of the United States will not be very dangerous by its ambition. That it will sweep its coasts of every hostile hold ; that Bermuda, and all such places, will come into the possession of the Americans in the course of the

next half century, no man can doubt, who has seen
how sagaciously they have already arranged their
frontiers, and who knows how to estimate their growing strength.   In fifty years it is physically certain
that these States will contain fifty millions of souls.
This number, supposing that the present marine
should increase only in a numerical proportion, would
give them a navy of rather more than two hundred
sail, of which one hundred and twenty would carry
more than fifty-four guns.   With an empire, compact,
natural, and so constituted as to require no artificial
défence, this alone would be a more available force
than three times the number employed in protecting
distant colonies and divided interests.   The game
which England has played with America, in their
two wars, by striking at the weak and most exposed
points, America will be able to play with England,
in the course of the next twenty years.   It would be
too dangerous an experiment to lie in her rivers and
bays, even now, with the advanced improvements in
steam ; and as to their ports, they will, shortly, be
beyond aggression.   The American citizen, a little
drilled, is as good a soldier, in a fort, as any man in
the world.   The last war abundantly proved that no
numbers can expel active and skilful seamen from
the ocean ; and any one can calculate what an efficient fleet of twenty sail might do against a divided
empire.   I know no more unsafe calculation than to
rely on the inactivity of an American sailor.

But it is a well-known fact, that the force and
wealth of nations are not so much in proportion to
their numbers as to their advancement in the arts of
life, and to their moral superiority.   In every thing
that constitutes general moral superiority, these people are already in the foremost rank.   Their population is getting compact; and as manufactures increase, and the usual divisions of employments follow,
they will become rich in a geometrical progression.

Should there be a necessity for such a force, there is far more probability that their marine will contain one thousand than two hundred sail in the year 1875.

Nor do I find a single plausible reason for disbelieving this result. Should a separation of the States occur, an event quite as improbable as any other act of suicide, and just as possible as all suicides, the commercial and manufacturing States would still keep together. I think, if any thing, their marine would be larger than if the confederation should exist as it now stands, since there would be but one opinion on its policy, and its size would clearly be a matter of greater necessity.

I know but one other material point to be considered in examining the American marine. With reference to its immediate growth, the finances of the country and the cost of ships are important. The debt of the United States is about 60,000,000 of dollars,* the revenue rather more than 21,000,000, without taxes. Including comparatively heavy sums paid to build fortifications, and a half million, each year, to the *increase* (not to the *repairs*) of the marine,† the whole expenditure is about 13,000,000 of dollars. This leaves an excess by which the debt will be entirely extinguished in a few more years of peace. A fair proportion of the moneys that shall then remain will, beyond a doubt, be used in fostering so interesting an arm of the public defence as the navy.

The American ships, considering their quality, are about as cheap as those of England. Some articles are less costly, others more expensive. I find that the Columbus, a ship on two decks, pierced for one

---

* It is actually 66,000,000, but the balance was created for the purchase of bank-stock, which pays an interest, and which can be sold without difficulty.

† This appropriation has been lately extended to six more years.—See note A. at the end of the volume.

hundred, and mounting about ninety-two or ninety-four guns, stands charged, nearly ready for sea, at 426,931 dollars; the North Carolina, launched, but not finished, at 343,251; Delaware ditto, at 375,735; and the Ohio* 308,000. The Potomac frigate was launched for 157,320 dollars, and the Brandywine, nearly completed for sea, for 261,876. The two latter are pierced for sixty guns, and actually mount fifty-six.†

Before closing this long, but I trust, to you, not tiresome, letter, I will allude to another topic. The Americans have been ignorantly and coarsely charged with deception on the subject of their navy. It has been said that they constructed vessels of extraordinary magnitude, and gave to them the appellations and rates of frigates. What is the fact? Frigates, as you very well know, were originally ships of one gun-deck, with a regular quarter-deck and forecastle, on both of which guns can be mounted. At first, the two latter decks were smaller than was necessary, and the frigates were rated at the precise number of guns that they carried. Thus a ship that formerly carried twenty-eight guns on her gun-deck, and ten guns on her quarter-deck and forecastle, was called, in the English navy, a thirty-eight. In course of time fourteen guns were placed on the quarter-deck of the same sort of ship (a little enlarged), and eight ports were cut in the forecastle, so that she could, and did, mount fifty guns. Some of them were even pierced

---

* In the state in which she was seen by Mr. De Roos, or nearly so.

† No American frigate, or ship of the line, with the exception of a 64 built for the Greeks, and recently *purchased* into the service, mounts, or has mounted, during the last five-and-twenty years, guns in the waist. The waists (since the last war) have been pierced for guns, in order that they may be shifted over to batter a town, or to defend a vessel at anchor, &c. &c. but hammocks are always stowed there as in other vessels of war.

for more. Between the frigates and the ships of the line was a sort of mongrel class that properly belonged to neither. They had the construction of the latter, though their force was but little superior to the former. These vessels were called fifties and forty-fours. When the Americans first formed their marine there was little method in its arrangement or classification. Ships like the English thirty-eights were commonly called thirty-sixes. But experience had shown that a larger-sized frigate might be built to advantage; and they were not disposed to perpetuate the mistaken notions of others. They constructed ships, on one deck, to carry thirty guns below (twenty-four pounders), and twenty-four guns on the quarter-deck and forecastle. But so far from attempting any deception in the manner of rating, they called them after the intermediate class already named, viz., forty-fours. Even the Chesapeake, the smallest thirty-eight (according to the English method of rating) ever known in their service, was, for a long time, through carelessness, or ignorance, termed a forty-four; because, at first, she actually mounted forty-four guns; while the New-York, a larger ship, though of fewer guns, was called a thirty-six. The Essex, a proper English thirty-two, was called a thirty-two; while the John Adams, and the Adams, both much inferior vessels, in size and in guns, were rated the same.

Now all these vessels were sent openly to sea, were visited freely, and were approved of or condemned by the officers of all the navies in the world. Some nations sneered at what the Americans deemed an improvement, and some imitated it. Time has shown that the latter were the wisest.

Deception is a word more unjustly applied to this nation than to any on earth. There is scarcely a secret even pretended to be kept in its whole government or police. Every year the fullest and most satisfactory documents, concerning its army, its finances and every thing else, are published to all who choose to read them. Their navy-yards and arsenals are open to every applicant. It is a singular fact that foreign officers have accused these people of a wish to practise deception, because they have discovered improvements in their navy-yards, while unreservedly enjoying, themselves, privileges that would, in their own countries, be denied to an American seaman. The officers of this country say that they are satisfied with the manner in which their own marine is conducted. If other people have a reason for changing their system of classification, let them do it, it is altogether an affair of their own. The object of rating at all is to understand the relative size and force of ships in the same service. It is not a matter of convention between nations. When an officer captures an enemy, or is captured by one, he is a fool if he does not state the actual force of his antagonist; he is only a knave when he conceals, or misrepresents it. Besides, they say, and justly enough, that the number of guns is no good criterion of the force of a vessel. An English thirty-two (old rate) and a thirty-six might, and often did, carry nearly the same number of guns (from forty to forty-four guns), but the latter is one-fourth larger, stronger, and heavier, and, of course, more formidable, than the former.*

That there was great inaccuracy in the rating of the American ships before and during the last war, is

---

* A ship carrying eighteen twenty-four pound carronades, and a ship of eighteen thirty-two pound carronades, would be rated the same, if the number of guns were to be the only guide; whereas, if one should be called a sixteen, and the other an eighteen, the mind would conceive a sufficiently just idea of the difference in force which actually existed. There are so many considerations that properly enter into the estimate of force in a vessel, that no one of them all can be safely taken as a rule.

certain; but it is just as certain it was oftener against their reputation than in their favour. They had three large frigates, and these they honestly called by the rates of vessels which fifty years since fought in the line. It must be remembered these three vessels have been built thirty years. They oftener over than underrated their other frigates. The same was true of their sloops of war. The Argus, (brig,) for instance, a vessel a third lighter every way than the regular eighteen, was rated in that class. The Nautilus, Vixen, Ferret, &c., were also overrated.

No nautical man, fit to command a vessel, would trust to any rate but that of his own judgment. If any people have got into difficulty by undervaluing their enemies, it is far more manful to confess their mistake, than to call improvements, which they are eager to imitate, by so coarse a term as deception. In this manner, clever men are, without bounds or moderation, deceiving the rest of mankind daily.

TO THE ABBATE GIROMACHI,

&c. &c.

Washington, ——

You ask me to write freely on the subject of the literature and the arts of the United States. The subjects are so meagre as to render it a task that would require no small portion of the talents neces sary to figure in either, in order to render them of interest. Still, as the request has come in so urgent a form, I shall endeavour to oblige you.

The Americans have been placed, as respects

moral and intellectual advancement, different from all other infant nations. They have never been without the wants of civilization, nor have they ever been entirely without the means of a supply. Thus pictures, and books, and statuary, and every thing else which appertains to elegant life, have always been known to them in an abundance, and of a quality exactly proportioned to their cost. Books, being the cheapest, and the nation having great leisure and prodigious zest for information, are not only the most common, as you will readily suppose, but they are probably more common than among any other people. I scarcely remember ever to have entered an American dwelling, however humble, without finding fewer or more books. As they form the most essential division of the subject, not only on account of their greater frequency, but on account of their far greater importance, I shall give them the first notice in this letter.

Unlike the progress of the two professions in the countries of our hemisphere, in America the printer came into existence before the author. Reprints of English works gave the first employment to the press. Then came almanacs, psalm-books, religious tracts, sermons, journals, political essays, and even rude attempts at poetry. All these preceded the revolution. The first journal was established in Boston at the commencement of the last century. There are several original polemical works of great originality and power that belong to the same period. I do not know that more learning and talents existed at that early day in the States of New-England than in Virginia, Maryland and the Carolinas, but there was certainly a stronger desire to exhibit them.

The colleges or universities, as they were some what prematurely called, date very far back in the brief history of the country. There is no stronger evidence of the intellectual character, or of the judicious ambition of these people, than what this simple fact furnishes. Harvard College, now the university of Cambridge—(it better deserves the title at this day)—was founded in 1638; within less than *twenty years* after the landing of the first settlers in New-England! Yale (in Connecticut) was founded in 1701. Columbia (in the city of New-York) was founded in 1754. Nassau Hall (in New-Jersey) in 1738; and William and Mary (in Virginia) as far back as 1691. These are the oldest literary institutions in the United States, and all but the last are in flourishing conditions to the present hour. The first has given degrees to about five thousand graduates, and rarely has less than three hundred and fifty or four hundred students. Yale is about as well attended. The others contain from a hundred and fifty to two hundred under-graduates. But these are not a moiety of the present colleges, or universities, (as they all aspire to be called,) existing in the country. There is no State, except a few of the newest, without at least one, and several have two or three.

Less attention is paid to classical learning here than in Europe; and, as the term of residence rarely exceeds four years, profound scholars are by no means common. This country possesses neither the population nor the endowments to maintain a large class of learned idlers, in order that one man in a hundred may contribute a mite to the growing stock of general knowledge. There is a luxury in this expenditure of animal force, to which the Americans have not yet attained. The good is far too problematical and remote, and the expense of man too certain, to be prematurely sought. I have heard, I will confess, an American legislator quote Horace and Cicero; but it is far from being the humour of the country. I thought the taste of the orator questionable. A learned quotation is rarely of any use in an argument, since few men are fools enough not to see that the application of any maxim to politics is liable to a thousand practical objections, and, nine times in ten, they are evidences of the want of a direct, natural, and vigorous train of thought. They are the affectations, but rarely the ebullitions of true talent. When a man feels strongly, or thinks strongly, or speaks strongly, he is just as apt to do it in his native tongue as he is to laugh when he is tickled, or to weep when in sorrow. The Americans are strong speakers and acute thinkers, but no great quoters of the morals and axioms of a heathen age, because they happen to be recorded in Latin.

The higher branches of learning are certainly on the advance in this country. The gentlemen of the middle and southern States, before the revolution, were very generally educated in Europe, and they were consequently, in this particular, like our own people. Those who came into life during the struggle, and shortly after, fared worse. Even the next generation had little to boast of in the way of instruction. I find that boys entered the colleges so late as the commencement of the present century, who had read a part of the Greek Testament, and a few books of Cicero and Virgil, with perhaps a little of Horace. But great changes have been made, and are still making, in the degree of previous qualification.

Still, it would be premature to say that there is any one of the American universities where classical knowledge, or even science, is profoundly attained, even at the present day. Some of the professors push their studies, for a life, certainly; and you well know, after all, that little short of a life, and a long one too, will make any man a good general scholar. In 1820, near eight thousand graduates of the twelve oldest colleges of this country (according to their catalogues) were then living. Of this number, 1,406 were clergymen. As some of the catalogues consulted were several years old, this number was of necessity greatly within the truth. Between the years 1800 and 1810, it is found that of 2,792 graduates, four hundred and fifty-three became clergymen. Here is pretty good evidence that religion is not neglected in America, and that its ministers are not, as a matter of course, absolutely ignorant.

But the effects of the literary institutions of the United States are somewhat peculiar. Few men devote their lives to scholarship. The knowledge that is actually acquired, is perhaps quite sufficient for the more practical and useful pursuits. Thousands of young men, who have read the more familiar classics, who have gone through enough of mathematics to obtain a sense of their own tastes, and of the value of precision, who have cultivated *belles lettres* to a reasonable extent, and who have been moderately instructed in the arts of composition, and in the rules of taste, are given forth to the country to mingle in its active employments. I am inclined to believe that a class of American graduates carries away with it quite as much general and diversified knowledge, as a class from one of our own universities. The excellence in particular branches is commonly wanting; but the deficiency is more than supplied by variety of information. The youth who has passed four years within the walls of a college, goes into the office of a lawyer for a few more. The profession of the law is not subdivided in America. The same man is counsellor, attorney, and conveyancer. Here the student gets a general insight into the principles, and a familiarity with the practice of the law, rather than an acquaintance with the study as a science. With this instruction he enters the world as a practitioner. Instead of existing in a state of dreaming retrospection, lost in a maze of theories, he is at once turned loose into the jostlings of the world. If perchance he encounters an antagonist a little more erudite than himself, he seizes the natural truth for his sheet-an-

chor, and leaves precedent and quaint follies to him
who has made them his study and delight. No doubt
he often blunders, and is frequently, of necessity, defeated. But in the course of this irreverent treatment,
usages and opinions, which are bottomed in no better
foundation than antiquity, and which are as inapplicable to the present state of the world, as the present
state of the world is, or ought to be, unfavourable to
all feudal absurdities, come to receive their death-
warrants. In the mean time, by dint of sheer experience, and by the collision of intellects, the practitioner gets a stock of learning, that is acquired in
the best possible school; and, what is of far more
importance, the laws themselves get a dress which
brings them within the fashions of the day. This
same man becomes a legislator perhaps, and, if particularly clever, he is made to take an active part in
the framing of laws that are not to harmonize with
the other parts of an elaborate theory, but which are
intended to make men comfortable and happy. Now,
taken with more or less qualification, this is the history of thousands in this country, and it is also an important part of the history of the country itself.

In considering the course of instruction in the
United States, you are always to commence at the
foundation. The common schools, which so generally
exist, have certainly elevated the population above
that of any other country, and are still elevating it
higher, as they improve and increase in numbers.
Law is getting every day to be more of a science, but
it is a science that is forming rules better adapted to
the spirit of the age. Medicine is improving, and in
the cities it is, perhaps now, in point of practice,
quite on a level with that of Europe. Indeed, the
well-educated American physician very commonly
enjoys an advantage that is little known in Europe.
After obtaining a degree in his own country, he passes
a few years in London, Edinburgh, Paris, and fre-

quently in Germany, and returns with his gleanings
from their several schools. This is not the case with
one individual, but with many, annually. Indeed,
there is so much of a fashion in it, and the custom is
attended by so many positive advantages, that its
neglect would be a serious obstacle to any very eminent success. Good operators are by no means
scarce, and as surgery and medicine are united in the
same person, there is great judgment in their practice. Human life is something more valuable in
America than in Europe, and I think a critical attention to patients more common here than with us,
especially when the sufferer belongs to an inferior
condition in life. The profession is highly respectable; and in all parts of the country the better sort of
its practitioners mingle, on terms of perfect equality,
with the highest classes of society. There are several
physicians in Congress, and a great many in the different State legislatures.

Of the ministry it is unnecessary to speak. The
clergy are of all denominations, and they are educated, or not, precisely as they belong to sects which
consider the gift of human knowledge of any importance. You have already seen how large a proportion of the graduates of some of the colleges enter
the desk.

As respects authorship, there is not much to be
said. Compared to the books that are printed and
read, those of native origin are few indeed. The principal reason of this poverty of original writers, is
owing to the circumstance that men are not yet
driven to their wits for bread. The United States are
the first nation that possessed institutions, and, of
course, distinctive opinions of its own, that was ever
dependent on a foreign people for its literature.
Speaking the same language as the English, and long
in the habit of importing their books from the mother
country, the revolution effected no immediate change

in the nature of their studies, or mental amusements. The works were re-printed, it is true, for the purposes of economy, but they still continued English. Had the latter nation used this powerful engine with tolerable address, I think they would have secured such an ally in this country as would have rendered their own decline not only more secure, but as illustrious as had been their rise. There are many theories entertained as to the effect produced in this country by the falsehoods and jealous calumnies which have been undeniably uttered in the mother country, by means of the press, concerning her republican descendant. It is my own opinion that, like all other ridiculous absurdities, they have defeated themselves, and that they are now more laughed at and derided, even here, than resented. By all that I can learn, twenty years ago, the Americans were, perhaps, far too much disposed to receive the opinions and to adopt the prejudices of their relatives; whereas, I think it is very apparent that they are now beginning to receive them with singular distrust. It is not worth our while to enter further into this subject, except as it has had, or is likely to have, an influence on the national literature.*

It is quite obvious, that, so far as taste and forms alone are concerned, the literature of England and that of America must be fashioned after the same models. The authors, previously to the revolution, are common property, and it is quite idle to say that the American has not just as good a right to claim Milton, and Shakspeare, and all the old masters of the language, for his countrymen, as an Englishman. The

---

* The writer might give, in proof of this opinion, one fact. He is led to believe that, so lately as within ten years, several English periodical works were re-printed, and much read in the United States, and that now they patronize their own, while the former are far less sought, though the demand, by means of the increased population, should have been nearly doubled. Some of the works are no longer even re-printed.

Americans having continued to cultivate, and to cultivate extensively, an acquaintance with the writers of the mother country, since the separation, it is evident they must have kept pace with the trifling changes of the day. The only peculiarity that can, or ought to be expected in their literature, is that which is connected with the promulgation of their distinctive political opinions. They have not been remiss in this duty, as any one may see, who chooses to examine their books. But we will devote a few minutes to a more minute account of the actual condition of American literature.

The first, and the most important, though certainly the most familiar branch of this subject, is connected with the public journals. It is not easy to say how many newspapers are printed in the United States. The estimated number varies from six hundred to a thousand. In the State of New-York there are more than fifty counties. Now, it is rare that a county, in a State as old as that of New-York, (especially in the more northern parts of the country), does not possess one paper at least. The cities have many. The smaller towns sometimes have three or four, and very many of the counties four or five. There cannot be many less than one hundred and fifty journals in the State of New-York alone. Pennsylvania is said to possess eighty. But we will suppose that these two States publish two hundred journals. They contain about 3,000,000 of inhabitants. As the former is an enlightened State, and the latter rather below the scale of the general intelligence of the nation, it may not be a very bad average of the whole population. This rate would give eight hundred journals for the United States, which is probably something within the truth. I confess, however, this manner of equalizing estimates in America, is very uncertain in general, since a great deal, in such a

I 2

question, must depend on the progress of society in each particular section of the country.

As might be expected, there is nearly every degree of merit to be found in these journals. No one of them has the benefit of that collected talent which is so often enlisted in the support of the more important journals of Europe. There is not often more than one editor to the best; but he is usually some man who has seen, in his own person, enough of men and things to enable him to speak with tolerable discretion on passing events. The usefulness of the American journals, however, does not consist in their giving the tone to the public mind, in politics and morals, but in imparting facts. It is certain that, could the journals agree, they might, by their united efforts, give a powerful inclination to the common will. But, in point of fact, they do not agree on any one subject, or set of subjects, except, perhaps, on those which directly affect their own interests. They, consequently, counteract, instead of aiding each other, on all points of disputed policy; and it is in the bold and sturdy discussions that follow, that men arrive at the truth. The occasional union in their own favour, is a thing too easily seen through to do either good or harm. So far, then, from the journals succeeding in leading the public opinion astray, they are invariably obliged to submit to it. They serve to keep it alive, by furnishing the means for its expression, but they rarely do more. Of course, the influence of each particular press is in proportion to the constancy and the ability with which it is found to support what is thought to be sound principles; but those principles must be in accordance with the private opinions of men, or most of their labour is lost.

The public press in America is rather more decent than that of England, and less decorous than that of France. The tone of the nation, and the respect for private feelings, which are, perhaps, in some measure, the consequence of a less artificial state of scciety, produce the former; and the liberty, which is a necessary attendant of fearless discussion, is, I think, the cause of the latter. The affairs of an individual are rarely touched upon in the journals of this country; never, unless it is thought they have a direct connexion with the public interests, or from a wish to do him good. Still there is a habit, getting into use in America, no less than in France, that is borrowed from the English, which proves that the more unworthy feelings of our nature are common to men under all systems, and only need opportunity to find encouragement. I allude to the practice of repeating the proceedings of the courts of justice, in order to cater to a vicious appetite for amusement in the public.

It is pretended that, as a court of justice is open to the world, there can be no harm in giving the utmost publicity to its proceedings. It is strange the courts should act so rigidly on the principle, that it is better a dozen guilty men should go free, than that one innocent man should suffer, and yet permit the gross injustice that is daily done by means of this practice. One would think, that if a court of justice is so open to the world, that it should be the business of the people of the world to enter it, in order that they might be certain that the information they crave should be without colouring or exaggeration. It is idle to say that the reports are accurate, and that he who reads is enabled to do justice to the accused, by comparing the facts that are laid before him. A reporter may give the expression of the tongue; but can he convey that of the eye, of the countenance, or of the form?—without regarding all of which, no man is perfectly master of the degree of credibility that is due to any witness of whose character he is necessarily ignorant. But every man has an infallible

means of assuring himself of the value of these reports. Who has ever read a dozen of them without meeting with one (or perhaps more,) in which
the decision of the court and jury is to him a matter
of surprise? It is true he assumes, that those who
were present knew best, and as he has no great interest in the matter, he is commonly satisfied. But
how is it with the unfortunate man who is wrong-
fully brought out of his retirement to repel an unjust
attack against his person, his property, or his character? If he be a man of virtue, he is a man of sensibility; and not only he, but, what is far worse, those
tender beings, whose existence is wrapped up in his
own, are to be wounded daily and hourly, for weeks
at a time, in order that a depraved appetite should be
glutted. It is enough for justice that her proceedings
should be so public as to prevent the danger of corruption; but we pervert a blessing to a curse, in
making that which was intended for our protection,
the means of so much individual misery. It is an
unavoidable evil of the law that it necessarily works·
some wrong, in order to do much good; but it is
cruel that even the acquittal of a man should be unnecessarily circulated, in a manner to make all men
remember that he had been accused. We have
proof of the consequences of this practice in England. Men daily shrink from resistance to base
frauds, rather than expose themselves to the observations and comments of those who enliven their
breakfasts by sporting with these exhibitions of their
fellow-creatures. There are, undoubtedly, cases of
that magnitude which require some sacrifice of private feelings, in order that the community should
reap the advantage; but the regular books are sufficient for authorities—the decisions of the courts are
sufficient for justice—and the utmost possible oblivion
should prove as nearly sufficient as may be to serve
the ends of a prudent and a righteous humanity.

Nothing can be more free than the press of this country, on all subjects connected with politics. Treason cannot be written, unless by communicating with an open enemy. There is no other protection to a public man than that which is given by an independent jury, which punishes, of course, in proportion to the dignity and importance of the injured party. But the utmost lenity is always used in construing the right of the press to canvass the public acts of public men. Mere commonplace charges defeat themselves, and get into discredit so soon as to be lost, while graver accusations are met by grave replies. There is no doubt that the complacency of individuals is sometimes disturbed by these liberties; but they serve to keep the officers of the government to their work, while they rarely do any lasting, or even temporary injury. Serious and criminal accusations against a public man, if groundless, are, by the law of reason, a crime against the community, and, as such, they are punished. The general principle observed in these matters is very simple. If A. accuse B. of an act that is an offence against law, he may be called on for his proof, and if he fail he must take the consequences. But an editor of a paper, or any one else, who should bring a criminal charge, no matter how grave, against the President, and who could prove it, is just as certain of doing it with impunity, as if he held the whole power in his own hands. He would be protected by the invincible shield of public opinion, which is not only in consonance with the law, but which, in this country, makes law.

Actions for injuries done by the press, considering the number of journals, are astonishingly rare in America. When one remembers the usual difficulty of obtaining legal proof, which is a constant temptation, even to the guilty, to appeal to the courts; and, on the other hand, the great freedom of the press, which is a constant temptation to abuse the trust, this fact, in itself, furnishes irresistible evidence of the general tone of decency which predominates in this nation. The truth is, that public opinion, among its other laws, has imperiously prescribed that, amidst the utmost latitude of discussion, certain limits shall not be passed; and public opinion, which is so completely the offspring of a free press, must be obeyed in this, as well as in other matters.

Leaving the journals, we come to those publications which make their appearance periodically. Of these there are a good many, some few of which are well supported. There are several scientific works, that are printed monthly, or quarterly, of respectable merit, and four or five reviews. Magazines of a more general character are not much encouraged. England, which is teeming with educated men, who are glad to make their bread by writing for these works, still affords too strong a competition for the success of any American attempts, in this species of literature. Though few, perhaps no English magazine is actually republished in America, a vast number are imported and read in the towns, where the support for any similar original production must first be found.

The literature of the United States has, indeed, too powerful obstacles to conquer before (to use a mercantile expression) it can ever enter the markets of its own country on terms of perfect equality with that of England. Solitary and individual works of genius may, indeed, be occasionally brought to light, under the impulses of the high feeling which has conceived them; but, I fear, a good, wholesome, profitable and continued pecuniary support, is the applause that talent most craves. The fact, that an American publisher can get an English work without money, must, for a few years longer, (unless legislative protection shall be extended to their own authors,) have a tendency to repress a national literature. No man will pay a writer for an epic, a tragedy, a sonnet, a history, or a romance, when he can get a work of equal merit for nothing. I have conversed with those who are conversant on the subject, and, I confess, I have been astonished at the information they imparted.

A capital American publisher has assured me that there are not a dozen writers in this country, whose works he should feel confidence in publishing at all, while he reprints hundreds of English books without the least hesitation. This preference is by no means so much owing to any difference in merit, as to the fact that, when the price of the original author is to be added to the uniform hazard which accompanies all literary speculations, the risk becomes too great. The general taste of the reading world in this country is better than that of England.* The fact is both proved and explained by the circumstance that thousands of works that are printed and read in the mother country, are not printed and read here. The publisher on this side of the Atlantic has the advantage of seeing the reviews of every book he wishes to print, and, what is of far more importance, he knows, with the exception of books that he is sure of selling, by means of a name, the decision of the English critics before he makes his choice. Nine times in ten, popularity, which is all he looks for, is a sufficient test of general merit. Thus, while you find every English work of character, or notoriety, on the shelves of an American book-store, you may ask in vain for most of the trash that is so greedily devoured in the circulating libraries of the mother country, and which would be just as eagerly devoured here, had not a better taste been created by a

---

* The writer does not mean that the best taste of America is better than that of England; perhaps it is not quite so good; but, as a whole, the American reading world requires better books than the whole of the English reading world.

compelled abstinence. That taste must now be overcome before such works could be sold at all.

When I say that books are not rejected here, from
any want of talent in the writers, perhaps I ought
to explain. I wish to express something a little different. Talent is sure of too many avenues to wealth
and honours, in America, to seek, unnecessarily, an
unknown and hazardous path. It is better paid in
the ordinary pursuits of life, than it would be likely
to be paid by an adventure in which an extraordinary
and skilful, because practised, foreign competition is
certain. Perhaps high talent does not often make the
trial with the American bookseller; but it is precisely
for the reason I have named.

The second obstacle against which American literature has to contend, is in the poverty of materials.
There is scarcely an ore which contributes to the
wealth of the author, that is found, here, in veins
as rich as in Europe. There are no annals for the
historian; no follies (beyond the most vulgar and
commonplace) for the satirist; no manners for the
dramatist; no obscure fictions for the writer of romance; no gross and hardy offences against decorum
for the moralist; nor any of the rich artificial auxiliaries of poetry. The weakest hand can extract a
spark from the flint, but it would baffle the strength
of a giant to attempt kindling a flame with a pudding-
stone. I very well know there are theorists who assume that the society and institutions of this country
are, or ought to be, particularly favourable to novelties and variety. But the experience of one month,
in these States, is sufficient to show any observant
man the falsity of their position. The effect of a
promiscuous assemblage any where, is to create a
standard of deportment; and great liberty permits
every one to aim at its attainment. I have never
seen a nation so much alike in my life, as the people
of the United States, and what is more, they are not

only like each other, but they are remarkably like that which common sense tells them they ought to resemble. No doubt, traits of character that are a little peculiar, without, however, being either very poetical, or very rich, are to be found in remote districts; but they are rare, and not always happy exceptions. In short, it is not possible to conceive a state of society in which more of the attributes of plain good sense, or fewer of the artificial absurdities of life, are to be found, than here. There is no costume for the peasant, (there is scarcely a peasant at all,) no wig for the judge, no baton for the general, no diadem for the chief magistrate. The darkest ages of their history are illuminated by the light of truth; the utmost efforts of their chivalry are limited by the laws of God; and even the deeds of their sages and heroes are to be sung in a language that would differ but little from a version of the ten commandments. However useful and respectable all this may be in actual life, it indicates but one direction to the man of genius.

It is very true there are a few young poets now living in this country, who have known how to extract sweets from even these wholesome, but scentless native plants. They have, however, been compelled to seek their inspiration in the universal laws of nature, and they have succeeded, precisely in proportion as they have been most general in their application. Among these gifted young men, there is one (Halleck) who is remarkable for an exquisite vein of ironical wit, mingled with a fine, poetical, and, frequently, a lofty expression. This gentleman commenced his career as a satirist in one of the journals of New-York. Heaven knows, his materials were none of the richest; and yet the melody of his verse, the quaintness and force of his comparisons, and the exceeding humour of his strong points, brought him instantly into notice. He then attempted a general satire, by giving the history of the early days of a *belle*. He was again successful, though every body, at least every body of any talent, felt that he wrote in leading-strings. But he happened, shortly after the appearance of the little volume just named, (Fanny,) to visit England. Here his spirit was properly excited, and, probably on a rainy day he was induced to try his hand at a *jeu d'esprit*, in the mother country. The result was one of the finest semi-heroic ironical descriptions to be found in the English language.* This simple fact, in itself, proves the truth of a great deal of what I have just been writing, since it shows the effect a superiority of material can produce on the efforts of a man of true genius.

Notwithstanding the difficulties of the subject, talent has even done more than in the instance of Mr. Halleck. I could mention several other young poets of this country of rare merit. By mentioning Bryant, Percival, and Sprague, I shall direct your attention to the names of those whose works would be most likely to give you pleasure. Unfortunately they are not yet known in Italian, but I think even you would not turn in distaste from the task of translation which the best of their effusions will invite.

The next, though certainly an inferior branch of imaginative writing, is fictitious composition. From the facts just named, you cannot expect that the novelists, or romance writers of the United States, should be very successful. The same reason will be likely, for a long time to come, to repress the ardour of dramatic genius. Still, tales and plays are no novelties in the literature of this country. Of the former, there are many as old as soon after the revolution ; and a vast number have been published within the last five years. One of their authors of romance,

---

* This little *morceau* of pleasant irony is called Alnwick Castle.

who curbed his talents by as few allusions as possible to actual society, is distinguished for power and comprehensiveness of thought. I remember to have read one of his books (Wieland) when a boy, and I take it to be a never-failing evidence of genius, that, amid a thousand similar pictures which have succeeded, the images it has left, still stand distinct and prominent in my recollection. This author (Mr. Brockden Brown) enjoys a high reputation among his countrymen, whose opinions are sufficiently impartial, since he flattered no particular prejudice of the nation in any of his works.

The reputation of Irving is well known to you. He is an author distinguished for a quality (humour) that has been denied his countrymen; and his merit is the more rare, that it has been shown in a state of society so cold and so restrained. Besides these writers, there are many others of a similar character, who enjoy a greater or less degree of favour in their own country. The works of two or three have even been translated (into French) in Europe, and a great many are reprinted in England. Though every writer of fiction in America has to contend against the difficulties I have named, there is a certain interest in the novelty of the subject, which is not without its charm. I think, however, it will be found that they have all been successful, or the reverse, just as they have drawn warily, or freely, on the distinctive habits of their own country. I now speak of their success purely as writers of romance. It certainly would be possible for an American to give a description of the manners of his own country, in a book that he might choose to call a romance, which should be read, because the world is curious on the subject, but which would certainly never be read for that nearly indefinable poetical interest which attaches itself to a description of manners less bald and uniform. All the attempts to blend history with romance in America, have been comparatively failures, (and perhaps fortunately,) since the subjects are too familiar to be treated with the freedom that the imagination absolutely requires. Some of the descriptions of the progress of society on the borders, have had a rather better success, since there is a positive, though no very poetical, novelty in the subject; but, on the whole, the books which have been best received, are those in which the authors have trusted most to their own conceptions of character, and to qualities that are common to the rest of the world and to human nature. This fact, if its truth be admitted, will serve to prove that the American writer must seek his renown in the exhibition of qualities that are general, while he is confessedly compelled to limit his observations to a state of society that has a wonderful tendency not only to repress passion, but to equalize humours.

The Americans have always been prolific writers on polemics and politics. Their sermons and fourth of July orations are numberless. Their historians, without being very classical or very profound, are remarkable for truth and good sense. There is not, perhaps, in the language a closer reasoner in metaphysics than Edwards ; and their theological writers find great favour among the sectarians of their respective schools.

The stage of the United States is decidedly English. Both plays and players, with few exceptions, are imported. Theatres are numerous, and they are to be found in places where a traveller would little expect to meet them. Of course they are of all sizes, and of every degree of decoration and architectural beauty known in Europe, below the very highest. The façade of the principal theatre in Philadelphia, is a chaste specimen in marble, of the Ionic, if my memory is correct. In New-York, there are two theatres about as large as the Théatre Français (in the interior), and not much inferior in embellishments. Besides these, there is a very pretty little theatre, where lighter pieces are performed, and another with a vast stage for melo-dramas. There are also one or two other places of dramatic representation in this city, in which horses and men contend for the bays.

The Americans pay well for dramatic talent. Cooke, the greatest English tragedian of our age, died on this side of the Atlantic; and there are few players of eminence in the mother country who are not tempted, at some time or other, to cross the ocean. Shakspeare is, of course, the great author of America, as he is of England, and I think he is quite as well relished here as there. In point of taste, if all the rest of the world be any thing against England, that of America is the best, since it unquestionably approaches nearest to that of the continent of Europe. Nearly one-half of the theatrical taste of the English is condemned by their own judgments, since the stage is not much supported by those who have had an opportunity of seeing any other. You will be apt to ask me how it happens, then, that the American taste is better? Because the people, being less exaggerated in their habits, are less disposed to tolerate caricatures, and because the theatres are not yet sufficiently numerous (though that hour is near) to admit of a representation that shall not be subject to the control of a certain degree of intelligence. I have heard an English player complain that he never saw such a dull audience as the one before which he had just been exhibiting; and I heard the same audience complain that they never listened to such dull jokes. Now, there was talent enough in both parties; but the one had formed his taste in a coarse school, and the others had formed theirs under the dominion of common sense. Independently of this peculiarity, there is a vast deal of acquired, travelled taste in

K 2

this country. English tragedy, and high English comedy, both of which, you know, are excellent, never fail here, if well played; that is, they never fail under the usual limits of all amusement. One will cloy of sweets. But the fact of the taste and judgment of these people, in theatrical exhibitions, is proved by the number of their good theatres, compared to their population.

Of dramatic writers there are none, or next to none. The remarks I have made in respect to novels apply with double force to this species of composition. A witty and successful American comedy could only proceed from extraordinary talent. There would be less difficulty, certainly, with a tragedy; but still, there is rather too much foreign competition, and too much domestic employment in other pursuits, to invite genius to so doubtful an enterprise. The very baldness of ordinary American life is in deadly hostility to scenic representation. The character must be supported solely by its intrinsic power. The judge, the footman, the clown, the lawyer, the belle, or the beau, can receive no great assistance from dress. Melo-dramas, except the scene should be laid in the woods, are out of the question. It would be necessary to seek the great clock, which is to strike the portentous twelve blows, in the nearest church; a vaulted passage would degenerate into a cellar; and, as for ghosts, the country was discovered, since their visitations have ceased. The smallest departure from the incidents of ordinary life would do violence to every man's experience; and, as already mentioned, the passions which belong to human nature must be delineated, in America, subject to the influence of that despot—common sense.

Notwithstanding the overwhelming influence of British publications, and all the difficulties I have named, original books are getting to be numerous in the United States. The impulses of talent and intelligence are bearing down a thousand obstacles. I think the new works will increase rapidly, and that they are destined to produce a powerful influence on the world. We will pursue this subject another time.—Adieu.

TO THE ABBATE GIROMACHI,

&c. &c.

FLORENCE.

Washington, ——

—You will be satisfied with these reasons for the abrupt conclusion of my last. I shall now tax your patience for a short continuation of the subject.

Although there are so many reasons why an imaginative literature should not be speedily created in this country, there is none, but that general activity of employment which is not favourable to study, why science and all the useful arts should not be cultivated here, perhaps, more than any where else. Great attention is already paid to the latter. Though there is scarce such a thing as a capital picture in this whole country, I have seen more beautiful, graceful, and convenient ploughs in positive use here, than are probably to be found in the whole of Europe united. In this single fact may be traced the history of the character of the people, and the germ of their future greatness. Their axe is admirable for form, for neatness, and precision of weight, and it is wielded with a skill that is next to incredible. Reapers are nearly unknown; but I have seen single individuals enter a field of grain in the morning, and

clear acres of its golden burthen, by means of the
cradle,* with a rapidity that has amazed me.　The
vast multitude of their inventions, as they are exhibited in the Patent Office in this city, ought to furnish
food for grave reflection to every stranger.　Several
large rooms are filled with the models, many of which
give evidence of the most acute ingenuity.　When
one recollects the average proportion of adults to
which the population must have been confined during
the last thirty-five years,† the number of their inventions is marvellous.　A great many of these models
contain no new principle, nor any new application
of an·old principle; but, as in such cases money has
been paid by those who deposit them there without an
object, it is fair to presume that they were inventions
so far as the claimants were concerned.　There are
so few means by which men, in remote districts of
this country, can profit by the ideas of other people
in these matters, that it is probable there are not a
dozen machines lodged in the office, of which the
parties concerned did not honestly believe themselves the inventors.　You may estimate the activity
of thought, which distinguishes the mass of this nation from all other people, by this fact.　It is in itself
a prodigious triumph to a young people to have given
form and useful existence to the greatest improvement of our age; but the steam-boats are not the only
gift of this nature, by many, that Europe has already
received from the western hemisphere.

The general accumulation of science in this country is exceedingly great, though it is quite likely that
few men have yet attained to a very eminent degree
of knowledge in any one particular branch.　Still it
is probable, that the amount of science in the United

---

* The writer does not know whether this implement is an
American invention or not.

† The whole period that the Patent Office has been in existence.

States, at this day, compared to what it was even fifteen years ago, and without reference to the increase of the population, is as five to one, or even in a still much greater proportion. Like all other learning, it is greatly on the advance.

In architecture the Americans have certainly no great reason to exult. They appear to have inherited the peculiarity of their ancestors, in all matters of mere taste. Their houses are mostly built of wood in the country and in the villages, and of bricks in the towns. There are, however, exceptions, in all cases, which reverse the rule. There are many farm-houses, seats, churches, court-houses, &c. in the country and smaller towns, which are of stone. Marble and granite are getting a good deal into use, too, in the more northern cities. The principal motive which controls their taste is economy. It is commonly cheapest to build of wood in the country, but where stone is at hand, and of a good quality, it begins to be preferred, in what may be called the second and third stages of the settlements. As the materials are cheap, the buildings are in common much larger than would be occupied by men of the same wealth in Europe. A house of forty or of forty-five feet front, and of thirty or thirty-five feet in depth, of two stories, with cellars, and garret, and with offices attached, is a usual dwelling for the owner of one or of two hundred acres of land, in a part of the country that has been under cultivation thirty or forty years. Such a man may be worth from five to ten thousand dollars. He has his growing orchard; fifty sheep; some eight or ten cows; a stock of young cattle; three or four horses; one or two yoke of oxen; hogs, poultry, and all the other provisions of a small farm. He grows his own maize; fattens his own pork; makes his own cider; kills his own beef; raises his own wheat, rye, and flax; and, in short, lives as much as possible on the articles of his own production. There are thousands and tens of thousands of these sturdy, independent yeomen in the eastern, middle and north-western States.

The villas and country-seats are commonly pretty, without ever attaining much elegance of size. A better sort of American country-house will cover perhaps sixty or seventy feet of ground in length, and from fifty to sixty in depth. There are some of twice this size; but I should say the first was a fair average. There are a great many a size smaller. The expense of building is, of course, in proportion to the general cost of every article in the particular place where the house is erected. I am told the best buildings in New-York cost from thirty to forty thousand dollars. A few are even much more expensive. But the town-houses, occupied by a majority of their gentlemen (those who own their own dwellings), cost probably something under twenty thousand.* These are the habitations of the rich, exclusively. They are every where exceedingly neat, prettily furnished, frequently with great elegance, and are always comfortable.

As some general idea of the state of the useful arts must have been obtained, in the course of my previous letters to the fraternity, I shall now pass to those which are intended exclusively to embellish life.

The United States, considered with reference to their means and opportunities, have been exceedingly prolific in painters. It is rather remarkable, that, in a country where active and less hazardous employ-

---

* The writer afterwards saw a row of buildings in New-York of the following cost and dimensions; twenty-five feet front, (in marble) fifty-five feet deep, and of three stories, besides the basement. The lots were two hundred feet in depth. The buildings were about as well finished as a third-rate London town-house. The cost of the whole was ten thousand dollars, and the rent six hundred dollars a-year. These houses were in the dearest city of America, but not in the dearest part of the town.

ments are so open to talent, men should take an inclination to a pursuit that is rarely profitable, and in which mediocrity is as annoying as success is triumphant. I cannot say that the majority of these gentlemen acknowledge that the fine arts are greatly encouraged in America, nor has it yet been my happy lot to enter a country in which artists and authors were very generally of opinion that the pen and the pencil received the rewards and honours which no one will deny they merit. A very great majority of the American artists are portrait painters. Some of them are highly esteemed by their own countrymen, and certainly there are a few of a good deal of merit. They are generally more distinguished for spirit and character, than for finish or grace; but it is quite evident that, as a class, they are rapidly improving. Drawing is the point in which they chiefly fail; and this, too, is probably an inherited defect, since most of them are disciples of the English school.

There are some highly respectable professional landscape painters. One of them (a Mr. Cole) possesses the rare faculty of giving to his pictures the impression of nature, to a degree so extraordinary, that he promises to become eminent. You know my eye is only for nature. I have heard both high eulogiums and sneering critiques on the powers of this young man, as an artist; some declaring that he has reached a point far beyond that attained by any of his competitors, and others denying that he knows how to make a sky look blue, *secundum artem*. To me his scenery is like the scenery from which he drew; and as he has taste and skill enough to reject what is disagreeable, and to arrange the attractive parts of his pictures, I only hope he will continue to study the great master from whom he has drawn his first inspirations. America has produced several historical painters. West, though a native of this country, and, perhaps with a pardonable vanity, claimed

as such by these people, was, to all intents and pur
poses an English artist. There are one or two of
his pupils who practise their skill here, and a few
others have aspired to the highest branch of their art.
One of them (Mr. Alston) is said to be employed on
a great and elaborate picture (the handwriting on
the wall;) and as his taste and merit are universally
admitted, a good deal is expected from his pencil.
It may serve to give you a better idea of the taste
for pictures in this country, or rather of the desire
which exists to encourage talent, if I mention the
price he is to receive for this work. A company of
gentlemen are said to have bought the picture, in
advance, by agreeing to pay ten thousand dollars.
I believe it is their intention to remunerate themselves by exhibiting it, and then to deposit the work
in some public place. Cabinet pieces, by this artist,
are readily sold for prices of between three hundred
and a thousand dollars, and the pencil of Cole is
employed as much as he pleases. There are many
other artists that paint portraits and landscapes, who
seldom want orders. The government of the United
States has paid Trumbull thirty-two thousand dollars
for the four historical paintings that are destined to
fill as many compartments in the rotunda, or the
great hall of the Capitol.

It is plain that the system of elementary education
pursued by this country, must bring an extraordinary
quantity of talent, within the influence of those causes
which lead to renown. If we suppose one hundred
men in America to possess the same amount of native
talent as one hundred men in any other part of the
world, more of it will, of necessity, be excited to
action, since more individuals are placed in situations
to feel and to improve their infant powers. Although
a certain degree of excellence in the higher branches
of learning and of art, may yet be necessary to create

a standard, and even for the establishments of higher schools or real universities, still the truth of this position is proved by the fact, that there already exists, among this people, a far more advanced state of improvement in all that relates to the familiar interests of life than among any other. It is true that a division of labour, and vast competition, may create a degree of minute perfection in many articles of European manufacture, that is not known in the same articles manufactured here; but I think it will be commonly found, in all such cases, that these wary people have counted the profit and the cost with sufficient accuracy. As circumstances vary, they instantly improve; and, once induced to persevere, they soon fearlessly challenge competition.

The purely intellectual day of America is yet in its dawn. But its sun will not arise from darkness, like those of nations with whose experience we are familiar; nor is the approach of its meridian to be calculated by the known progress of any other people. The learned professions are now full to overflowing, not so much with learning as with incumbents, certainly, but so much so, as to begin to give a new direction to education and talents. Writers are already getting to be numerous, for literature is beginning to be profitable. Those authors who are successful, receive prices for their labours, which exceed those paid to the authors of any country, England alone excepted; and which exceed even the prices paid to the most distinguished authors of the mother country, if the difference in the relative value of money in the two countries, and in the luxury of the press, be computed. The same work which is sold in England for six dollars, is sold in the United States for two. The profit to the publisher is obtained out of a common rate of per centage. Now, as thirty-three and a third per cent. on six thousand

L

dollars, is two thousand,* and on two thousand dollars, only six hundred and sixty-six, it is quite evident, that if both parties sell one thousand copies of a work, the English publisher pockets three times the most profit.   And yet, with one or two exceptions, and notwithstanding the great difference in the population of the two countries, the English bookseller rarely sells more, if he does as many, copies of a book, than the American.   It is the extraordinary demand which enables the American publisher to pay so well, and which, provided there was no English competition, would enable him to pay still better, or rather still more generally, than he does at present.

The literature of the United States is a subject of the highest interest to the civilized world ; for when it does begin to be felt, it will be felt with a force, a directness, and a common sense in its application, that has never yet been known.   If there were no other points of difference between this country and other nations, those of its political and religious freedom, alone, would give a colour of the highest importance to the writings of a people so thoroughly imbued with their distinctive principles, and so keenly alive to their advantages.   The example of America has been silently operating on Europe for half a century ; but its doctrines and its experience, exhibited with the understanding of those familiar with both, have never yet been pressed on our attention.   I think the time for the experiment is getting near.

A curious inquiry might be raised as to the probable fate of the English language, among so many people having equal claims to its possession.   I put this question to my friend, who has kindly permitted me to give you the substance of his reply.   You will

---

* This calculation supposes one-third of the price to go to the trade in discount, one-third to the expenses, and the other third to constitute the joint profit of the author and publisher.

at once understand that this is a subject which requires a greater knowledge of the matter in dispute, than what I, as a foreigner, can claim :—

" In order to decide which nation speaks the English language best, it becomes necessary to refer to some standard. If it be assumed that the higher classes in London are always to set the fashion in pronunciation, and the best living writers in England are to fix the meaning of words, the point is clearly decided in their favour, since one cannot see on what principle they are to be put in the wrong. That the better company of London must set the fashion for the pronunciation of words in England, and indeed for the whole English empire, is quite plain ; for, as this very company comprises all those whose manners, birth, fortune, and political distinction, make them the objects of admiration, it becomes necessary to imitate their affectations, whether of speech or air, in order to create the impression that one belongs to their society. It is absurd to think that either parliament, or the stage, or the universities, or the church, can produce any very serious effect on the slighter forms of utterance adopted by this powerful caste. The player may hint at the laws of prosody for ever, unless his rule happens to suit the public ear, it becomes no more than the pronunciation of the stage. The fellow, when he gets beyond his cloisters, is glad to conceal the habits of retirement in the language of the world ; and as for the member of Parliament, if he happen to be of the caste, he speaks like the rest of them ; and if not, he is no better than a vulgar fellow, who is very glad to conceal his provincialisms by having as little said about them as possible. In short, the bishop might just as well expect to induce the exquisite to wear a copy of his wig, or the representative of Othello, to set the fashion of smooty faces, as either of them to think of giving the tone to pronunciation, or even to the meaning of words. A secret and lasting influence is no doubt produced by education; but fashion is far more imperious than even the laws of the schools. It is, I think, a capital mistake, to believe that either of the professions named, produce any great impression on the spoken language of England. They receive more from fashion than they give to it; and they each have their particular phrases, but they rarely go any farther than their own limits. This is more or less the case in all other European nations. The rule is more absolute, however, in England than in France, for instance, because the former has no academy, and because men of letters have far less circulation, and, of course, far less influence in society there, than in the neighbouring kingdom. The tendency of every thing in England is to aristocracy. I can conceive that the King of England might very well set a fashion in the pronunciation of a word, because, being the greatest aristocrat of the nation, the smaller ones might be ambitious of showing that they kept enough of his company to catch his imperfections of speech; but, as for the King of France, he sits too much on a pinnacle for men to presume to imitate his blunders. A powerful, wealthy, hereditary, but subsidizing aristocracy, rules all things in England; but, while wit gives up to the King and *la charte*, the control of politics in France, it asserts its own prerogative over every other interest of the empire, religion, perhaps, a little excepted.

"There exists a very different state of things in America. If we had a great capital, like London, where men of leisure, and fortune, and education, periodically assembled to amuse themselves, I think we should establish a fashionable aristocracy, too, which should give the mode to the forms of speech, as well as to that of dress and deportment. Perhaps the influence of talent and wit would be as much felt in such a town as in Paris; for it is the great peculiarity of our institutions to give more influence to talents than to any one other thing. But we have no such capital, nor are we likely, for a long time to come, to have one of sufficient magnitude to produce any great effect on the language. In those States where many men of leisure and education are to be found, there are large towns, in which they pass their winters, and where, of course, they observe all those forms which are more or less peculiar to themselves. The habits of polite life, and even the pronunciation of Boston, of New-York, of Baltimore, and of Philadelphia, vary in many things, and a practised ear may tell a native of either of these places, from a native of any one of the others, by some little peculiarity of speech. There is yet no predominating influence to induce the fashionables of these towns to wish to imitate the fashionables of any other. If any place is to possess this influence, it will certainly be New-York; but I think, on an examination of the subject, that it can be made to appear that an entirely different standard for the language must be established in the United States, from that which governs so absolutely in England.

" If the people of this country were like the people of any other country on earth, we should be speaking at this moment a great variety of nearly unintelligible patois; but, in point of fact, the people of the United States, with the exception of a few of German and French descent, speak, as a body, an incomparably better English than the people of the mother country. There is not, probably, a man (of English descent) born in this country, who would not be perfectly intelligible to all whom he should meet in the streets of London, though a vast number of those he met in the streets of London would be nearly unintelligible to him. In fine, we speak our language, as a nation,

L 2

better than any other people speak their language.*
When one reflects on the immense surface of country
that we occupy, the general accuracy, in pronunciation and in the use of words, is quite astonishing.
This resemblance in speech can only be ascribed to
the great diffusion of intelligence, and to the inex-
haustible activity of the population, which, in a manner, destroys space.

" It is another peculiarity of our institutions, that
the language of the country, instead of becoming
more divided into provincial dialects, is becoming,
not only more assimilated to itself as a whole, but
more assimilated to a standard which sound general
principles, and the best authorities among our old
writers, would justify. The distinctions in speech
between New-England and New-York, or Pennsylvania, or any other State, were far greater twenty
years ago than they are now. Emigration alone
would produce a large portion of this change; but
emigration would often introduce provincialisms without correcting them, did it not also, by bringing acute
men together, sharpen wits, provoke comparisons,
challenge investigations, and, finally, fix a standard.

" It has been a matter of hot dispute, for the last
twenty years, in which of our large towns the best
English is spoken. The result of this discussion
has been to convince most people who know any
thing of the matter, that a perfectly pure English is
spoken nowhere, and to establish the superiority, on
one point in favour of Boston, on another in favour
of New-York, and so on to the end of the chapter.
The effect of all this controversy is, to make men
think seriously on the subject, and thinking seriously
is the first step in amendment. We do amend, and

* Of course the writer calls Italy one nation, and all Germany
one nation, so far as language is concerned.

each year introduces a better and purer English into our country. We are obliged, as you may suppose, to have recourse to some standard to settle these contentions. What shall this standard be? It is not society, for that itself is divided on the disputed points; it cannot be the church, for there is none that will be acknowledged by all parties; it cannot be the stage, for that is composed of foreigners, and possesses little influence on morals, politics, or any thing else; nor the universities, for they are provincial, and parties to the dispute; nor Congress, for that does not represent the fashion and education of the nation; nor the court, for there is none but the President, and he is often a hot partisan; nor the fashions of speech in England, for we often find as much fault with them as we do with our own. Thus, you see, we are reduced to the necessity of consulting reason, and authority, and analogy, and all the known laws of language, in order to arrive at our object. This we are daily doing, and I think the consequence will be, that, in another generation or two, far more *reasonable* English will be used in this country than exists here now. How far this melioration or purification of our language will affect the mother country, is another question.

"It is, perhaps, twenty years too soon to expect that England will very complacently submit to receive opinions or fashions very directly from America." [What she will do twenty years later, is a question that little concerns us, dear Abbate, since I have not, and you ought not to have, any very direct interests in the fortunes of posterity.] "But the time has already arrived, when America is beginning to receive with great distrust fashions and opinions from England. Until within the last fifteen years, the influence of the mother country, in all things connected with mere usages, was predominant to an incredible extent; but every day is making a greater change.

" On a thousand subjects we have been rudely provoked into comparisons,—an experiment that the most faultless generally find to be attended with hazard. We are a bold though a quiet people, and names and fashions go for but little when set in opposition to the unaccommodating and downright good sense of this nation. It may be enough for an Englishman that an innovation on language is supported by the pretty lips of such or such a belle of quality and high degree; but the American sees too many pretty lips at home, to be very submissive to any foreign dictation of this sort. I think it plain, therefore, that the language must be reduced to known general rules, and rules, too, that shall be respected as such rules should be, or else we shall have a dialect distinct from that of the mother country. I have not, however, the slightest apprehensions of any thing of the kind arriving, since any one who understands the use of figures can estimate the probable influence of the two nations half a century hence. I think it will be just as much the desire of England then to be in our fashion, as it was our desire twenty years ago to be in hers, and for precisely the same reason. The influence of fifty millions of people, living under one government, backed by enormous wealth, extended intelligence, a powerful literature, and unrivalled freedom, cannot be very problematical, in the eyes of any man who is capable of regarding the subject free from prejudice or passion. I very well know there is a fashion of predicting the separation of our States, and a consequent disorganization of society, which would certainly weaken that influence. These predictions were made fifty years ago with rather more confidence than they are made now, and those who know most in the matter, treat them with very little deference. But, admitting that they should be realized, in what particular will the result materially affect the question before us? A division of this republic into two or three republics, is the utmost that can be expected. There would still exist those intimate relations between the parts of our present empire which find their support in a conformity of principles, and our intercourse and literature would necessarily be essentially the same. I cannot see that the impression on the language would in any degree be weakened, except that, by dividing our power, we might retard a little the period when the weight of that power should obtain its natural and necessary preponderance. You may be assured, that, in thinking on this subject, I have not forgotten that history supplies sufficient evidence that small communities may exercise a vast influence over larger; but I do not know where to find a precedent for a large community, possessing equal activity and intelligence, submitting to be controlled, either morally or politically, by one physically much weaker. Our own history already furnishes a striking example of the very reverse; and as we are bent on perpetuating all the means of our present independence, it is fair to presume that we shall gain a moral ascendancy in the world, in proportion as we gain physical force. If a pretty duchess can now set a fashion in speech, what will not a combination of two hundred millions of persons do, (the number is not at all exaggerated if we carry the time forward a century and a half,) more especially if all of them shall happen to possess a reasonable knowledge of the use of letters.

"You may have a curiosity to know something of the present state of the language in America. I have already said that there is no patois throughout the whole of this country. There is broken English among the Germans, French, and other foreigners, but nothing that is very widely distinct from the language of London. Still there are words of perfectly provincial use, most of which were brought from certain parts of the mother country, and which have been preserved here, and a few which have been introduced from wantonness or necessity. There is much more difference in intonation, and in the pronunciation of particular words, than in the use of terms unknown to England. The best English is spoken by the natives of the middle States, who are purely the descendants of English parents, without being the descendants of emigrants from New-England. The educated men of all the southern Atlantic States, especially the members of those families which have long been accustomed to the better society of their towns, also speak an English but little to be distinguished from that of the best circles of the mother country. Still there are shades of difference between these very persons, that a nice and practised ear can detect, and which, as they denote the parts of the Union to which they belong, must be called provincialisms. These little irregularities of language solely arise from the want of a capital.

"Throughout all New-England, and among most of the descendants of the people of New-England, the English language is spoken with more or less of an intonation derived, I believe, from the western counties of England, and with a pronunciation that is often peculiar to themselves. They form so large a proportion of the entire population of the country, that some of their provincialisms are getting to form a part of our ordinary language. The peculiarity of the New-England dialect (the term is almost too strong) is most discernible in the manner in which they dwell on the last word of a sentence, or the last syllable of a word. It is not properly drawling, for they speak very quick in common, much quicker than the English; so quick, indeed, as to render syllables frequently indistinct : but, in consequence of the peculiar pause they make on the last word, I question if they utter a sentence in less time than those who dwell more equally on its separate parts.* Among men of the world and of education, this peculiarity is, of course, often lost, but education is so common, and the state of society so simple in New-England, as to produce less apparent distinction in speech and manners than it is usual to find elsewhere.

"Another marked peculiarity of New-England is in the pronunciation of a great many words. The fact that a vast improvement has occurred in this respect within the last thirty years, however, goes to prove the truth of what I have just told you, no less than of the increasing intelligence of the nation.

"When I was a boy, I was sent from a middle State, for my education, to Connecticut. I took with me, of course, the language of my father's house. In the first year I was laughed out of a great many correct sounds, and into a great many vulgar and disagreeable substitutes. At my return home to pass a vacation, I almost threw a sister into fits by calling one of her female friends a 'virtoous *an*-gel,' pronouncing the first syllable of the last word like the article. It was in vain that I supported my new reading by the authorities of *the university*. The whole six weeks were passed in hot discussions between my sister and myself, amidst the laughter and merriment of a facetious father, who had the habit of trotting me through my Connecticut prosody by inducing me to recite Pope's Temple of Fame, to the infinite delight of two or three waggish elder brothers, who had got their English longs and shorts in a more southern school. It was at a time of life when shav-

---

* The phrase of "I wonder if he did," is very common in New-England. It is usually uttered "I wonder if he de-e-e-e-ed," with a falling of the voice at the last word, to nearly an octave below the rest of the sentence. Sometimes there is more than one resting point, in a sentence of any length.

ing was a delight instead of a torment. I remember they were always sure of drawing me out by introducing the subject of my beard, which I pedantically called *berd;* or, for which, if pushed a little harder than common, I gave them a choice between *berd* and *baird.* Even to this hour, it is rare to find a native of New-England who does not possess some of these marked provincialisms of speech. By a singular corruption, the word *stone* is often pronounced *stun,* while *none* is pronounced *noane,* or nearly like *known.* The latter is almost a shibboleth, as is *nothing,* pronounced according to the natural power of the letters, instead of *nuthing.* I think, however, a great deal of the peculiarity of New-England pronunciation is to be ascribed to the intelligence of its inhabitants. This may appear a paradox; but it can easily be explained. They all read and write; but the New-Englandman, at home, is a man of exceedingly domestic habits. He has a theoretical knowledge of the language, without its practice. Those who migrate lose many of their peculiarities in the mixed multitudes they encounter; but *into* New-England the current of emigration, with the exception of that which originally came from the mother country, has never set. It is vain to tell a man who has his book before him, that *cham* spells *chame,* as in *chamber;* or *an, ane,* as in *angel;* or *dan, dane,* as in *danger.* He replies by asking what sound is produced by *an, dan,* and *cham.* I believe it would be found, on pursuing the inquiry, that a great number of their peculiar sounds are introduced through their spelling-books, and yet there are some, certainly, that cannot be thus explained. It is not too much to say that nine people in ten, in New-England, pronounce *does, dooze,* when the mere power of the letters would make it nearer *doze.* There is one more singular corruption, which I shall mention before I go farther south, and which often comes from the mouths of men, even in Boston, who, in other respects, would not be much criticised for their language : the verb *to show* was formerly, and is even now, spelt *shew*, and *shewed* in its participle ; I have heard men of education and manners, in Boston, say, "he *shew* me that," for, he *showed* me that.

"With these exceptions, which are sufficiently numerous, and the hard sound they almost always give the letter *u*, the people of New-England speak the language more like the people of Old-England than any other parts of our country. They speak with a closer mouth, both physically and morally, than those who live further south and west. There is also a little of a nasal sound among some of them, but it is far from being as general as the other peculiarities I have named.

" The middle States certainly speak a softer English than their brethren of the east. I should say, that when you get as far south as Maryland, the softest, and perhaps as pure an English is spoken as is any where heard. No rule on such a subject, however, is without many exceptions in the United States. The emigration alone would, as yet, prevent perfect uniformity. The voices of the American females are particularly soft and silvery ; and I think the language, a harsh one at the best, is made softer by our women, especially of the middle and southern States, than you often hear it in Europe.

"New-York, Philadelphia, and Baltimore, have each their peculiar phrases. Some of the women have a habit of dwelling a little too long on the final syllables, but I think it is rare among the higher classes of society. I don't know that it exists at all, as far south as Baltimore. As you go further south, it is true, you get a slower utterance, and other slight varieties of provincialism. In Georgia, you find a positive drawl, among what are called the "crackers." More or less of this drawl, and of all the peculiar sounds, are found in the south-western and western States; but they are all too new to have any fixed habits of speech of their own.

"The usual vulgar phrases which are put into the mouths of Americans, are commonly caricatured, though always founded in truth. 'I guess,' is a phrase of New-England. It is used a great deal, though not as often, as 'you know,' by a cockney. It proceeds, I think, from the cautious and subdued habit of speaking which is characteristic of these people. The gentlemen rarely use it, though I confess I have heard it, interlarding the conversation of pretty lips that derived none of their beauty from the Puritans. You see, therefore, that it has been partially introduced by the emigrants into the middle States. Criticism is here so active, just now, that it is rapidly getting into disuse. The New-Yorker frequently says, 'I suspect,' and the Virginian, 'I reckon.' But the two last are often used in the best society in the mother country.*

"The difference in pronunciation and in the use of words between the really good society of this country and that of England, is not very great. In America, we can always tell an Englishman by what we are pleased to call his provincialisms (and, quite half the time, the term is correct,) I was struck at the close resemblance between the language of the higher classes in the mother country, and the higher classes of my own, especially if the latter belong to the middle States. There are certainly points of difference, but they as often proceed from affectation in individuals, as from the general habits of the two countries. Cockneyisms are quite as frequent in the language of an English gentleman, as provincialisms

---

* The negroes have a habit of saying, "you sabber dat," for, you know that; can this be one of their African terms, or is it a corruption of "saber," or of "savoir," that has found its way to the continent from the neighbouring islands?

in the mouth of an American gentleman of the middle States. I now use the word gentleman in its strict meaning. I have heard many people of high rank in England, for instance, pronounce 'yours' as if it were spelt 'yers.' If affectations are to become laws, because they are conceived in the smoke of London, then they are right; but, if old usage, the rules of the language, and the voices of even educated men are to prevail, then are they wrong. This is but one among a hundred similar affectations that are detected every day by an attentive and critical ear. But mere rank, after all, is not always a criterion of correct pronunciation in an Englishman or an Englishwoman. I have met with people of rank who have spoken in very perceptible provincial dialects. Parliament is very far from being faultless in its English, putting the Irish, Scotch, and aldermen out of the question. I have heard a minister of state speak of the 'o-casion,' with a heavy emphasis; and just before we sailed, I remember to have burst into involuntary laughter at hearing a distinguished orator denounce a man for having been the 'recipient of a bribe of ten guineas.' The language of Parliament is undeniably far more correct than that of Congress; but when it is recollected that the one body is a representation of the aristocracy of a condensed community, and the other a representation of the various classes of a widely-spread people, the rational odds is immensely in our favour. I am not sure that one, who took pleasure in finding fault, might not detect quite as many corruptions of the English language in the good society of the mother country, as in the good society of our own. The latter, strictly considered, bears a less proportion to our numbers, however, than the same class bears to the population of England. The amount of the whole subject I take to be simply this: allowing for all the difference in numbers, there is vastly more bad English, and a thousand times more bad gram-

mar spoken in England than in America; and there
is much more good English (also allowing for the difference in numbers) spoken there than here. Among
the higher and better educated classes, there are
purists in both countries, who may write and talk to
the end of time; innovations have been made, are
made, and will be made in both countries; but as
two nations now sit in judgment on them, I think
when words once get fairly into use, their triumph
affords a sufficient evidence of merit to entitle them
to patronage.

TO THE COMTE JULES DE BÉTHIZY,

&c. &c.

Washington, ——

If I have said nothing for a long time, concerning
your distinguished countryman, it has not been for
want of materials. The *éclat* which attends his passage through the country, is as brilliant as it was the
day he landed; but were I to attempt to give you a
continuous history of the ceremonies and pageants
that grow out of his visit, my letters would be filled
with nothing else. One of the former has, however,
just occurred here, which may have a particular interest. I shall, therefore, attempt to describe a few
of its outlines. Before proceeding to this task, permit me to mention one circumstance, that has struck
me with peculiar force, and which I beg you will
communicate to our friend the Abbate, when next
you write to him.

At Philadelphia, after a triumphal entry, in which
something like twenty thousand of the militia were

under arms, the citizens of all classes, according to custom, paid visits of congratulation to their guest, who received them in that famous hall, which has become celebrated for being the place where the separation of a portion of this continent from Europe was first solemnly declared. Among the thousands who crowded around the venerable Frenchman, were all the clergy of the city. They were more than sixty in number, and at their head appeared the Bishop of the Protestant Episcopal Church, with the Bishop of the Roman Catholic Church at his side. The former, who is a native of the country, and one of its oldest divines, delivered the sentiments of his brethren ; but had the latter, who is a foreigner, been of a greater age, and of longer service, he would, undoubtedly, have been selected to have performed the same ceremony. It is much the fashion, in Europe, to say there is no religion in the United States, for no better reason than that there is no church establishment, and, consequently, no exaltation of one particular sect, and a consequent depression of all others. But you will allow there is one evidence of a Christian spirit, that is not always found elsewhere, viz. charity. Although, in theory, all denominations in the United States are equal before the law, there is, in point of fact, no country in the world that is more decidedly Protestant than this, and yet, I do believe, it would give scandal to the whole nation, to learn that a slight, or an offence of any nature, were given to a priest, merely because he happened to belong to the Roman Catholic communion.

La Fayette arrived in Washington some time before the meeting of Congress. He had an appropriate reception from the inhabitants of the district, and was received into the house of the President. But his time was too precious to be unnecessarily lost. All were anxious to see him, and he was, apparently, just as anxious to see all. Leaving Washington, after a short residence, he paid a visit to Virginia, where he found Jefferson and Madison, the two last Presidents, living in retirement, and where he must also have spent several delightful days on the theatre of that brilliant campaign, where, though but a boy, he foiled all the sagacity and activity of an experienced and enterprising general, (Cornwallis,) and prepared the way for the final and glorious success with which the war of 1776 was terminated.

On his return to this place, it was announced that the House of Representatives intended to give him a public and solemn reception. He was received by the Senate in a simple, and more private, but in an affectionate manner. I was in their hall, on this occasion, and was greatly struck with the quiet dignity of the ceremony. There was a short address, and a simple reply, after which La Fayette was invited to take his seat on the sofa, by the side of the President of the Senate.* He afterwards frequently visited the Senate chamber, to hear the debates, and, on all these occasions, he was seated in the same place. There was something noble, as well as touching, in the sight of a veteran returning to the scene of his services, after a life like that of La Fayette, and of being thus received so familiarly and affectionately into the bosom of the highest legislative body of a nation, that was enjoying a prosperity and ease far exceeding that known to any other people.

On the day of the more public ceremony in the hall of the Representatives, every one was seen mounting the Capitol hill at an early hour. We got places, as usual, on the floor of the house, where we could both hear and see. The galleries were

---

* The Vice-President of that day, being often indisposed, rarely presided, and a President *pro tem.*, according to a custom, performed his duties. The Vice-President (Mr. Tompkins) died soon after.

crowded to overflowing, being filled with fine women
and well-dressed men.   The body of the house was,
of course, occupied by none but the members, while
the inner lobbies, or the circular space along the
walls, and behind the Speaker's chair, were occupied
by those who, of right, or by virtue of sufficient influence, were allowed to enter.

The Speaker of the House of Representatives is a
man of singular talents, and of great native eloquence.
In person he is tall and spare, and he is far from being graceful in his ordinary air and attitudes.   His
countenance is one of those in which a pleasing
whole is produced by parts that are far from being
particularly attractive.   In face and form, Mr. Clay
(the Speaker) is not unlike the pictures of the last
Pitt, nor is he unlike him in the power of addressing
public bodies.   Notwithstanding these defects of the
physique, few men are capable of producing as great
an effect as Mr. Clay, when he is placed in situations
to exhibit his talents.   His gesticulation is graceful,
and exceedingly dignified, his utterance slow, distinct, and gentlemanly, and his voice one of the
sweetest imaginable.*

At the appointed hour, the doors of the hall were
thrown open, and a simple little procession advanced
with dignity into the body of the house.   It was composed of the Senators of the United States, preceded
by a delegation of the lower house, who had been
sent to invite them to attend at the approaching ceremony.   They were in pairs; the Senators of each
State walking together.   Forty-eight chairs were
placed near the Speaker for their reception, and, after
exchanging bows with the members of the lower

---

* The Attorney-General of the United States (Mr. Wirt)
has the sweetest voice the writer ever heard in a public
speaker.   It is something in the style of that of Mr. Peel,
though nothing can be more different than their usual manner of speaking.

house, who were standing, the whole were seated together. As the Senators never wear their hats, the Representatives, on this occasion, took their seats uncovered. A few minutes after, M. George La Fayette and the secretary of the general, were shown into the hall and provided with places.

The doors now opened again, and a deputation of twenty-four members of Congress (one from each State) slowly entered the hall. In their front was La Fayette, supported by their chairman and a representative from Louisiana. The whole assembly rose; the guest was led into the centre of the hall, and then the chairman of the deputation said, in an audible voice,

"Mr. Speaker, your committee have the honour to introduce General La Fayette to the House of Representatives."

A sofa had been placed for La Fayette, and he was now invited to be seated. Both houses resumed their chairs, and the guest occupied his sofa. A short pause succeeded, when the Speaker rose with deliberation and dignity. The instant the tones of his sweet voice were heard in the hall, a silence reigned among the auditors that equalled the stillness of death. La Fayette stood to listen. The address was evidently *extempore*, but it was delivered with the ease of a man long accustomed to rely on himself, in scenes of high excitement. He was evidently moved, though the grace of manner and the command of words were rather heightened than suppressed, by his emotions. I shall endeavour to give you the substance of what he said:

"General,—The House of Representatives of the United States, impelled alike by its own feelings, and by those of the whole American people, could not have assigned to me a more gratifying duty, than that of presenting to you cordial congratulations on the occasion of your recent arrival in this country.

In compliance with the wishes of Congress, I assure you of the very high satisfaction which your presence affords on this early theatre of your glory. Although but few of the members who compose this body, shared with you in the war of our revolution, all have learned from impartial history, or from faithful tradition, a knowledge of the perils, the sufferings, and the sacrifices which you voluntarily encountered, and of the signal services which you performed in America, and in Europe, for an infant, a distant, and an alien people. All feel and own the very great extent of the obligation under which you have placed the nation. But the relations in which you have ever stood to the United States, interesting and important as they have been, do not constitute the only motive for the respect and admiration of this House.   Your consistency of character, your uniform devotion to regulated liberty, through all the vicissitudes of a long and arduous life, command its profound admiration. During the recent convulsions of Europe, amidst, no less than after the dispersion of, every political storm, the people of the United States have beheld you, true to your principles, erect in every danger, and cheering, with your well-known voice, the votaries of liberty; a faithful and fearless champion, ready to shed the last drop of that blood which here you had already so freely and so nobly spilt in the same holy cause.

" The vain wish has been sometimes indulged that Providence would allow the patriot to return to his country after death, and to contemplate the changes to which time had given birth. To the American this would have been to view the forest felled, cities built, mountains levelled, canals cut, highways constructed, the progress of the arts, the advancement of learning, and the increase of population.

" General,—Your present visit is a realization of the consoling object of that wish.   You stand in the midst of posterity. Every where you must have been struck with the physical and moral changes which have occurred since you left us. This very city, bearing a name dear to you and to us, has since emerged from the forest which then covered its site. In one thing you behold us unaltered; the sentiment of continued devotion to liberty, and of ardent and profound gratitude to your departed friend, the father of his country, and to you and to your illustrious associates in the field and in the cabinet, for the multiplied blessings which surround us, and for the very privilege which I now exercise of addressing you. This sentiment, now fondly cherished by more than ten millions of people, will be transmitted, with unabated vigour, down the tide of time to the latest posterity, through the countless millions who are destined to inhabit this continent."

During this discourse, La Fayette was visibly affected. Instead of answering immediately, he took his seat, which he retained for a minute, struggling to conquer his feelings; then rising, he replied in English, and with powerful feeling, nearly as follows. I think the slight evidence of a foreign idiom, which his reply contains, adds to its interest.

"Mr. Speaker, and Gentlemen of the House of Representatives—While the people of the United States, and their honourable Representatives in Congress, have deigned to make choice of me, one of the American veterans, to signify in his person their esteem for our joint services and their attachment to the principles for which we have had the honour to fight and bleed, I am proud and happy to share those extraordinary favours with my dear revolutionary companions. Yet, it would be, on my part, uncandid and ungrateful not to acknowledge my personal share in those testimonies of kindness, as they excite in my breast emotions which no words are adequate to express.

" My obligations to the United States, Sir, far exceed any merit I might claim. They date from the
time when I have had the happiness to be adopted
as a young soldier, a favoured son of America; they
have been continued to me during almost half a century of constant affection and confidence; and now,
Sir, thanks to your most gratifying invitation, I find
myself greeted by a series of welcomes, one hour of
which would more than compensate for the public
exertions and sufferings of a whole life.

" The approbation of the American people, and of
their representatives, . for my conduct during the
vicissitudes of the European revolution, is the highest
reward I could receive. Well may I stand firm and
erect, when in their names, and by you, Mr. Speaker, I am declared to have, in every instance, been
faithful to those American principles of liberty, equality, and true social order, the devotion to which, as
it has been from my earliest youth, so it shall continue to be a solemn duty to my latest breath.

" You have been pleased, Mr. Speaker, to allude
to the peculiar felicity of my situation, when, after
so long an absence, I am called to witness the immense improvements, the admirable communications,
of the prodigious creation of which we find an example in this city, whose name itself is a venerated
palladium; in a word, all the grandeur and prosperity of those happy United States, who, at the same
time they nobly secure the complete assertion of
American independence, reflect on every part of the
world the light of a far superior political civilization.

" What better pledge can be given of a persevering
national love of liberty, when those blessings are evidently the result of a virtuous resistance to oppres-
sion, and of institutions founded on the rights of man
and the republican principle of self-government?

" No, Mr. Speaker, posterity has not begun for-
me, since, in the sons of my companions and friends,

I find the same public feelings, and, permit me to add, the same feelings in my behalf, which I have had the happiness to experience in their fathers.

" Sir, I have been allowed, forty years ago, before a committee of a Congress of thirteen States, to express the fond wishes of an American heart. On this day, I have the honour, and enjoy the delight, to congratulate the representatives of the Union, so vastly enlarged, on the realization of those wishes, even beyond every human expectation, and upon the almost infinite prospects we can with certainty anticipate. Permit me, Mr. Speaker, and Gentlemen of the House of Representatives, to join to the expression of those sentiments, a tribute of my lively gratitude, affectionate devotion, and profound respect."

A deeper silence never pervaded any assembly than that with which the audience listened to this answer. There was so much of nature, of sincerity, and of affection in the manner of the speaker, and quite evidently so little of preparation in the language of his reply, that it produced a vastly greater effect than any studied discourse, however elegant in phraseology and thought.

After a short pause of a few minutes, during which many of the members were manifestly stilling their awakened feelings, the gentleman who had announced La Fayette arose, and impressively moved that the house should now adjourn. The question was put and carried, and then all present, members and spectators, crowded about their guest, to renew welcomes and felicitations which were reiterated for the thousandth time.

I do not know that the Americans have any particular tact in their manner of conducting ceremonies, perhaps, on the contrary, they are not much practised in their mysteries; but, as natural feelings are as little disturbed as possible, I have ever found in the receptions, greetings, and *fêtes* they have given to La Fayette, a simplicity and touching affection that has gone directly to the heart. The veteran himself has manifested, on all occasions, a wonderful tact and readiness. Notwithstanding the gravity and earnest air he has so often been compelled to encounter, he has, in every instance, managed to strip the ceremony of the stiffness of preparation, and to give to the interviews the warmth and interest that should distinguish a meeting between a parent and his children.

After the business of the morning was ended, Cadwallader and myself joined a small party which continued about the person of La Fayette, whom we accompanied to his lodgings. The heart of the old man was full, and he took an evident delight in recurring to those events of the revolution which redounded to the credit of a people, in whose history and character he seems to take the same pride that a fond father would feel in witnessing the advance of a promising son. During our ride, he mentioned several little circumstances that are worthy of repetition; but the limits of this letter must confine me to two.

In the year 1779 and 1780, La Fayette commanded the light infantry of the American army. Most of the soldiers were natives of New-England, or of the middle States. With these troops he was sent from the north to act against Cornwallis, in that memorable campaign in which he did himself so much honour by his prudence and spirit, and which terminated in the capture of the latter. On reaching Baltimore, the effects of climate, and of a removal from home, became quite apparent on the spirits of his men. They conversed among themselves of the dangers of a summer passed in the low counties of Virginia, and for a few nights there were repeated desertions. It was of the last importance to put a stop to a feeling that threatened destruction to the service. The young Frenchman took counsel of his own heart, and acted accordingly. He issued a general order, in which he set forth the dangers of the climate, and the hazards and hardships of the contemplated service in the plainest language, concluding by calling on those who felt unequal to the trial to present themselves, in order that they might be embodied and sent back to the main army, since it was absolutely necessary that he should know the precise force on which he might depend. Not a man came forward to claim the promised favour; and, what is far more remarkable, not another desertion occurred. The second anecdote is still more worthy of relation.

Throughout the whole of the war of 1776, the American army was rarely exempted from severe suffering. They had to contend with disease and hunger; were often without shoes, even in winter, and frequently without ammunition.* On one occasion, it is known that famine actually pervaded the grand army while it lay at no great distance in front of general Howe, who was at the head of a powerful and an admirably appointed force. During the campaign of 1780, La Fayette, who, you will remember, was an American general, was joined by a small French force. He continued to command as the senior officer. There was a scarcity in the camp, and it became necessary to resort to severe measures in order to provide for the allies. He boldly issued an order that no American should receive a mouthful until the French soldiers were furnished with full

---

* The writer made an acquaintance with two veterans of that war, while in America. One of them assured him he marchèd into the battle of Trenton (he was a lieutenant, and it was in the depth of winter) without a shirt; and the other, who was in the cavalry, assured him, that by charging at the battle of Eutaw into a thicket of black-jacks, (a sort of thorny bush,) where the English infantry had thrown themselves, after the principal rencontre, he lost a far more important vestment, which he was not able to replace, until he luckily found a piece of tow-cloth in the highway.

rations, and for several days the camp exhibited the singular spectacle of one portion of its inmates being full fed, while the other was on an exceedingly limited allowance. What renders the forbearance of the native troops still more worthy of praise, is the fact, that the officer who commanded the dangerous distinction, was a countryman of those who were well fed: yet no man heard a murmur! To me it seems, that the mutual confidence exhibited in this fact, is as creditable to him who dared to issue the order, as to those who knew how to submit to it without complaint.

TO THE PROFESSOR CHRISTIAN JANSEN,

&c. &c.

Washington, ———

—It was a week before I recovered from the shock of such an alarm. But on more mature thought, (especially when I came coolly to reflect on some recent dangers through which I had myself passed in triumph, as well as on the numberless instances in which I had felt symptoms of the same disorder,) I began to consider your cause as far from hopeless. We become more liable to these attacks as we advance in life, and I warn you of being constantly on your guard against them. I also beg leave to recommend exercise and change of scene as the most effectual cure. I am fully persuaded that had not fortune made us all travellers, we should long since have ceased to be the independent beings we are. Waller spoke, in his last letter, of a Venetian beauty,

in language that seemed ominous; but I know too
well that deep inward eccentricity of the man, which
he so prettily calls *mauvaise honte*, to dread any thing
serious from the affair. I think his eminently impartial manner of viewing things, will for ever save him
from the sin of matrimony. Besides, the girl is only
descended from two doges of the fifteenth century,
and four or five old admirals of the thirteenth and
fourteenth, a genealogy that surely cannot pretend to
compete with the descent of a Somersetshire baronet,
whose great-grandfather was an alderman of Lin-
coln, and whose great-grandmother was the youngest
daughter of a British officer. If you doubt the truth
of the last circumstance, I refer you to the half-pay
list of lieutenants of dragoons, in the reign of George
the Second.

You have made a much more formidable request
than you appear to think, when you desire that I will
give you a detailed account of the system of jurisprudence, of the laws, and of the different courts of
this country. The subject, properly and ably considered, would require a year of time, and infinitely
more legal science than I can lay claim to possess.
Still, as I may tell you some things of which you are
as yet a stranger, I shall not shrink from the task of
communicating the little I do know, under the stale
plea of incompetency.

About a week after our arrival in this place, Cadwallader and myself had descended from the hall of
the House of Representatives to the caucus, and we
were about to leave the Capitol, when my friend
made a sudden inclination to the left, motioning for
me to follow. He passed into the basement of the
northern wing of the edifice. I had seen but a few
minutes before, by the naked flag-staff, that the Senate had adjourned,* and, was about to say as much,

---

* A flag is kept flying over the wings in which the two houses
meet, when they are in session, and they are struck as either

when I observed, that in place of ascending the stairs which led to their chamber, he proceeded deeper into the lower apartments of the wing. Opening a simple door, we entered a spacious, but low and far from brilliant apartment. It was lighted only from one of its sides. Directly in front of the windows, and a little elevated above the rest of the floor, sat seven grave looking men, most of whom had passed the meridian of life. They were clad in simple black silk robes, not unlike those worn by the students of universities, and most of them were busily occupied in taking notes. Immediately in their front, some ten or twelve respectable men were seated, who had nothing in attire to distinguish them from the ordinary gentlemen of the country. There were two or three others who had the air of being inferior *employés* of some grave and important body; though, with the exception of the black silk robes, I saw no other badges of office. On the right, and on the left, there were benches in rows, and perhaps thirty or forty more gentlemen were seated on them, listening to what was said. Among these auditors, there might have been a dozen genteel looking women. This assemblage was composed of the judges, the advocates, the officers, and the suitors of the Supreme Court of the United States. All present who did not come within one or the other of the above-mentioned denominations, were, like ourselves, merely curious witnesses of the proceedings.

We staid an hour listening to the argument of a distinguished advocate. He was a member of Congress from one of the eastern States, and by the simplicity of his language, and the acuteness and force of his thoughts, he was clearly a man who would

body adjourns. These are signals that enable people at a distance to learn whether the Senate, or lower house, are still together or not.

have done credit to any tribunal in the world. The manner of the speaker was rather cold, but it was dignified, and he paid the highest compliment to his auditors, by addressing all he said to their reasons. The judges listened with grave attention, and indeed the whole scene wore the air of a calm and a highly reasonable investigation.

My attention was given more to the severe simplicity which marked the aspect and proceedings of this powerful tribunal, than to the particular subject before it. I found high authority again reposing with confidence on the most naked ceremonials, and I again found it surrounded by an air of deep reverence, which proves how little the vulgar auxiliaries of our eastern inventions are necessary to insure it respect and obedience. On no other occasion was I ever so completely sensible of the feebleness of an artificial, or of the majesty of a true, because a natural dignity, as on this. I have heard the wigs, and robes, and badges of office of half the tribunals of Europe laughed at, even by those who become familiar with their absurdities; but I do not know on what the most satirical wit could seize, in a body like this, to turn into ridicule. It is no small proof of the superiority that is obtained by the habit of considering things in their direct and natural aspects, that wigs, and other similar encumbrances, which are heaped upon the human form, with us, in order to heighten respect, in this country are avoided, in order to protect those, who should be venerated, from undeserved ridicule.

Considered in reference to its functions, and to the importance of the trusts which it discharges, the Supreme Court of the United States is the most august tribunal of the world. It may not yet be called upon to decide on causes which involve as great an amount of property, perhaps, as some of the courts of England; but, as the wealth and power of this country shall increase with its growth, the matters it decides will become still greater; and it now produces a mighty influence on the interests of the whole Union. You will better understand the subject, if we take a rapid view of the judicial system of the confederation, as it is connected with those of the several States.

You already know that the theory of the American government assumes that all power is the natural and necessary right of the people. The accidental circumstances of colonization had thrown the settlers into a certain number of bodies politic, before the era of their revolution. Until that event arrived, each province was entirely distinct and independent of all the others, except as they had common relations through their allegiance to the crown of England, and through those commercial and general interests which united them as the subjects of the same empire.

For the purpose of achieving their independence, the different provinces entered into a compact which partook of the nature of an intimate and indissoluble alliance. The articles of the confederation were a sort of treaty, that was not, however, limited to definite, but which embraced general objects, and which was to know no limits to its duration, but such as necessity must put to all things. Still it was little more than an intimate alliance between thirteen separate and independent governments. Money was to be raised for avowed and general purposes; but it was done in the way of subsidies rather than of taxation. Each State collected its own resources in its own manner, and it had fulfilled most of its obligations to the confederation when it had paid its quota, and when it permitted the few public agents appointed by the Congress to discharge the particular trusts that were delegated.to the Union.

Notwithstanding this imperfect and clumsy organization of their general government, the inhabitants of the United States were, even at that early day, essentially the same people. They had the same views of policy, the same general spirit, substantially the same origin,* and a community of interests that constantly invited a more intimate association. The country was scarcely relieved from the pressure and struggle of the war of the revolution, before its wisest citizens began to consider the means of effecting so desirable an object. Peace was concluded in 1783 ; and, in 1787, a convention was called to frame a constitution for the United States. The very word *constitution* implies the control of all those interests which distinguish an identified community. If we speak with technical accuracy, the convention of 1787 was assembled for the purpose of improving an existing compact, rather than for the purpose of creating one entirely new. But it will simplify our theory, and answer all the desirable purposes of the present object, if we assume that the States entered into the bargain perfectly unencumbered by any pre-existing engagements.

Under this view of the case, each State possessed all the rights of a distinct sovereignty, when it sent its delegates to the convention. There was no power which of necessity belongs to any other government of the world, that each of these States could not of itself exercise, subject always to the restrictions of its own institutions and laws. But then, each State possessed the power of altering its own institutions as it saw fit; it had its own laws, its own tribunals, and it preserved its policy in all things, except that, in point of fact, by the ancient confederation, it was

---

* A gross error exists in Europe, on the subject of the mixed character of this people. The whole population of Louisiana, for instance, but a little exceeded 75,000 souls (blacks included,) in 1810. It was ceded to the Union in 1804.

bound not to enter into wars, and certain other engagements, with foreign nations, without the rest of
the States being parties to the transaction.

The constitution of 1787 wrought a vital change
in this system. The Americans now became one
people in their institutions, as well as in their origin
and in their feelings. It is important to remember
that the two latter induced the former circumstance,
and not the former the latter.

You can readily imagine that the principal point
to be decided in a body which had professedly assembled with such intentions, was that of the continuation or annihilation of the State governments. There
were not a few in favour of the first policy, though
the influence of those who supported the authority
of the States happily prevailed. I say happily, since,
I think, it can be made plain that the existence of
the Union at the present hour, no less than its future
continuance, is entirely dependent on the existence
of the government of the several States.

In consequence of the policy that prevailed, a
species of mixed and complicated government was
established, which was before unknown to the world,
but which promises to prove that territory may be
extended *ad libitum* without materially impairing the
strength of a country by its extent. It strikes me,
that as the confederation of the United States is the
most natural government known, that it is consequently the only empire on whose stability the fullest
confidence can be placed. It is a superstructure
regularly reared on a solid foundation, and not a
tower from which a number of heavy and ill-balanced
dependants are suspended. As to the prognostics of
its dissolution, they are founded on theories that are
getting to be a little obsolete; and the best argument
that is urged to prove their truth, after all, is merely
the fact that the confederation of the United States
has not existed more than the full term of fifty years

during the last half century. Perhaps it may console these impatient reasoners to know, that, while the records of the country are certainly limited to the brief period named, so far as improvement, wealth, power, and a general advancement are concerned, it has every appearance of having been in existence two or three centuries.

In order to effect the material objects of the new confederation, it became necessary that the States should part freely with their power. The principle was adopted that every thing which was necessary to the general welfare should be yielded to the general government, while the States should, of course, retain all the rest of their authority. But, with a view to give the utmost efficiency to the new system, an executive, courts, and subordinate functionaries were created, who were to act on the people sometimes through, but oftener without, the intermediate agency of the State authorities. As our present business is with the courts, we will confine ourselves to that branch of the subject.

Although the several States preserve the outlines of the judicial institutions which they inherited from their ancestors, there are not, probably, two in the whole confederation whose forms of jurisprudence are precisely the same. There is necessarily a difference in the policy of a large State and the policy of a small one; in that of a large, *new* State and that of a large *old* one; in that of a State without and in that of a State with slaves; in a commercial and in a purely agricultural State; and, in short, in a society which exists under the direct influence of certain interests, and in a society which exists under the influence of certain others. You may trace in this power of accommodating their minute policy to their own particular condition, and, what is probably quite as important, to their own pleasure, one of the great reasons for the durability of the Union.

Had I the necessary knowledge to impart it, you would not possess the patience to read a detailed account of the shades of difference which exist in the jurisprudence of twenty-four separate communities. I shall therefore take the outline of that of New-York, the most populous of the States, and point out its connexion with that of the Union. It will be sufficiently exact to give you an idea of the whole.

The foundation of the laws of New-York, is the common law of England. Some of the provisions of this law, and a few of its principles, have been destroyed by the constitution of the State, which, of course, has substituted the maxims of a republic for those of a monarchy. Statute law has changed, and is daily changing certain other decrees of the common law, which are found to be inapplicable to the peculiar state of this society. I know no better evidence of the boldness and usefulness of reform, as it exists in this country, than is to be found in the early changes they made in the common law. It is now near half a century since they destroyed the right of entail, the trial by battle, the detestable and unnatural law of the half-blood, and a variety of other similar usages that are just beginning to become obnoxious to European censure. The Americans themselves say that New-York has still a great deal to do, and daily complaints are heard against impediments to justice, which are to be traced to the usages of a comparatively dark age.*

The lowest tribunal known to the laws, is what is

---

* There are people who may find it curious to know, that the advancement of public opinion, and the consequent security of liberty, is making bold inroads on those practices which are known to have given birth to political rights. In the State of Louisiana, and, the writer believes, in one or two others, the use of a jury is dispensed with, in all civil cases, in which it is not demanded by one of the parties. It is said that more than five-sixths of the civil actions are tried by the court. Still the *right* of a trial by jury is guarantied by the constitution of the United States.

called a justices' court, or the suits before a justice
of the peace.   In each county there is also a regular
court for the trial of criminal causes, and for the
common pleas of that county.   The presiding officers
of these courts are termed judges; they are commonly
five in number, and are sometimes aided by what are
called assistant justices.   In the older counties these
judges are usually men of education, and always men
of character.   They are frequently lawyers, who continue to practise in the higher courts, and they are
often men of landed estate, yeomen of good characters and influence, and sometimes merchants.   Their
criminal duties are not unlike those of the quarter
sessions in England.   Executions in civil actions issued out of this court, take effect on all property
found within the limits of the county, and judgments
are liens on real estate, according to priority of date,
without reference to the courts where any other similar claims may be recorded.

The State is next subdivided into judicial circuits.
For each of these circuits there is one judge.   This
officer presides at the circuit courts, assisted by the
judges of the county; and as the judgments obtained
under verdicts in this court are perfected before the
supreme court of the State, they have a lien on all
property belonging to the party concerned within the
bounds of the State.   Both of these courts take cogni-
zance of crimes.

The supreme court (of the State of New-York) is
composed of three judges.   They constitute a court
of law, to which appeals are made from the inferior
tribunals.   The judges do not regularly preside at any
of the circuits, though it is within the scope of their
powers to do so if they please.*   They settle all causes,

---

* There has been a recent change in the courts of New-
York.   A few years since there were five judges of the supreme court, and they tried all causes at Nisi Prius, holding
the circuits in person.   It was found that the business accu-

and the reports of their proceedings form the ordinary books of precedents.

There is a chancellor who hears and decides in all cases where equity is claimed, and who exercises the usual authority in granting injunctions against the consummation of proceedings at law. In many of the States, the equitable power is lodged in the same courts as the legal, the judges hearing causes on what is termed the equity side. The chancellor of the State is purely a law officer, exercising no other functions, and holding his commission by the same tenures as the judges. In one or two of the States, however, the governor acts as chancellor.

The Senate of the State, (of New-York,) assisted by the chancellor and judges of the Supreme Court, form a tribunal for appeals, and for the correction of errors in the last resort. Their decision is final, unless the defendant should happen to be a foreigner, or a citizen of another State, in which case the cause can be carried into the courts of the United States* under certain circumstances. This court is not known to many of the States.

The jurisdiction of the courts of a State, embraces most of the ordinary interests of life. Nearly all offences against persons and things, whether considered in reference to the protection of the individual, or in

---

mulated, and, in order to repair the evil, the circuit judges were appointed; those of the supreme court were reduced in number, and the common duties of the latter were limited to the terms. The better opinion in the State is, that this departure from a practice which has been sanctioned by so many centuries is not successful. A return to the former system is already contemplated, with an increase of the judges, that shall make their whole number equal to the labour they have to undergo.

* The plaintiff, being an alien, or a citizen of another State, can do the same thing in the first stages of the suit. But it is impossible to be minute in a work like this; the writer merely aims at giving a general idea of the system of the jurisprudence of the United States.

reference to the dignity and security of society, can be tried before some one of the tribunals mentioned. In many cases the tribunals have concurrent power, those of the United States always being supreme, when they have a right to interfere at all.

The lowest tribunal established by the United States is that of the district courts. The rule is to make each State a district for the trial of causes under the laws of the Union, though some of the larger States are divided into two. Each of these courts has its particular judge, its recording, and its executive officers. The latter are called marshals; they exercise all the ordinary duties of an English sheriff.* Original causes are tried before the district judge. If A. should fail in the conditions of an ordinary contract made with B., the latter would bring his suit in the county in which the former resided, or in the supreme court of the State, as he might please; but if the contract had direct reference to matter which is exclusively controlled by the laws of the United States, he would probably bring his action in the circuit court of the State in which the defendant lived. In matters that arise from seizures under the customs, or that affect any other of the direct interests of the United States, the *District Court* is always competent to proceed. If process issues on execution from the courts of the State, it is to the sheriff; but from the United States' courts it is directed to the marshal. The same distinction is observed for the execution of sentences under the respective criminal laws of the two authorities. Thus, it would be possible, as in the cases of an ordinary murder and of piracy, for two convicts to issue from the same gaol, and to go to the same gallows, though the one should be hanged under the orders of a sheriff, and the other under the orders of a marshal. Though

---

* Each county has a sheriff under the laws of the State.

there are no points of collision, in matters of mere dignity, the marshal is a man of more importance than a sheriff, inasmuch as his bailiwick embraces a whole State instead of a county; and he executes the supreme law of the land, though, in fact, his functions are often limited to a course of concurrent, or rather to a division of familiar powers.*

Each State also forms a district for the circuit courts of the United States. At the circuit, a judge of the supreme court of the United States presides, assisted by the judge of the district. They hear original cases, and such appeals as, by law, can be brought from the tribunals of the State. It frequently happens, that actions affecting parties residing in different States, are brought in the courts of a particular State, because the property in dispute lies there, and the defendant then carries his appeal to one of the circuit courts of the United States. You will see that, of necessity, the laws of the several States must be known to the judges of these circuits, as a great deal of their power goes no further than to take care that these laws shall not infringe on the rights which are guarantied by the confederation.

The judges of the supreme court of the United States sit once a year, to hear appeals and questions of law. They have all the equity powers which are necessarily incident to justice, there being no chancellor of the United States. Their decisions are final, no appeal lying to any other body of the land. This dignified and powerful tribunal not only decides on the interests of individuals, but on the interests of

* The United States have, as yet, no gaols. There is such perfect understanding between the two authorities, that the States lend their gaols, court-rooms, &c. to the officers of the United States, though it is probable that, ere long, provision will be made for both. A convict, sentenced to hard labour by a court of the United States, is sent to the Penitentiary of the State where he is convicted, the former defraying any excess of expense over the fruits of his earnings.

States. Communities that are, even now, larger than the smallest kingdoms of Europe, can come before them, in their corporate capacity, as suitors and defendants.

The affairs of this immensely important tribunal, have ever been conducted with surprising dignity and moderation. The judges are amenable to public opinion, the severest punishment and the tightest check in a free community, and their corruption can be punished by impeachment. An instance of the latter occurred during high party times, and while the doctrines of Europe were more in fashion than they are at present, but the accused was not found guilty.

The duties of the supreme court are often of a highly delicate nature, but the judges have contrived to create a great degree of reverence for, and of confidence in, their decisions. As the population of the country increases, the number of the judges will be increased to meet its wants.*

You know that steam was first successfully applied to boats in America. The celebrated Fulton obtained a law (in the State of New-York) creating a monopoly of its use in his favour for a term of years. At first, the experiment was deemed so hazardous, that he enjoyed this exclusive right without molestation. But, when the immense profits of the speculation became apparent, men began to question the legality of the monopoly. Boats were built without the consent of the assignees of Fulton. The chancellor of the State of New-York, regarding the act of his own legislature, granted an injunction, prohibiting their use. The parties then joined issue, and the case was carried through the courts of the State, until it reached the Court of Errors, where it was decided in favour of the law of the State. New parties appealed to the circuit court of the United States, as citizens

---

* It has recently been raised to nine.

of another State, and as citizens claiming the protection of the laws of the confederacy. It was contended that the law of New-York was unconstitutional, inasmuch as the States had conceded the right to protect inventions, &c. &c. to the general government, and that no State had a right to grant a monopoly on waters, that might interfere with the commerce of the whole country. So the supreme court decided, and, since that decision, there has been an end of the monopoly. Many of the States have enacted laws, of different natures, that have always been treated with great reflection and candour, but which have been as effectually destroyed by this court.

In respect of mere dignity, the judges of the supreme court of the United States stand foremost over all others. A judge of the district court is, as a rule, perhaps, about equal to a judge of the supreme court of a State, though these parallels are entirely arbitrary. In point of variety of power, the judges of the States have much the most; but, in point of importance, those of the United States are the greatest, since appeals can be made to, but not from, them.

You can easily imagine that numberless questions of jurisdiction between the courts of the confederation and those of the States, still remain to be decided. Although the laws of the United States, when constitutional, are called supreme, yet there are points where the two authorities must of necessity meet. To take a strong case, the life of the citizen is, in most instances, to be protected by the laws of the State; but it is possible to conceive a case in which some of the rights that are fairly enough incidental to the discharge of the powers ceded to the United States, might impair the force of a State law for the protection of the life of its citizen. In such a case reason must decide the limits of the two authorities, as it has had to decide the limits of concurrent authorities elsewhere. It would be folly to say always

O 2

that the United States law being paramount, should prevail. In fact, in such questions, it is not supreme, even in theory; for the States, having reserved to themselves all the power they have not expressly yielded to the United States, have clearly the same claim to the rights incidental to the powers reserved, as the United States possess to the rights incidental to the powers which have been conceded. The courts of the States (which are bound to know and respect the authority of the United States) might have a natural leaning to extend these incidental powers, and it is in fixing their limits that the supreme court of the United States, which is placed above all petty and local interests, exhibits most of is usefulness and majesty.

A species of natural law.is growing up under this system, that promises to be eminently useful, inasmuch as it is adapted to actual necessity. I am a great venerator of those laws which are enacted by custom, since I entertain the opinion that the stamp of usage is worth a dozen legislative seals, especially in a community where men, being as free as possible, have every opportunity of consulting the useful.

The States have conceded all power to Congress to regulate commerce. Now, Congress has jurisdiction over more than twenty degrees of latitude. It has not, however, yet seen fit to establish quarantine regulations for the numerous ports within its jurisdiction, though it is scarcely possible to imagine any measure which more intimately affects commerce than these laws. But the States do continue to pass quarantine laws, under their natural right to protect the lives of their citizens. Should any State, under this plea, attempt to pass such laws, however, as would operate unjustly towards another State, the court of the United States might then pronounce a decision affecting the question. There is as yet a divided opinion, in theory, on the subject of this right, while the practice is just what it ought to be; that is to say, those who are most familiar with the subject provide for its wants, and should any abuses arise, there is a power in the country competent to put them down.

As its institutions get matured by time, the power of the confederation is every day receiving strength. A vast deal of constitutional law, however, remains to be decided; but as new cases arise, the ability to make discreet decisions, grows with experience. Laws are enacted to meet the regulations necessary to the common good, and as the legislators are themselves citizens of the States to be governed, and one body of them (the Senate) are the legal protectors of their corporate rights, there is little fear that the general government will ever reach that point of authority that shall make it weak, by setting it up in opposition to a force that it would vainly strive to subdue. It may appear paradoxical, but the secret of the actual durability of this confederation consists in its apparent weakness. So long as the influence of the several States shall be of sufficient importance to satisfy their jealousy, I think it will endure; and so long as the present representative system shall prevail, there is every motive to believe the States will possess, with a reasonable portion of the power, a share in all the honour, and the profit, and the security of being members of an Union that must shortly stand foremost among the nations of the earth.

The true balance of power, which elsewhere is found to exist in the hands of individuals, exists here in the hands of legislative bodies, who are the direct representatives of those whose interests are controlled by the government.

TO SIR EDWARD WALLER, BART.

&c. &c.

Washington, ———

A GREAT event has just been decided in this city.
The ceremony of the election of a President of the
United States, for the four years which shall commence on the fourth day of March next, took place
yesterday. The circumstances which led to the peculiar forms of this choice, the characters of the candidates, and the probable result that it will have on
the policy of the country, may not be without interest
to one who studies mankind as generally as yourself.

The first President, you know, was Washington.
He was succeeded by the Vice-President, the elder
Adams.* At the end of four years, a hot contest occurred between Mr. Adams and Mr. Jefferson, the
President and Vice-President of the day, for the
chair. In order to give you a proper understanding
of the case, it will be necessary to explain the law
for the election to this high office.

You know that the sovereignty of the States is
represented by the Senate. Thus, Rhode Island,
with 70,000 inhabitants, has two members in the
Senate, as well as New-York with 1,700,000. But
the members of the lower house, which is the connecting link between the States, are apportioned

---

* An absurd story is told by a recent traveller, or a pretended traveller, in the United States, concerning the wish of Mr
Adams, *when Vice-President*, to have the title of " Highness,
and Protector of our Liberties," given to the President of the
United States. It is said he introduced a resolution to that
effect in the *Senate*. Now, it happens, independently of the
gross folly of the title, that the *Vice-President*, who is merely a
presiding officer, has no right to introduce any law or resolution
into the *Senate* at all.

according to the population. The State of Rhode Island has, therefore, two Representatives, and the State of New-York thirty-four. In all ordinary cases of legislation, each individual, whether a Senator or a Representative, gives one vote. While New-York has, consequently, eighteen times more influence in the lower house than Rhode Island, in the upper house they are equal. It is in this division of power that another system of the checks and balances of this government is to be traced.

For the election of the President, bodies are especially convened that are at other times unknown to the constitution. They are called electoral colleges, of which there are as many as there are States. These colleges are composed of citizens chosen in each State, in such a manner as its own laws may prescribe. They are sometimes elected by the legislatures, sometimes in districts by the people, and sometimes again by the people in what is called a general ticket; that is to say, every citizen votes for the whole of the electors that his State is entitled to choose. The number is determined by the population of the State. The number of Representatives is added to the two Senators, and the amount forms the body of the electors. Thus New-York, having thirty-four Representatives and two Senators, chooses thirty-six electors; while Rhode Island, having but two of each class, is limited to four electors.

Within a certain number of days after their own election, the electors of each State meet at some indicated place, and form the several colleges. The time is fixed at so short a period as to prevent, as much as possible, the danger of corruption. There is undoubtedly a preconcert between parties, and an understanding in the way of pledges; but there cannot well be any direct bribery on the part of powerful individuals. Each elector gives one vote for President, and another for Vice-President. As the constitution formerly stood, the citizen who received the greatest number of votes, provided they made more than half of the whole number, was chosen for the former office, and the citizen who received the next greatest number, under the same provision, was chosen for the latter office. The constitution has, however, been changed, so as to make it necessary that each vote should express for which officer it is given. These votes are counted in the presence of the college, and of any body else who may choose to attend, and the result is properly authenticated and sent to the Department of State; the President of the Senate opens and compares the returns in the presence of both houses of Congress, after which the result is officially announced to the country. But as the votes of each State are known the day they are actually given, the public press uniformly anticipates the public documents by several weeks. If there should be no election, the final choice is referred to Congress.

In 1801, the contest between Mr. Adams and Mr. Jefferson had a singular termination. Mr. Pinckney, of South Carolina, was the candidate for the Vice-Presidency, supported by the friends of the former; and Mr. Burr, of New-York, the candidate supported by the friends of the latter. Adams was the head of what was called the federal party, and Jefferson the head of the democrats.* The election of 1801 was

* A singular mistake is prevalent in Europe, concerning the origin and objects of the two great political parties, which, for twenty years, nearly equally divided the people of the United States. It is often asserted, and sometimes believed, that the federalists were the secret friends of a monarchy, and that the democrats were, what their name would imply, the only friends of the people. The gross absurdity of this belief is completely exposed, by the fact, that a great majority of the people of New-England and of New-York were, for a long time, federalists; and it is difficult to conceive that the mass of communities, so completely republican in practice, should entertain a *secret* wish to overthrow institutions which they had been the

the first triumph of the democrats.   Mr. Adams and
Mr. Pinckney were both handsomely defeated; but,
by an oversight of the electors, Jefferson and Burr
received the same number of votes in the colleges.

---

first to form, and which were so completely confirmed by long
habit.   Washington was, undoubtedly, a federalist, as, indeed,
were a very large proportion of the ancient officers and patriots
of the revolution.   But this party was more lukewarm in the
cause of the French revolution, than the other, and its members
were the advocates of a rather stronger government than the
democrats.   It is also true, that, as some of its leaders acknowledged more of the maxims of the ancient monarchy than their
opponents, all those who had a bias in favour of the mother
country joined their ranks, and served to keep alive an impression which their enemies, of course, industriously circulated,
that the party leaned to aristocracy.   It was easy to raise this
cry, both for the reasons named, and because a large proportion
of the men of wealth in the middle and eastern States, were
enrolled in its ranks.   But there can be no greater absurdity
than to suppose, that any party has existed in America, since
the revolution, with an intention of destroying, or, indeed, with
the intention of seriously modifying, the present form of government.   When the constitution was formed, and before all its
principles were settled by practice, it was to be expected that
men should differ on the subject of the *degree* of change that was
prudent; but, as early as the year 1800, the federalists and the
democrats were, essentially, nothing more than two great parties, struggling for place, and who adopted different politics
about as much for the purpose of opposition as for any other
reason.   This got to be eminently the case a few years later,
when the federal party grew desperate in the minority, and lost
sight of character altogether, in the conduct it pursued on the
subject of the war with England.   Some of the eastern politicians, during that war, believing the moment favourable to
a final effort, concerted a plan, by which the whole of the eastern, and some of the middle States were to unite in an attack
on the policy of the general government, the result of which
was to be the expulsion of the administration.   This plan gave
rise to the famous Hartford Convention.   The opponents of the
Hartford Convention accused its founders of a design to divide
the Union.   It is difficult to say what crude projects may have
floated in the heated brains of individuals of that body, but this
is a country in which individuals do less than elsewhere, especially in matters of great moment.   The New-England States
themselves would never have encouraged a scheme so destructive to their own interests; but, had they entertained the wish,
it would have been a mad policy without the connivance of
New-York, a State that was then, and has been since, daily

This left the question of the presidency to be still decided, as the constitution then prescribed that the choice should be in favour of the candidate who had the greatest number of votes, provided always that he had a majority of the whole number.

The choice of a President, by the provisions of the constitution, now devolved on Congress. In the event of a referred election, the Senators have no voices, the Representatives of each State in the lower house giving but one vote; so that the final decision is made by the States, and not by the people. In 1810, there were sixteen States in the confederation. By a singular coincidence, two of these States had a tie in themselves; so that they defeated their own votes; and of the remainder, eight gave their votes

---

draining them of their population, and which already numbers nearly, if not quite, as many souls as all New-England united. It is well known that the great body of the federalists of New-York refused to join the convention, even with a view to remonstrate, at the time when the country was engaged single-handed against England. The best evidence of what would have been the fate of an attempt to separate the Union, is to be found in the fact that the people of New-England themselves treat with great coldness, the principal members of the Hartford Convention, although most men acquit them of entertaining so mad a scheme. But the federal party was destroyed by the policy it pursued in the war. The Hartford Convention was its dying effort, and its last moments were as impotent as those of any other worn-out nature. The older members of the party sometimes act together, now, from habit and intimacy, but the generation that is just appearing on the stage, already read of the party struggles in which their fathers were engaged as matters of history. There is no such party known in the United States, as a party unfriendly to their institutions, though, doubtless, there are still a few men living who retain some of their ancient attachment for the sort of government under which they were born. It is worthy of remark, that the children of these men are almost always decided democrats, and in many instances, the complete success of the confederative system has overcome the prejudices of old and bigoted tories. It must be remembered, also, that though a majority of the people of Massachusetts, Connecticut, &c. were willing to try the experiment of the Hartford Convention, there were powerful minorities in every State concerned, without counting the influence of all the rest of the Union.

for Mr. Jefferson and six for Mr. Burr. You should be told that the same law which referred this question to Congress requires that the successful candidate should have a majority of *all* the States. Mr. Jefferson, therefore, required nine votes for success, which was the number necessary to make a majority of sixteen.

The members of Congress voted thirty-five times on this interesting question, and always with the same result. At length, a member or two belonging to the States which had lost their votes by a tie, changed their minds, and gave their voices for Jefferson. This decided the matter, and placed that distinguished statesman in the chair for the next four years. At the expiration of the regular period of service, he was re-elected; but, imitating the example of Washington, he retired at the end of his second term.

Until now the Vice-President had been the successor of the President : but although Mr. Burr, having the next greatest number of votes, was necessarily Vice-President for the first of Mr. Jefferson's terms of office, he was superseded at the second election. The constitution had been altered so as to stand as at present, making it necessary to indicate the situation it is intended the candidate shall fill. A veteran of the revolution, but a man past the expectation of further preferment, had been selected to supply the place of Mr. Burr. The friends of the administration now turned their eyes on the Secretary of State, as a successor to the President of the day. This gentleman (Mr. Madison) was elected, and a sort of change in the descent of power was effected. After a service of two terms, Mr. Madison also retired, and the Secretary of the time being (Mr. Monroe) became the successful candidate. The second term of this gentleman's service is now near its close, and he retires too, as a matter of course. You are not to suppose that the constitution prescribes any other limits

to the presidency of an individual, but that of a new
election every four years ; but the example of Washington, and, perhaps, the period of life to which all
the Presidents have attained, after filling the chair for
two terms, have induced them, in succession, to decline elections for a third.

On the present occasion, an entirely new state of
politics presents itself. The old party distinctions
of federalists and democrats are broken down, and
the country is no longer divided into two great political factions. Mr. Adams, the Secretary of State (and
a son of the second President,) is considered by a
great number of people as the natural and the best
successor to Colonel Monroe. When I say natural,
you must confine the meaning of the word to a natural expediency, and not to any natural right. His
claims consist of a long experience in the politics of
the country, great familiarity with foreign diplomacy,
and the intimate connexion that he has so long had
with the particular measures of the existing administration. He is a man of extensive acquirements, great
honesty, and unquestionable patriotism. He is also
a northern, or, as it would be expressed here, an
eastern man (coming from New-England ;) and hitherto Virginia has given four out of the five Presidents.
But the circumstance of birth-place has far less influence than you would suppose in a government like
this. It is worthy of remark, that while Europeans
are constantly predicting sectional divisions in this
country, the people of the country themselves appear to think very little about them. Mr. Adams
has both a warm support and a warm opposition in
the northern States, it being evident that men follow
the bent of their humours or judgments, without
thinking much on the question of north and south.
It is an important circumstance, which always should
be remembered in considering this subject, that though
the south has, in consequence of its physical inferiority

and peculiar situation, a jealous watchfulness of the north, that the north regards the south with no such feelings. It is clear that the sentiment must be active enough in both to induce men to overlook their interests, before it can produce any important changes.

Mr. Crawford, the Secretary of the Treasury, was another candidate for the Presidency; Mr. Calhoun, the Secretary of War, was a third; Mr. Clay, the Speaker of the House of Representatives, a fourth and General Jackson, a Senator of Tennessee, was a fifth.

The two first of these gentlemen sit in the cabinet with Mr. Adams, and present the singular spectacle of men united in administering the affairs of the nation, openly and honourably opposed to each other in a matter of the greatest personal interest.

Mr. Crawford was for a long time thought to be the strongest candidate. He is said to have been a man admirably qualified to fill the high station to which he aspired; but a paralytic attack had greatly weakened his claims, before the meeting of the colleges. His friends, too, had committed a vulgar blunder, which is more likely to be fatal here than in any country I know. They commenced their electioneering campaign by bold assertions of their strength, and the most confident predictions of success. I have heard a hundred men of independence and of influence say that disgust, at having themselves disposed of in this cavalier manner, disinclined them to a cause that they might otherwise have been induced to support. It is the opinion of Cadwallader that Mr. Crawford would not have succeeded, had his health not so unhappily suffered. He was but little known to the northern States, and men of character and talents always choose to have at least the air of judging for themselves. He succeeded, however, in receiving enough votes to include his name among the three highest candidates, and consequently he came before Congress on the final question.

Mr. Calhoun, who is still a young man, and who probably aimed as much as any thing at getting his name prominently before the nation, to be ready for a future struggle, prudently withdrew from the contest. As he is universally admitted to be a man of high talents, he was put up, in opposition to the celebrated Albert Gallatin, for the Vice-Presidency; and as that gentleman declined the election, Mr. Calhoun was chosen by the colleges nearly unanimously.

Mr. Clay had many warm friends, and was supported by his own State (Kentucky) with great zeal; but he failed in getting his name included on the list of the three highest. He is a self-created man, of unquestionable genius, and of a manner and eloquence that will always render him formidable to his opponents, and of immense value to his political friends. His direct interest in this election, however, ceased, of necessity, with the returns of the colleges.

General Jackson is a gentleman who has long been employed in offices of high trust in his own State, but who only came prominently before the nation during the late war. He is a lawyer by education, and has filled the civil stations of a judge, a member of Congress, and, lastly, of a Senator. In early life he served as a soldier, during the struggle for independence; but he was much too young to be distinguished. As a military man, his merit is unquestionable. He led two or three difficult expeditions against the Indians of the south with great decision and effect, and with an uniformity of success that has been rare indeed against the savages of this continent. In consequence of the skill and energy he displayed on these occasions as a general of militia, he received a commission in the regular army, soon after the declaration of war against Great Britain. Fortunately, he was chosen to defend New-Orleans against the formidable attack of that country. He was lying a short distance above the town, with a small body of men,* when it was unexpectedly announced that the enemy had landed at a point, whence a forced march of two or three hours would put them in possession of the place. Mustering as many of his motley troops as he could spare from other points of defence, (something less than sixteen hundred men,) he led them to the attack against a regular and much superior force, whom he attacked with a spirit and effect which left an impression that he was far stronger than the truth would have shown. By this bold measure, he gained time to throw up entrenchments and to receive reenforcements. Before his works were completed, or one-half of the necessary troops had arrived, the British risked the celebrated attack of the 8th of January. They were repulsed with horrible slaughter to themselves, and with an impunity to the defendants that was next to a miracle. The works were entered at an incomplete point; but all who presented themselves were either slain or captured. The great modesty of the account of his success given by General Jackson, is as worthy of commendation as was his indomitable resolution. Contrary to the usage of the times, he gave his opinion that the loss of the enemy was several hundreds less than what they acknowledged it to be themselves, and, indeed, nearly a thousand less than what further observation gave him reason to believe it actually was. If the decision of this extraordinary man was so brilliantly manifested in the moment of need, his subsequent

* Less than three thousand men. As late as the 29th December, General Jackson, in an official letter, states his whole force at three thousand effectives. In the report of the battle of the 8th January, he says, that though a detachment of Kentucky militia had arrived, they added but very little to his force, as most of them were unarmed.

prudence is worthy of the highest commendation.
Although he had not hesitated an instant to attack
nearly twice his force on the open plain, when
nothing short of desperate courage could save the
town, he did not allow success to lure him from a
position which experience had shown he could maintain. He suffered his beaten, but still greatly superior enemy to retire unmolested; and it is probable
that, had they asked for succour, he would cheerfully
have yielded them assistance to embark.*

---

* The force with which General Jackson defended New-
Orleans, according to the official returns, was less than 6000
men, imperfectly armed and organized: and all of whom, with
the exception of a few marines and sailors, and two battalions
of new levies for the army, in all about one thousand men, were
the citizens of the country. It is believed that, sailors and marines included, General Packenham landed nearly ten thousand men. It would be a curious study, to those who had any
desire to sift the truth, to examine the documents of England
and America in relation to the events of their two wars. The
writer must say he has met many Americans who are familiar
with the documents of England, but he never yet met one Englishman who was familiar with those of America. Nations lose
nothing by looking a little closely into their own affairs, as well
as into those of other people. One circumstance first drew the
writer into a closer investigation of these subjects, than he might
otherwise have been induced to undertake. He will relate it.

It is well known that, in 1814, a bloody battle was fought
near the great cataract of Niagara. The American general
says, that a brigade of his army met a portion of the British
army, and engaged it. That he arrived with reenforcements,
the enemy reenforcing at the same time; that he was much annoyed by certain pieces of artillery, stationed on an eminence
that formed the key of the English position; that he carried this
hill at the point of the bayonet, and captured the artillery; that
the enemy made three desperate attempts to regain the position
and their guns, in all of which they were defeated, and that they
finally relinquished the attempt. He gives his enemy a small
superiority of force, and he conveys an implied censure against
the officer third in command, (he and his second in command
having been obliged to retire, from their wounds,) for not secur-
ing the fruits of this victory on the morning succeeding the day
of the battle. So much for the American. On the other hand,
the English general gives a sufficiently similar account of the
commencement of the battle. He also admits the charge up
the hill, that " our artillerymen were bayoneted by the enemy
in the act of loading;" that " our troops having for a moment

General Jackson obtained immense popularity in the country by this brilliant success. His political honesty is unquestionable, and his patriotism without a blot. Still his want of experience in matters of state, and even his military habits, were strongly urged against him. The former may be a solid objection, but, it is more than absurd, it is wicked to urge the military character of a citizen, who meritoriously leaves his retirement in the hour of danger to carry those qualities with which nature has endowed him, into the most perilous, and commonly the least requited service of his country, as an argument against his filling any station whatever. A thousand falsehoods have been circulated at the expense of General Jackson, and even some admitted inequality of temper has been grossly exaggerated. Notwithstanding the industry and affected contempt of the adversaries of this gentleman, he received more of the electoral votes than the highest of the three candidates in the returned list.

---

been pushed back, some of our guns remained for a few minutes in the enemy's hands;" that they were, however, soon recovered; and that, instead of his making attacks for the recovery of the lost position, the Americans were the assailants; and that they were uniformly defeated in their attempts. He estimates the force of the Americans at nearly double what their official reports state it to have been. Both parties nearly double the (presumed) loss of their enemy; and the American, though something nearer to the admission of the Englishman than the Englishman was to the admission of the American, estimated the force of his enemy considerably over the official account.

The writer was struck with these official discrepancies. The documents were uttered to the world under the same forms, in the same language, and by people acknowledging the same moral influences. He was induced to exclaim, Where is the truth of history? The writer knows nothing more of the merits of this question than is contained in the documents he has examined, and which any one may also examine, who has a curiosity equal to his own. The circumstance should, however, teach moderation to partisans, as it abundantly proves that the data on which they found their opinions cannot always be of the most unexceptionable nature.

The day of the final decision by Congress was one of great interest here. All the candidates were on the spot, in the discharge of their official duties, and large bodies of their friends had assembled to witness, and, if possible, to influence the result. Cadwallader obtained a convenient position, where we both witnessed the whole manner of the election.

Although three names were returned to Congress for the choice, it was universally understood that the selection would be made between Messrs. Adams and Jackson. It would have been indecent in the representatives to prefer Mr. Crawford over two men, both of whom had received nearly double the number of the popular votes that had been given in his favour, though by the constitution they certainly had a right to elect which of the three they pleased. It was thought that the representatives of those States in which the electors had given their votes for this gentleman, would make a single demonstration in his favour, and then give their voices for one or the other of the two candidates, who, it was well known, must eventually succeed.

The gallery of the hall of Congress was crowded nearly to suffocation. The Senators were present as a sort of legal witnesses of the election, and many men of high political consideration were in the lobbies and behind the desks. In short, every one was there who could gain admission by art or influence. The arrangements for this important proceeding were exceedingly unpretending, though remarkably imposing by their simplicity, and that air of grave composure which usually reigns over all the legislative proceedings of this country.

The members of the different States were now seated together, since they composed so many separate colleges which, on this momentous question, were to pronounce the voices of their particular communities. Here, sat the numerous and grave-looking representation of the powerful State of New-York, and by their side was a solitary individual, who, in his own person, held all the authority that was to be exercised on that important day, by the younger community of Indiana. This gentleman, and one or two others, were men of peculiar importance in an event like this, since accident had placed them individually on a level with large bodies of enlightened and discreet men. Still it is not probable that they dared to depart from the known wishes of the people they represented, so direct and certain is the punishment which usually attends popular displeasure in this country.

At the appointed hour, the States began to collect the voices among themselves. The members voted by ballot, having established for that purpose, a set of simple forms by which the votes were collected and reported to tellers appointed to receive them by the house. Fraud was impossible, since each college knew the precise number of its votes, and each individual deposited his ballot with his own hand. The duty was soon performed by the smaller States, and a moment of breathless suspense succeeded while the representatives of New-York were collecting their votes. The friends of Mr. Adams had counted on twelve States with great confidence, but the number and the peculiar policy of the members from New-York had rendered their vote more doubtful. The result was, however, soon known on the floor of the house, as was quite apparent by the look of suppressed triumph that was playing about the eyes of certain partisans, and the air of forced composure that was assumed by their adversaries.

The result was communicated to the Speaker, (who had himself been a candidate before the electoral colleges,) and then it was officially announced "that *thirteen* States had given their votes for John Quincy Adams, for President of the United States during the four years, commencing on the fourth of March next, and that the said John Quincy Adams was duly elected."*

While the sweet, clear, voice of Mr. Clay was announcing this important news, I never witnessed a more intense silence in any assembly. The stillness continued a moment after his words had ceased, and then followed the low hum of whispers, and immediately after, a half involuntary and feeble clapping of hands was heard in the galleries. This little burst of exultation on the part of some indiscreet spectators, gave me an opportunity of witnessing the manner in which the American legislators maintain order and assert their dignity. "Sergeant-at-arms, clear the galleries!" commanded the Speaker, in a voice, that of itself hushed the slightest sound of approbation. The officers of the house instantly performed their duty, and in a few moments those spacious and commodious seats which were so lately teeming with conscious human countenances, presented nothing to the eye but its magnificent colonnade and long rows of empty benches.

The house soon adjourned, and every body quitted the Capitol, some filled with joy they could ill suppress, and others evidently struggling to conceal the defeat of expectations which had probably been more fed by hope than reason. The important question was, however, irretrievably decided by a first vote, notwithstanding hundreds had anticipated that a struggle similar to that of 1801 was about to occur again.

The election had been conducted with great heat, especially in the public prints, and so much seeming violence of denunciation had been used during the discussion, that I confess I was induced to look about me, as we quitted the edifice, in quest of the legions that were to tame so many unquiet spirits, and to

---

* Thirteen States being a majority of the twenty-four which now compose the Union, were necessary to a choice.

teach them submission to an authority that exercised its functions in forms so simple as those I had just witnessed. I had heard so much of revolution, and of the disorders of popular governments, that it did not appear possible a question which, an hour before, had filled the minds and voices of men with so much bitterness, could peaceably subside in quiet, and in submission to a force that was invisible.

During the preceding week, more than one foreign functionary had whispered in my ear something that implied a sneer on the folly of periodically throwing society so near the verge of dissolution, by enlisting the passions of the community in a question that embraced so many important interests as these frequent elections; and one of them had intimated an expectation that, in the event of his failure, there would be a rising in favour of a military hero, who was not accustomed to defeat. I remembered the reply of my quiet yeoman in the stage-coach, and did not certainly carry my expectations quite so far; but still it was inconceivable that passions which had been so strongly excited, should subside without at least some of the usual indications of a disappointed resentment.

While descending Capitol hill, we met a warm partisan of the unsuccessful candidate, who was known to us both. "Well, ———," said Cadwallader, "what do you intend to do now? Your man has, beyond all hope, lost the day." "We shall change the face of things four years hence," was the answer. The reply was given in the tone of one who seemed conscious that he and his friends had been mistaken in their force, but who, at the same time, felt that legal means of obtaining a triumph were always before him. I must acknowledge, when I found that one of the most violent partisans I had ever met, was for deferring his schemes of revenge to a day so distant as four years, and that he even then contemplated to effect his object by means of the ballot-box,

I began to despair of seeing a revolution in America during my visit. It is true, that the defeated party have begun already to raise a clamour against corruptions and bargains; but it is very evident that they are doing it as mariners place an extra anchor to windward, to be in readiness for the tempest which is known to come on periodically.*

The result of this election, and the sudden calm that succeeded to so much apparent warmth, have again led me to reflect on the vague and imperfect impressions which we get in Europe, of the actual political condition of America. During the war of 1812, one saw monthly accounts, in the journals of England, that this, or that, State of the confederation was on the verge of a separation from the Union, and that distress had driven men to madness and all sorts of political desperation. If these accounts were published in good faith, they imply an inconceivable ignorance of the actual state of the country; for, unless the opinions of intelligent men of all parties grossly deceive me, there never has been one hour since the adoption of the present constitution, when probably one thousand *natives* of the whole United States have seriously contemplated any such event as likely to be near. If the paragraphs to which I allude, were

---

* The writer had an excellent opportunity of witnessing the effect of the American institutions, shortly after the event above described, while on a visit to the city of Philadelphia. A foreigner, who conducted a paper in that city, was so profoundly ignorant of the people among whom he lived, as to invite a meeting of the citizens of Pennsylvania, in order to provide the means of marching to Washington to put down Mr. Adams, who, it was affirmed, had been elected by means of corruption. Curiosity drew thousands of spectators to the appointed spot, in order to see what would be done at such a meeting. No officers appeared to oppose it, and yet the affair ended in the utter disdain of the whole community. The miserable intruder on the peaceful habits and common sense of the Americans was too much despised to be punished for his impudence, though he could not escape contempt and ridicule.

published with a view to deceive the people of Europe, it has induced the inevitable consequences of a wilful ignorance, viz. disappointment. I am perfectly satisfied, that a vast majority of the citizens of this country have more confidence in their own institutions than in those of any other nation; nor can I find, on a reasonably close examination of the subject, that they are so very wrong. One thing is certain, that other nations have made much nearer approaches to their opinions, during the last half century, than they have made to the opinions of other nations.*

I have conversed freely on this matter with my friend Cadwallader. I cannot say that he discusses the subject with particular gravity; but one of his remarks struck me as possessing singular force. "How is it," he said, "that you, or any stranger who enters our country, can and does freely discuss the danger of a dissolution of our confederacy, or the probability that we shall one day become a monarchy, and that, too, without giving offence or finding any difficulty in meeting with disputants? or how is it that an American never goes into an European country, Switzer-

---

* What are all the changes that have occurred in so many kingdoms on the continent of Europe, but approaches to the American system? It is certainly the fashion, and for obvious reasons, to look to England as a model for the new constitutions, but what is England herself about? The American would say, that the recent repeal or alteration of the Test Act, the state of the Catholic question, the disfranchisement of rotten boroughs, the improvement of the common law, and, in short, the whole plan of rational reform which now pervades England, rests on principles, that rather than abandon, his ancestors preferred to emigrate. When a man states this undeniable truth, with a view to exult in the superior penetration of his own people, he should be reminded how very far the most faultless are from perfection in any thing; but when an European insolently and ignorantly assumes that the United States are existing in a state of political insecurity, every day and every hour, the citizen of the latter country has a natural right to throw these stubborn facts into the teeth of such supercilious commentators.

land, perhaps, excepted, without finding men, let their breeding be what it may, who very unequivocally let him know that they consider his government as a chimerical project, and the constitution of his empire exceedingly frail; while, on the other hand, if the American attempt a comparison between his own government and that of his assailant, he is generally silenced by cold looks and an averted eye? It is odd that all this sensitiveness, more especially as the parties exhibiting it rarely fail of being bold enough on the subject of American democracy, should abide in the midst of such conscious security. We all of us know, that most Europeans so far identify themselves with their soil as to believe they have a moral superiority over the American that is exactly in proportion to the antiquity of their governments; but *we* also know a fact that commonly escapes their acuteness. The practices of Europe form part of our experience; while Europe knows nothing of our practices. Answer me one thing. Why does America trouble herself so little about the governments of Europe, while all Europe is demonstrating on paper that our republics cannot endure? I think, when you find the motive of this marked difference, you will not be far from the secret consciousness which the two parties have in the strength and durability of their respective systems."

The evening of the day of the election was one of those on which Mrs. Monroe opens the doors of the White House to the motley assemblage I have already described. Great curiosity was felt by every one to be present, because it was known that the principal personages, who had been so recently exerting themselves in the question which was just decided, were in the habit of paying their respects, on these occasions, to the wife of the first magistrate. We went at ten.

Perhaps the company on this evening was a little

more numerous than on the preceding drawing-room. It was composed of the same sort of visiters, and it was characterized by the same decency of exterior and of deportment. ,We found the President and Mrs. Monroe in their usual places; the former encircled by a knot of politicians, and the latter attended by a circle of women, of rather brilliant appearance. Most of the Secretaries were near, conversing cheerfully, like men who had just got rid of an irksome and onerous toil; and I thought, by the placid air of the venerable chief justice, that he was well content that the harassing question was decided. The assistant justices of the supreme court were also present, near the person of the President; and a group had collected in the same room; in the midst of which I discovered the smiling features and playful eye of La Fayette. The Speaker was known to have favoured the election of Mr. Adams, and I thought I could trace secret satisfaction at the result in a countenance that his height elevated above those of most of his companions. There was no coarse exultation on the part of the victors, nor any unmanly dejection on that of the defeated. Several of the latter spoke to us; and, in reply to the laughing condolences of my friend, they made but one remark—" We shall see what the next four years will do."

" How do you do, General Jackson?" said Cadwallader, as we passed out of one drawing-room into another. The unsuccessful candidate returned the greeting with his usually mild and graceful mien. I watched his manly and marked features narrowly, during the courteous dialogue that followed; but, with all my suspicions, it was impossible to trace the slightest symptoms of a lurking disappointment. He left us laughing and conversing cheerfully with some ladies, who induced him to join their party. A minute before, he had been seen congratulating his successful rival with great dignity, and with perfect good nature.

We now entered the last apartment of the suite, with the hope of finding a cooler atmosphere. A group of men, among whom perhaps a dozen women were intermingled, had collected about some object of common interest. Drawing near, I caught a glimpse of the cold air which, in contrast to an uncommonly fine and piercing eye, forms so remarkable an expression in the countenance of Mr. Adams. He was certainly in good spirits; though, had we not known his recent victory, it is probable that his manner would not have been at all remarked. He soon extricated himself from the crowd, and spoke to two or three of us who stood together. "Why have you not been to see us lately?" he inquired of a member of Congress, from Virginia: "Mrs. Adams complains that you were not at her last evening." "I have been there so often this winter, that I began to think it necessary to be absent for the sake of form." "Is that the etiquette?" "We must ask this question of you;" returned the Virginian, laughing, in allusion to the Secretary's well-known strictures on the subject; "*you* are our authority in all matters of etiquette." "Well then," returned the President elect, with great good humour, and with the tact of a courtier; "I pronounce it to be always etiquette for Mr. —— to visit Mrs. Adams."*

* Mr. Adams and General Jackson are again candidates for the presidency. As the contest is as yet confined to these two, and it is so shortly to be decided (in December of 1828,) it is probable that one of them will be chosen. What the writer now states, he says understandingly. A good deal is certainly said concerning the inexperience of General Jackson, and some press the circumstance of his chief merit being military, as a reason against him. There is not a man in the Union who, however, seriously apprehends any danger from his election. It is false that he is not supported by wary and prudent men. The writer can name a hundred gentlemen in the middle States of education, of fortune, and of religion, too, who are his warm

TO SIR EDWARD WALLER, BART.

&c. &c.

Washington, ———

YESTERDAY, while walking with Cadwallader on the banks of the Potomac, we saw a group of gentlemen, in the. midst of whom we distinguished the animated features of La Fayette, moving towards a steam-boat that was waiting their arrival. A moment of explanation induced us to join the party, which was about to visit the tomb of Washington.

Mount Vernon, an estate which the hero inherited from an elder brother, lies on the river at the distance of about two hours' sailing towards the sea. The boat was rather more crowded than was desirable for such a visit ; but the circumstances left us no choice. We passed the little city of Alexandria on our route, and reached the point of destination within a reasonable time of our departure.

The estate of Mount Vernon was left by the will of its late possessor to his nephew, Mr. Bushrod Washington, who has long been one of the assistant justices of the supreme court of the United States. The country, immediately about the dwelling, is much wooded ; the land being neither particularly level, nor yet very uneven. The house stands on a rather

friends. The question is altogether one of men, there being scarcely a measure of policy that is likely to be much affected by the result. A great deal of the popularity of General Jackson is owing to an injudicious and presuming opposition, which has foolishly ascribed a danger to his success, that is as false, as his friends are determined to manifest it is ridiculous. But men may well hesitate about rejecting so tried a patriot, and so experienced a statesman, as Mr. Adams.

sudden rise, which may be elevated more than a hundred feet above the level of the water. The ascent from the river is quite precipitous, though the ground falls away to the north and to the south, with rather more regularity. The building is placed on the highest point; a position which scarcely leaves room for a very narrow lawn between it and the brow of the declivity in front. In the rear, the formation of the ground is level, for some distance, and tolerably extensive gardens communicate with the inner or back court.

The house of Mount Vernon is constructed of a frame-work, whose interstices, I am informed, are filled with bricks. The exterior covering is of planks, concealed in such a manner as to give it, at a little distance, the appearance of being made of hewn stone. The interior finish is like that of any other better sort of mansion. The length of the whole edifice cannot greatly exceed one hundred feet; and I should think that, in depth, it is something less than fifty. There are, however, two semicircular chains of offices, which project from each of its ends towards the rear, something in the form of sweeping galleries. These additions serve to give the building much more of an air of size from the side of the gardens than from that of the river. Towards the east (the river front) there is a colonnade which supports a roof that is continued from the main edifice. Though the pillars are very simple, the effect of a colonnade, so lofty and so long, is rather striking; and, on the whole, it leaves an impression that the house was one not altogether unworthy of its simple but illustrious possessor.

The interior of the building is exceedingly irregular, though far from inconvenient. I had full leisure for its examination, while a solemn scene was taking place at the tomb. La Fayette had been permitted to go to this sacred spot, unattended by any except the immediate members of the two families. I was permitted, by an especial favour, to pass up the ascent by another path, and to examine the rest of the grounds and the mansion.

There was but one considerable apartment in the dwelling. This was a drawing-room that occupied the whole width of the house, with a proper proportion of its length. The rest of the rooms were small, and of arrangements to prove that they were constructed before the master of the mansion was in the habit of receiving more guests than fell to the share of a private gentleman. Most of the furniture was of the time of the hero. It was exceedingly simple, though I thought it quite good enough, in fashion and in form, for a country residence. The principal drawing-room had more the air of a reception-room than the others, which were altogether in a quiet, comfortable, and domestic taste. There was a library, that is rather large for America, but which, in Europe, would be thought very small for the habitation of a man of any eminence.

I looked on all these things with a deep and increasing emotion. The house, at the moment, with the exception of Cadwallader and myself, and a domestic who showed us through the rooms, was entirely empty. More than once, as my hand touched a lock to open some door, I felt the blood stealing up my arm, as the sudden conviction flashed on my mind that the member rested on a place where the hand of Washington had probably been laid a thousand times. That indescribable, but natural and deeply grateful, feeling beset me, which we all are made to know when the image of a fellow-mortal, who has left a mighty name on earth, is conjured before us by the imagination in the nearest approaches to reality that death, and time, and place, and the whisperings of an excited fancy, will allow. There was a sort of secret desire, rather than an expectation, of finding something more than what reason told me to expect; and

I passed from parlour to parlour, in my haste, until
my companions were left behind, and I found myself
alone in a sort of upper office of the mansion. I shall
never forget the sensation that I felt, as my eye gazed
on the first object it encountered. It was an article
of no more dignity than a leathern fire-bucket; but
the words " Geo. Washington" were legibly written
on it in white paint. I know not how it was, but the
organ never altered its look until the name stood before my vision distinct, insulated, and almost endowed
with the attributes of the human form. The deception
was aided by all the accessories which the house
could furnish. Just at that instant, my friend, who is
a man of tall stature and grave air, appeared in the
adjoining door, without speaking. I felt the blood
creeping near my heart with awe, nor did the illusion
vanish until Cadwallader passed before me, and laid
a hand, with a melancholy smile, on the words, and
then retired towards the grounds, with a face that I
thought he would gladly conceal.

We were shown into the gardens and green-
houses. In the latter, the domestic culled us a bou-
quet of hot-house flowers; and, turning to a box
which lay at hand, he took a sheet of paper, and,
enveloping their stems, presented them to my friend.
Cadwallader received them thoughtfully ; but his
mind was too much occupied at the moment to attend
to so trifling an occurrence. We had returned to the
city, and were at our late dinner, when his eye seemed riveted, by some charm, on the paper that encircled this little offering. Scattering the flowers on
every side of him, he laid the paper on the table, and
read its contents with breathless eagerness. It proved
to be a sheet torn from a farming journal of the mod-
ern Cincinnatus, which had been kept in his own
hand. The writing was distinct, though there were
many technical abbreviations : the pages were without blot or erasure, and the precision of the language

and the minuteness of the details were rigidly exact.
The precious morsel was divided, and each of us took
his portion, like men who were well content with the
possession of some sacred relic.

When we left the green-house, we were joined by
the party of the veteran Frenchman. We had parted at the margin of the water, and each of us had
found subjects for reflection that were alike pleasing
and painful. Just before we separated, there had
been a little hesitation in the choice of the path that
led to the mansion. " Let me show you the way,"
cried M. George La Fayette, eagerly, but with evident emotion : " I know all the paths of Mount Vernon." Twenty-five years before, during the exile of
his natural parent, he had been intrusted to Washington, as to a second father, and he now rushed forward, full of his recollections, to point out a route
that time and momentous scenes in another hemisphere, had not blotted from his memory. I shall
not attempt to describe what passed at the vault
during the visit of La Fayette. He was powerfully
affected, and the recess of the dead was opened to
his admission. When he joined us, it was evident
that his feelings had been wrought up to a high and
painful point ; and I thought his eye wandered over
the familiar objects of the dwelling, as if every thing
keenly reminded him that he who gave them life and
interest, had passed away from the moving scenes of
the earth into the solemn quiet of the place he had
just quitted. We took the occasion of his absence
from the spot, to go ourselves to the tomb. As Cadwallader knew the way, I had no other companion.

The family vault of Mount Vernon stands near the
brow of the declivity, at a little distance from the
mansion, and at the point where the ground begins
to fall away to the south. It is as plain and simple
as can be well imagined. The excavation in the
earth is neither large nor deep, and the small portion

of the work that is visible in front, is a dead wall of
bricks. The door was low, humble and unornament-
ed—a more meek and fitting passage to the narrow
house of the dead than thresholds and arches of mock-
ing architecture. The earth is rounded over the
summit of the vault, and a few stunted and sickly
cedars have taken root on and about it.

I have stood by the side of many a boasted and
admired tomb; but by none with the awe and reverence with which I gazed on this. The dark days
of the revolution, the gloom and difficulties which
threatened the first hours of the present government,
the cheerful and prosperous scenes through which I
had so recently passed, crowded on my memory, and
produced a teeming picture in which the most prominent object was the form of the man whose ashes
were mouldering beneath my feet.

I have ever been an ardent, and were there not so
much reason to support me, I might say an enthusiastic admirer of Washington. His character, unlike
that of the heroes of other days, is most illustrious
when seen at the nearest approach. Those who
lived the closest to his person, and who possessed
the best opportunity of studying his moral qualities,
are touched with the deepest reverence for his vir-
tues. The narrative of his private deeds is the
counterpart of the history of his public acts. They
were alike founded on the immutable principles of
justice and truth. Men already regard him with the
admiration with which they gaze at a severe statue
of antiquity. He stands, naked of meretricious ornament, but grand in the majesty of reason.

Some, who know little of the history of the man,
or of his nation, confound the images of his renown,
by blending his merit with deeds that it was the fortune of no one to perform in America. This was not
the country of Alexanders and Napoleons.

The useful career of Washington commenced at

an age when men are occupied in fitting themselves
for the active scenes of life.   Before he had attained
his majority, he was employed by his native province
in situations of high trust.   Even at that early period
of life, he had established a character for firmness,
integrity, prudence, disinterestedness, and humanity,
which attended him to the peaceful grave in which
I found his venerated ashes.   There was an unpre
tending, but imposing dignity thrown about the person and character of this extraordinary youth, that
distinguished him in every future scene.   As a soldier, his career had been circumscribed, as a politi-
cian, he had enjoyed no opportunities to earn distinction, and yet, when the hour of trial came, the eyes
of a nation sought him anxiously.   The Congress of
the Union, composed of men from differently constituted and distant provinces, summoned him by a
common impulse to lead its armies.   The influence
of his character had been silently extending itself
over the vast regions whose fortunes were trusted to
his care.   His rise to power was degraded by no intrigue ; its exercise was stained by no abuse.   The
times required that a people, jealous beyond precedent of their rights, should trust a large portion of
their destinies to the keeping of a single man.   They
calmly, dispassionately, and wisely made their election ; confidence was nobly bestowed, meekly received, and gloriously requited !

The sword of Washington did not leap from its
scabbard with the eagerness of military pride, or with
the unbridled haste of one willing to make human
life the sacrifice of an unhallowed ambition.   It was
deliberately drawn at the call of his country, but with
a reluctance that came deep from the heart, and with
a diffidence that acknowledged the undisputed dominion of his God.   He went forth to battle with
the meekness of a mortal, the humanity of a Christian, the devotedness of a patriot, and the resolution

of a victor. As his object was limited by a righteous moderation, so were his intentions to achieve it, bounded only by success. In the air, the declarations, and the pledges of such a man, we are not to look for dramatic effect, or promises that were made to be forgotten. He took the trust his country offered, because it was the pleasure of that country he should do so; and when its duties were excellently performed, he returned it to the hands from whence it had come, with a simplicity which spoke louder than a thousand protestations. The integrity of such a mind needed no stimulants from the pages of history Its impulses were drawn from a higher source. Its self-denial was not a victory over opportunity, and occasion, and power, and all the natural promptings of busy man; but it was a silent, enduring, principled, and unconquerable will to refuse to admit temptation. So far as the human heart can be judged by outward symptoms, there never was a moment when this true hero ever suffered his thoughts to change their righteous and devoted direction; there never was a moment when men, in the least competent to speak on the subject, ever suspected him of any other object than patriotism. It is impossible to look closely into the conduct and motives of this man, and not to feel that his simple rule of morals said, self before dishonour, my country before self, and God before all.

It is the common fate of heroes to suffer by intimacy; but the private life of Washington was as beautiful, as his public was glorious. The latter was no more than an expansion of those principles which controlled the former. The same sternness of integrity, the same simplicity of purpose, could always be traced in that familiar conduct in which most men fail. It is a fact worthy of remark, that his most confidential correspondence is still in existence, inviting scrutiny, and challenging comment. There was a time when reverses and calumny, and weari-

ness of suffering, had made a party of his countrymen impatient of his government. A few misguided
individuals would have elevated a chief of untried
abilities to the post he filled. The machinations of
his enemies were known to Washington. Accident,
rather than merit, had placed his rival in a situation
to reap a glory far exceeding that which had then
fallen to the share of any leader in the contest. But
the issue of events still rested on contingencies.
Washington saw the crisis from a distance, and though
unfortunate, and opposed to a victorious and powerful foe, he stripped himself of force, in order to insure a good to his country, that would probably hasten
his own downfall. But the nation saw the sacrifice
and too well knew the estimate of merit to be deceived. Still it required that a high reward should
be bestowed on the successful general. He received
another trust, and sank under an incompetency that
no longer was supported by the extraordinary talent
of subordinates. Then it was that the soul of Washington was exhibited in its native power. The bruised
spirit of foiled ambition was solaced, and so solaced,
that the disappointed rejoiced in the sympathy of
success.

The character of Washington was Doric, in all
its proportions. Its beauty is the beauty of harmony
between purpose and means, and its grandeur is owing to its chaste simplicity. Like the order of archi-
tecture to which I have ventured to ascribe a resemblance, it is not liable to the details of criticism. You
see it in its majesty of outline, in its durability, and
in its admirable adaptation to usefulness ; but it rests
on a foundation too firm, and it upholds a superstructure too severe, to be familiarly dissected. His fame
already resembles that which centuries have produced for other men, while it owes no portion of its
purity to the mist of time. Truth, bold, clear, and
radiant, is the basis of his renown; and truth will

bear his name to posterity in precisely the same simple and just attributes as it was known to those who lived in his immediate presence.

The age has been prolific of character, and it should be prolific in the lessons it conveys. I think a mighty moral is taught by the careers of Washington and Napoleon. A parallel between these eminent men is impossible; but a comparison is easy indeed. To say that the former lived for others, and the latter solely for himself, is to say no more than what most men see, and feel, and acknowledge. To endeavour to magnify the exploits of the latter, by putting them in contrast with those of the former, would be unjust, since accident and not merit was at the bottom of this distinction. It should, however, never be forgotten, that the first achieved all he aimed at, which was all that man should do; and that the last failed, from an incompetency of estimating his own powers. The error of the latter is the more unpardonable, since, to gross want of judgment, must be added unworthiness of purpose; nor is it in any degree lessened by the circumstance that he sinned in the presence of so bright and so glorious an example. If there be any so weak as to believe the asseverations of Napoleon, that he fought for aught but self, let them try his patriotism by the same test as that of Washington. It is true that, in mere extent of achievement, the hero of France vastly outstripped the patriot of America; but the latter not only wanted a theatre for his actions, but he was often deficient in means. Merit is of a nature too comparative to be rashly reduced to results; but strip these men of their accidental and adventitious advantages, and regard them steadily. The military career of Napoleon was run in the current of prosperity, while that of Washington was a constant, but manly struggle, against a combination of the most adverse circumstances. In addition to this important fact, the one considered his troops as the devoted instruments of his own purposes, and he used them accordingly; while the other looked on his followers not only as the sole guardians of a country to which they were devoted, but as an important portion of that community for whose happiness he was contending. Napoleon was greatest in prosperity; but the fame of Washington is as equal as his character.

They who believe that America would not have been free without Washington, neither understand the part he acted, nor the people who intrusted him with power. The war of 1776 was purely a war of principle. Remonstrance and petition had been exhausted, and no duty of forbearance was neglected. All that justice, and temper, and mercy required, had been done before the sword was drawn at all. When it was determined to resist, it became necessary to choose a leader worthy of a cause so righteous; one who would give dignity to the quarrel in the eyes of nations; who would secure confidence at home, and who could command respect from those who were bent on submission to their will. These difficult duties did Washington perform, in a manner to exceed the hopes of the most sanguine. His enemies never dared to assail his integrity. No man was ever sufficiently hardy to affect to distrust his motives. While he wielded a power little short of that of a dictator, and wielded it firmly and with steadiness, the governed never knew uneasiness. So far from aiming at an unjust purpose, he checked, not with Roman severity, but with the directness and simplicity of an honest man, the least approach to that disorder or disaffection in his troops, which, if any thing could do it in a country like this, would have effected the views of a personal ambition. On all occasions, he steadily regarded duty, and disregarded self. Nor were opportunities wanting, of which a man less pure might be tempted to profit. The dis-

content of his unrequited army at the close of the
contest, might have deluded a less devoted patriot;
and ambition itself could not desire a better pretext
for urging a stronger government on the nation, than
the resistance to the law, which occurred in the
powerful State of Pennsylvania so soon after his
election to the presidency. Perhaps history does
not record an instance of an insurrection which
threatened to be more dangerous to infant institutions than this; and it is certain that history does
not record an instance in which resistance to the
laws was more promptly, and at a less expense of
blood, subdued. But the glory of Washington is to
be sought in the whole tenor of his life; in the bright
example, and in the stern lesson of virtue that he
has exhibited to the age, and which he has bequeath-
ed to posterity. He is the only public man, since
the general use of letters has rendered communication easy and judgments critical, that has, by common consent, purchased an imperishable, and, what
is far more glorious, an unsullied name.

It is cheering to virtue to know how lasting and
more certain are its rewards, than the temporary and
doubtful fame which attends the mere conqueror.
In what but the accidental attributes of a more advanced state of civilization, does Napoleon materially
differ from Jenghis Khan? His contemporaries are
already treating him with severity; and, before another age is passed, and passion and personal antipa-
thies shall have ceased, his career will lose one-half
of its lustre by the active agency of truth. How
different has been the lot of Washington! He has
not yet been in his tomb for half the life of man, and
the world have already placed him at the side of the
brightest names of antiquity. The young, and the
restless, and the weak of mind, may still find matter
of applause in the career of Napoleon; but it is the
thoughtful, the good, and the experienced, who see

the most to admire in the deeds, and the most to reverence in the character of Washington.

Until I stood by the side of the grave of this illustrious man, I had never ceased to reproach his country with neglect, in not having reared a monument of marble to his memory. But as I lingered, for near an hour, about the humble vault which holds his remains, it was impossible not to feel how much stronger is the impression left by character, in a place where no accessories of art exist to distract its musings. If I were an American, it would be the wish nearest to my heart to see the estate of Mount Vernon pass into the keeping of the nation, in order that it might be preserved, as nearly as possible, in its present condition. The vault should be kept in the touching and peaceful quiet in which it is now seen; and when foreigners ask for the monument of their hero, let them be referred, with honest pride, to that liberty, and to those institutions which grew on the confidence of the world, under his wise and patriotic guidance. If there be a name in the records of history that can afford to stand before the eyes of criticism devoid of artificial aid, it is that of the man who now sleeps beneath a few stunted cedars, and within mouldering walls of brick, on the banks of the Potomac.

R 2

TO THE PROFESSOR JANSEN,

&c. &c.

Philadelphia, ———

CONGRESS necessarily rose on the night of the 4th of March. You must have learned from my previous letters, that a Congress lasts but two years, commencing on the 4th of March of one year, and terminating on the 3d of March of the year but one following. Of course it would be necessary to convene the new members, in order to proceed in legislation after the prescribed period. This can be, and has been, done, in times of need, but the usual practice is to let the bodies separate, at the end of what is called the "short session." The terms of short and long session are easily explained. The constitution requires that Congress should assemble on the first Monday in December of each year, unless it has adjourned to a different period, or is expressly convened by a call from the President. On the first year of the service of the members, it is plain they may sit as long as they please; but on the second, their term of service expires on the 3d of March. As one-third of the Senators, and perhaps about the same number of the Representatives, usually retire every two years, it would be necessary to summon those who supply their places, should the public service require an immediate continuation of the legislative duties. The Senate sometimes sits a day or two after the lower house has adjourned, in order to attend to what is called executive business (the approval of nominations to office.) The practice is, I believe, uniform, at the end of a presidential term, in order to give the new incumbent an opportunity to name his cabinet. In all such cases, the new Senators are summoned in time to attend. Of course, no legislative business can then be done.

Late on the evening of the 3d of March, Congress rose; but, in point of fact, the change of executive power was not made until the President elect took the oath of office. This ceremony took place about noon of the following day. In 1801, when Mr. Adams, the elder, went out of office, he made sundry nominations which were confirmed by the old Senators on the evening of the 3d of March. Mr. Jefferson, his successor, refused to ratify these appointments. He took the ground that, as President, he had the power to appoint to office, the Senate only possessing, in effect, a veto. Now, the new functionaries had not received their commissions, and no one could, constitutionally, sign them but the actual President; this, the actual President refused to do, and of course there were no appointments, since it is by no means incumbent on the President to appoint an officer, even after the Senate has approved of his name, the power of the latter going no farther than their negative. It could be of no moment, except in the appointment of a judge, whether the President appointed these officers or not, since, in all other cases, he possesses the power of removal, the commissions invariably running—"this commission to continue in force during the pleasure of the President of the United States for the time being."

The President absolutely appoints certain inferior officers of the government, such as midshipmen, masters, gunners, &c. &c., in the navy, and all the cadets that enter the army; but, in point of fact, a great deal of republican equality is observed in the distribution of even these small favours. The plan is to give to each State officers in proportion to its representatives; still the absolute selection is with the President. All the postmasters in the country, who are, in truth, only deputies of the postmaster-general, receive their commissions from the latter officer. Of course the President, who can at any time remove the postmaster-general, has a controlling voice in all the superior appointments of that department. The Secretaries also appoint their own clerks, and there is a considerable patronage in the hands of the Secretary of the Treasury, who names several hundred officers, in the different custom-houses, that receive salaries of between five hundred and a thousand dollars each. The constitution indicates certain officers who *shall* be nominated to the Senate. It then goes on to say, that all others must be similarly appointed, unless Congress, by law, shall see fit to trust the power in the President, or in the heads of departments. As yet, Congress has seen fit to do both ; but should the trusts be abused, it always possesses the power to repeal its own enactments.

A great deal is said in Europe concerning the economy of this government. It is the subject of much ridicule, and of high praise, on our side of the Atlantic. In order to form a just opinion on the subject, it is necessary to ascertain some of the leading facts.

You will always remember, that as there exists a double form of government, there are double sets of officers to be paid. This circumstance, however, does not add in any great degree to the expense, since no duty is performed twice. The President of the United States receives a salary of twenty-five thousand dollars a year. This sum can neither be increased nor diminished during his term of service. He is also supplied with a furnished house. On this salary the President can live like a gentleman who receives a good deal of company, and it is thought he may even lay by a reasonable excess yearly. Perhaps, considering the nature of the government, the income is about what it should be. The heads of departments receive six thousand dollars each, and no house. Their salaries are too low, since they scarcely afford the means of creditable subsistence to men in their public situations. It is probable, however, that the country will, ere long, erect buildings for the residence of these officers, and increase their pay a little. There is no plausible reason why it should be so much inferior to that of the President. The chief justice of the United States receives five thousand dollars a year, and each of the assistant justices four thousand five hundred. The judges of the district courts are paid from eight hundred to three thousand dollars a year, according to the amount of their services. The Vice-President gets five thousand dollars a year. The members of Congress receive eight dollars a day, each, while at Washington, and eight dollars for every twenty miles of their route in going and returning. Ministers plenipotentiary receive nine thousand dollars a year salary, the same sum for an outfit, and one-fourth of it to defray the expenses of their return home. This pay is much too small, certainly; and it is as unwise in its generality, as in its amount. It is unjust to pay a man who is compelled to live in London, for instance, the same sum as a man who is compelled to live in Madrid. It is unwise to neglect to use, in a rational degree, an influence that other people acknowledge, whatever may be its inherent merit, or whatever may be the opinion of the people of the United States themselves on the subject. Their motive in sending ministers abroad, is interest: and we, who know the effect of a little appearance in our hemisphere, know that he is a gainer who consults the prejudices of those with whom he is required to dwell. But independently of this truth, which must, however, be taken with a proper degree of qualification, in many places, the agents of this government cannot subsist with a proper degree of comfort on their salaries. No man can maintain the establishment of a private gentleman and educate four or five children well, on two thousand pounds a year, in London. Consuls receive no pay (as such.) The collectors of the customs are paid in proportion to their duties, limiting the receipts to less than five thousand dollars a year. A similar plan is observed with postmasters, and sundry other officers ; the maximum of pay varying according to the importance of the office. Although the higher functionaries of this government are not often paid as well as they should be, the lower officers are very generally well rewarded. Salaries of two or three thousand dollars, for situations of no great dignity, are not uncommon, and there are many subordinates who receive from eight to twelve hundred. In short, the object, though it sometimes fails, is to make all classes of men comfortable, without furnishing the means of a useless splendour to any. The errors that have undoubtedly been made, are the unavoidable results of a popular government in which official men are sometimes reluctant to incur a responsibility that leads to no very important results. I think that time will correct them ; and, should it not, the evil is one of far less magnitude than that which is entailed by a lavish expenditure of the public money.

The whole of the civil, diplomatic, and miscellaneous expenses of this government, for the year 1826, were 2,600,177 dollars. This is, however, exclusive of the cost of the State governments, and the cost of collecting the revenue. The latter is about 750,000 dollars. The military expenditure was 6,243,236 dollars. But the greater part of this sum was for the erection of fortifications, for ordnance, arming the militia, Indian department, and pensions of soldiers of the revolution, &c. The actual cost of the army, pay, subsistence and clothing included, was about 2,000,000 of dollars. That so extensive a country can protect itself at so cheap a rate, is in some measure owing to its remote situation, but chiefly to its institutions, which trust its defence to the citizens. A vast deal is clearly gained, by thus limiting resistance to its foreign enemies. I do not think that the pressure of a crowded population can produce any material difference, since the present system of America must ever make it the interest of a great majority to preserve order. A soldier in the army receives five dollars a month pay, with his clothes and victuals. The officers are paid according to rank.* The other expenses of the army are of a temporary nature, and furnish no clue to future estimates.

The navy of the United States, for the same year (1826) cost 4,218,902 dollars. But this sum is also liable to a great deal of explanation. The United States, to be in readiness to meet any emergency, maintain a corps of about 950 officers. Their present policy is to foster this corps, and consequently no one member of it is put on half-pay, except at his own desire. The pay and subsistence of the officers, and the pay of the men, actually afloat (rather more than 5,000 in all,) somewhat exceeds a million of dollars. In this number, too, about one-tenth are quarter-deck officers. Much of the money is for the expenses of navy-yards, and the ordinary. About 300,000 dollars are for the provisions of the men. The rest is for the increase of the navy, arrearages, and for the support of the marine corps, of whom

---

* A soldier enlists for five years. He receives the following articles of clothing during that period, viz. five uniform coats; three cotton jackets with sleeves; three woollen ditto ditto; ten pairs of gray woollen overalls; ten pairs of drilling ditto; three fatigue frocks; five trowsers; ten pairs of laced boots; ten ditto shoes; ten flannel shirts: ten cotton ditto; ten pairs of stockings; ten ditto socks; two leathern stocks; one great coat; three blankets; five pairs of wings; four pompons; two cockades and eagles; four bands and tassels; one leathern cap-cover, plate, scales and ball; one forage-cap, and ten pairs of flannel drawers.

nearly 1,000 are employed. The latter are, of course, in addition to the sea officers and seamen. It would be troublesome to separate the several parts of these expenditures in such a manner as to give a clear and simple statement of each and all of them; but as the American government publishes the most minute documents on these subjects, it is in the power of any one to do it who has sufficient interest in the subject to pursue so elaborate an inquiry. I shall content myself with the main results, coupled with such facts of a general nature, as I think may reward you for the pain of deciphering my letters.*

---

* In the January number (LXXIII.) of the Quarterly Review, there is an article on the United States of America. The reviewer speaks boldly of the American navy, for he professes to treat of a work written by an English naval officer, who, in his turn, had also written a little decidedly on the same subject. In a note attached to the end of this volume, the writer has endeavoured to show in what points his information differs from that of both reviewer and reviewed, in respect to this important branch of the American policy. His present object is, however, confined to expenditure. In page 279 of the said Review, is the following sentence: "With this small number of men" (4,268,) "the establishments of the dock-yards on a very limited scale, and the civil branches of the service, a mere trifle, the sum expended for the naval department in 1826, was 4,222,952 dollars, or close upon one million sterling. In the printed report of the secretary of the treasury, now before the writer, Letter F. page 39, is a minute statement of the expenditure of the naval establishment for the year 1826. The gross amount is 4,218,902 dollars, 45 cents. From this Report the following items are extracted: "Repairs of vessels, 485,970; ship-houses, 44,296; gradual increase of the navy, 793,704; ten sloops of war, 506,163; prohibition of slave trade, 22,220; pay and subsistence of marine corps (which is not included in the before mentioned number of men,) 219,686:" and no less a sum than 294,380 for improvements and additions to navy-yards, besides a number of small miscellaneous items, that make together about 110,000 more. The figures are all meant to represent dollars, and together they make 2,576,419, or something more than one-half the sum that the reviewer has taken for premises by which he wishes to show that the Americans maintain a small force at an enormous expense. Not one of the items here enumerated, properly belongs to the expense of the small number of men, the civil branches of the service, or the establishments of the dock-yards, unless additions and improvements

All the appointments of a captain of the navy, in command of a shore station, are worth something less than four thousand dollars a year, exclusive of a house. When in command of a vessel, his pay is considerably less. There is a difference made in the case of a vessel of a very small size, though the commander of a 44 receives as much as the commander of a 74. But the pay of both the army and navy should not be considered as permanently established, especially of the latter service, which is just beginning to receive, in all its branches, that grave attention that its vital importance to the security and dignity of the nation demands.

You will perceive that, as a rule, the inferior agents of the American government are better paid than the same description of individuals in the employment of almost any other nation, while the higher officers receive less.*

The positive annual expenses of the American government are not far from 13,000,000 dollars. Of this sum, rather more than three millions and a half are for the interest of the national debt. But the odd half million is met by the dividends of bank stock, for the purchase of which several millions of the

---

to the latter can be thus considered. Independently of all this, the balance not only supports the service afloat, &c. &c. but it keeps *all* the officers of the navy (with perhaps a dozen voluntary exceptions) on *full pay*. The writer here leaves the matter between the Secretary of the Treasury of the United States, and the contributor to the Quarterly Review.—See Note A. end of the volume.

* The expenditure for the year 1828, is estimated as follows: the result rarely differing materially from these calculations. Civil, diplomatic, and miscellaneous, 1,828,385 dollars; military service, including fortifications, ordnance, Indian department, provisions, arming of militia, &c. 4,332,091 dollars; naval service, including the gradual increase of the navy, 3,788,349 dollars, making a total for the regular expenses of the government, including sums previously voted for erecting forts and building ships, of 9,947,125 dollars. The interest of the debt is not contained in this amount.

debt were created. The actual outgoings, therefore, for the current service of the country, all improvements and constructions included, are within 10,000,000 dollars. Every thing is so much on the advance in the United States, that it is difficult to arrive at an exact understanding of what is meant by current expenditure. Thus, of 2,600,177 dollars, which formed the amount of the civil, miscellaneous and diplomatic head of the account (for the year 1826,) near 1,200,000 dollars were miscellaneous enough, as the charges included 188,000 dollars for light-houses, near 300,000 for canal stock, and more than 200,000 for old claims arising out of the war of 1812. The real civil list of that year, exclusive of diplomacy, was 1,256,745 dollars, and the cost of all the diplomacy of the country was 180,103 dollars. This trifling sum supported the whole expense and contingencies, in short, the entire cost of more than twenty different missions in Europe, Africa, and America. It is worthy of remark, that the diplomacy of this country is managed about as well as that of most nations; and I am of opinion, that, when its power shall become sufficiently great to be dreaded, it will be found to be still more successful.

The clear revenue of the United States, from the customs alone, is now (1828) about 20,000,000 of dollars. As this source of receipts produces in itself a great excess over all the outgoings, there are no direct impositions laid by the general government. The debt is in the course of rapid extinguishment, and as the interest is annually diminished, the ability of the country to increase its expenditure is of course increased. Notwithstanding this prosperous state of the public purse, the most rigid economy is observed; a circumstance that it is idle to say is produced by any other cause than the direct agency of the people on the administration.

Thus far we have not touched on the salaries of

the State governments at all. They are graduated,
however, on the same scale of expense, the richest
and largest of these communities rarely paying as
much to the public servants as the general government. There is undoubtedly, in some few instances,
as in the legislatures and judiciaries, a double set of
officers to support; but, when one remembers the
great extent of the country, it will be seen that, under
any other form of government, it would be impossible
to avoid this expense. No single set of judges could
travel over this great surface in times sufficiently
short to administer justice equally and promptly, nor
could one great and central legislative body enact all
the local laws that are absolutely necessary to a
country so new and so vast.

The only reply that the enemies of America (and
they are all the enemies of liberty) can urge, when
her example is pointed to in support of the doctrine
of economy, is founded on the fact of the double form
of its government, and the additional expense that is
consequently incurred. I know of but two ways in
which we can arrive sufficiently near the truth to
ascertain whether this additional cost raises the expenses of the American to the level of those of the
European or not. The one (and is it not infallible ?)
is to compare the amount of contributions paid by the
parties; and the other is to attempt to reach the cost of
governing some particular portion of the confederacy,
and then to make the necessary comparisons between
it and some equal community in our hemisphere.
We will endeavour to do both.

The State of New-York contains one-seventh of
the entire population of the Union. One-seventh
of 2,600,177 dollars, the whole amount of the " civil,
diplomatic, and *miscellaneous* expenses " of the general government for the year (1826) is 371,453. This
dividend includes more than one million of miscellaneous expenditure, such as " light-houses," " stock in

canal companies," and " payment of claims for buildings destroyed in the war;" but no matter, we will
take the amount in gross. Now the whole expenditure of the civil list of the State of New-York, is about
350,000 dollars. The two sums make 721,453 dollars. Here you have 1,700,000 inhabitants receiving
justice at their own doors, internal protection, legislation in the utmost convenient form possible, and *all*
the more general advantages of government, for the
sum of less than half a dollar a head annually. If you
divide the military and naval expenses of the United
States by seven, you have the entire pecuniary charge
that they defray, not only for the current expenses,
but for the material provisions they are making for
future defence.* The States are at no other material expenses than those attached to the civil list,
unless it be for the purpose of domestic *improvements*, and even a great portion of the latter is thus
defrayed, in the salaries of the *employés*.

Of incidental expenses the American pays less,
considering his means, than the inhabitant of any
other nation. Their city corporations, with the exception of one or two, are cheap, and little or no
money is expended in mere show. There are no
church establishments, and the religious contributions
are therefore voluntary. Still the clergy are supported. There are various manners of doing this, as you
may suppose, in a country so diversified in condition.
In many of the old congregations, there are endowments which have grown in value with the growth
of the country, and which now serve to relieve the
people of a large portion of the expense. A farm
bought for that purpose, and a house erected when
land and materials were cheap, become valuable and
useful in time. There is a common practice of

---

* It should be remembered that all the expenses of the general government (in time of peace) are paid by the importation
duties.

erecting a church by contributions, and then renting the pews, for the support of the clergyman. No general rule is, however, applicable to this particular branch of expense; but as no one taxes himself beyond his own pleasure, and as churches are, for the circumstances, exceedingly numerous, it is fair to presume that the population do not find the expense of supporting the clergy burthensome. Trifling additional taxes are also laid in the counties and towns to defray local expenses, and, among others, for the maintenance of the common schools. These taxes also vary according to circumstances, the county which is building a court-house and jail, or which is engaged in any other public work, paying more at the moment than the county which has already discharged that duty. The *whole* tax paid on a farm valued at 5,000 dollars in one of the older counties of New-York, was five dollars. This included every charge for that year, though the assessment is subject to variations, being sometimes more and sometimes less. As the United States, in point of fact, imposes no taxes in time of peace, this charge was all the owner of this farm had to pay (as such) for the entire protection of government. It is true he contributed something in the way of duties on imported goods, but that is a contribution that depended entirely on his personal expenditure. The impositions of the general government are, as you already know, commonly much lighter than those laid in other commercial nations.

In order to make a correct estimate, however, of the comparative rate of the taxes paid by the American, it is necessary to consider the value of what he receives. He is required to pay for improvements in the country, which produce a direct influence on the increasing value of his property. The income and the price of his farm keep equal pace with the growth of the settlement in which he lives. He enjoys the means of giving a creditable education to his children, within a reasonable distance of his own dwelling, and all for the sum included in the State tax, if the cost of school-books, paper, &c. be excepted. He is certainly compelled to devote more or less of his time to working the highways,* but then he takes care that the route by his own door shall be kept in as good order as that by the door of any body else.

As a whole, the public impositions in America, including taxes, duties, labour, militia service, clergy, and every thing else, are exceedingly light. But it is absolutely impossible to give any particular example which shall not be liable to so much exception as to destroy it as a rule. · So much of the contribution is returned in the way of improvements which affect the value of the property taxed, that, had I all the statements in my head, I do not know that I could give you a clear idea of their relative amount. All those local impositions which exist in other countries, as octrois, &c. &c. are utterly unknown here.

I have heard it imputed to America as a fault, that her system leads to the loss of time and money in excessive litigation. It is said that there are more suits at law here, than among any similar number of people in the known world. Although I cannot pretend to say that the fact is so, I should be surprised to learn that it was otherwise.

The whole territory of the United States covers 2,000,000 of square miles. It is true that the title to more than half of this immense surface still exists in the government, where a vast deal of it will probably continue for ages. But, in order to bring our

---

* This imposition is laid according to the property of the individual. A commutation in money at a very reduced rate is allowed, but it is impossible to give its amount, since it is an assessment that diminishes with the improvement of the country.

calculations within the bounds of exactitude, let us again look at New-York. This State has 46,000 square miles of territory, which is owned among, we will say (1828,) 1,750,000 people. Now, to every foot of this land there is a title somewhere. Very little, indeed, is the property of the State. Here, then, is a plain and direct resaon why the 1,750,000 inhabitants should have more questions about land titles than the same number any where else, simply because they are the owners of more of the article in dispute. Land is also greatly subdivided in all the older parts of America, and of course each subdivision has its separate title. Then the rapid transfer of property which is incidental to the condition of a country in progress of settlement, multiplies conveyances, and each new conveyance opens the way to litigation. The revolution, with its changes, also gave birth to disputes which time is just beginning to settle, as indeed it is beginning to settle all other controversies that grow exclusively out of the transfers of real estates.

The United States are, again, a more commercial nation, compared with their population, than any other in the world. Among such a people legal disputes must, of necessity, arise. Justice is comparatively cheap, and easy of access. Men have confidence in her decrees; and the fear of power, influence, and corruption, is unknown. In such circumstances, wrong-headed persons, who are ever apt to fancy themselves in the right, make their appeals to the tribunals boldly. I do not believe that the system of the United States encourages litigation, except as it brings all men before the court on terms not of nominal, but of a true equality. Still I can believe, that the great number of low practitioners of the law who are scattered up and down the country, do induce men to enter rashly into legal contests.

In the older and more regulated States, litigation is far less frequent, *cæteris paribus*, than in those that are more new. The same is true of the proportion of taxes, as compared to the value of property. I am of opinion that, were it not for the great number of country lawyers in America, it would be found that litigation is less resorted to than in many other countries, notwithstanding the unavoidable causes of contention which exist in a new country. The number of the lawyers is undeniably an evil; but, besides being an evil which is likely to correct itself, and which is already beginning to correct itself, it is one that is not without its advantages. They serve to keep alive an active knowledge of their rights among the people; and although much abused as pettifoggers, they make, in common, exceedingly useful and intelligent local legislators.

There is a great fashion of decrying men of moderate acquirements in all things, as if life were not more a matter of experience than of theories. It is much easier to assume than to prove, that a set of profound thinkers would legislate better for a community than a set of active and half-educated men, who are familiar with the practices of the world. All the common passions of man are as well, and perhaps better known to the latter than to the former, and after legislation has provided against the dangers that are coincident to their existence, one must seek the rest of its duties in the world and not in books. But what says experience? It would be difficult to find any one country on earth in which the laws are better adapted to promote the true interests of the community, than in the most, I am not sure I could not say the least, favoured of the States of this republic. And yet legislation is the business of practical men altogether. At all events, they have contrived to obtain quiet and security at a cheaper rate than other people, and that, too, in many cases under all the unpropitious circumstances of great dispersion and the first stages of society.

It is a rule which applies to all salaries in this country, that little or no allowances are made for the support of mere dignity. The dignity of government is supposed to rest in the people themselves; and among their other provisions for its support, they have taken care to retain most of the money. The President receives a larger sum certainly than is necessary for his mere subsistence; but then the President is liable to a vast number of expenses that other functionaries escape; and, in his case, it is thought politic to bid a little higher than common, in order to command talent. It is not too much to say, that the President of the United States, if a prudent man, can save quite as much money out of his salary, each year, as a first-rate lawyer in practice would gain; and I confess I see but one reason why he has the smallest right to ask any more. He has generally reached a time of life when he retires, that forbids further exertion; and perhaps it is wisest to attach a degree of consideration to this high office, which shall preclude men from descending subsequently to inferior duties. The latter point, however, is one that will certainly admit of dispute, and I do not think the former as strong as it first appears. Necessity will teach men the value of prudence and exertion in early life; nor is this the country that ought to wish to see its chief magistrate setting an example of useless, but attractive splendour. There are no vices so contagious as the corruptions which flow from the excessive use of money; for the desire to possess it, is a passion that all men feel, since it is the medium by which all the ordinary good of life is obtained. The accountableness af the public agents, and the simplicity of men of station, are matters of so vast importance in a republic, that the one should never be neglected, and as little occasion as possible should be given to make any serious innovations on the other.

We have just had a proof that the government of the United States knows how to give with grace and liberality on a proper occasion. When La Fayette first came to America, he did not proceed on his distant and hazardous expedition empty-handed. The new States were then so poor, and they had been kept, by the operation of colonial policy, so completely dependent on the mother country for supplies, that the contributions of an individual were not without moment to them. The arms and money of the young Frenchman were scarcely less acceptable than his sword and his heart. They had amply returned his love; but it still remained to discharge a debt whose obligations were scarcely less sacred.

During the last session, a bill was introduced, appropriating two hundred thousand dollars in money, and a township of land, to extinguish this debt. It was not pretended that the money borrowed, or rather given (for the devotion of La Fayette to the cause he had espoused knew none of the forms of bargaining).had not been already returned. But the Americans know that their venerable friend has long been a heavy sufferer by the revolution in his own country, and they also know that he took little account of the pecuniary interests of this life. The bill was not passed in enthusiasm, and with the hurry of dramatic effect, but it went through the forms of legislation with calmness and dignity. It was even resisted by one or two sturdy republicans, who paid a tribute to the manliness of the nation, by openly contending that, as the infirm and poorer agents of the revolution were still unrequited, they could not vote to bestow money on another, for services that were performed in common. But a vast majority of the two houses were of opinion that injustice to a part was no apology for injustice to the whole, and the case before them was one of too disinterested and too brilliant service to admit of a parallel.

The claims of La Fayette on America, cannot, surely, be likened to the claims of even Washington. The immortal patriot of this country owed his allegiance, his services, and his life, to the land of his birth; and his exceeding merit is in the faith and ability with which he discharged the duties. But nature had imposed no such obligation on La Fayette. We may admire and extol the filial piety of the child in its degree; but without it, altogether, the offspring would become a reproach and a subject of scorn before mankind. The stranger who yields his aid under the influence of a general philanthropy, is alone entitled to deep and unqualified gratitude, since the universal obligations of society create indissoluble connexions between the members of families and the citizens of the same communities.

But there was still a loftier claim, in the case of La Fayette, to the homage of a nation. His devotion to the cause of America was a devotion to the interests of humanity. The service he performed was chivalrous in its conception, bold in its moral attributes, and fearless in its execution. He dedicated youth, person, and fortune, to the principles of liberty; and it was fitting that an example should be given to the world, that he who had suffered in such a cause was not to go unrequited. In this view of the case, it was just as incumbent on the Frenchman to receive, as it was the duty of the American to bestow. At a time when the servants of despotism and abject submission are receiving such ample gifts for their devotion, it is encouraging to see one splendid instance, at least, of virtue, and disinterestedness, and patient suffering, receiving a portion of the worldly rewards that should be the exclusive property of men devoted to the good of mankind.

TO THE COMTE JULES DE BÉTHIZY,

&c. &c.

Washington, ——

I HAVE just witnessed one of the most imposing ceremonies of this government; I allude to the inauguration of the President of the United States. It took place about noon, on the 4th of March, when the power of the late incumbent ceased, and that of his successor commenced. It was simple in its forms, but it may possess sufficient interest to amuse a few leisure minutes.

Every body was in the Capitol by the appointed hour. As it is altogether a ceremony of convention (with the exception of the oath of office) such persons were admitted to be spectators, as the officers who controlled the proceedings chose. But in a country like this, exclusion must proceed on a principle, and on such a principle, too, as shall satisfy the reason of the community. In the first place, the galleries of the hall of the House of Representatives were thrown open to every body; a measure that in itself served to commence with a system of equality. The floor of the house was next occupied, as a matter of course, by the Senators and Representatives. The foreign ministers and their suites, the officers of the government, including those of the army and navy, ex-members of Congress, and citizens of eminence from distant States, and finally strangers, who were deemed worthy of attention, composed the rest of the assembly.

The officers of the army and navy appeared in uniforms; and as there were a great many handsome and well-dressed women present, the scene was sufficiently gay. But here all attempts at display ceased. There were no guards, no processions, no wands, no robes, nor any of the usual accompaniments of an European ceremony.

At the proper time, the President (Mr. Monroe) and the President elect (Mr. Quincy Adams) entered the hall, accompanied by the great officers of state, the judges of the supreme court, &c. &c. The two former took their seats on the sofa of the Speaker, while the others occupied chairs that had been reserved for them. After a short pause, the chief justice of the United States arose, and ascended to the little elevation on which the sofa stands. He held in his hand the sacred volume. Mr. Adams then took the oath, in the presence of the assembly, with solemnity and distinctness. The form was as follows : " I do solemnly swear (or affirm) that I will faithfully execute the office of President of the United States, and will, to the best of my ability, preserve, protect, and defend, the constitution of the United States."

With this brief but impressive office, a change in the executive power of this vast republic was effected. The moment Mr. Adams had pronounced the words just quoted, he was the chief magistrate of a great nation, and his predecessor retired to the station of a private citizen.

After a momentary delay, the new President commenced what is called his " inaugural address." It was long, and it was delivered with earnestness and apparent sincerity. It is customary to recognise, on this occasion, the leading principles of the constitution, and for the new functionary to make some manifestation of the particular course of policy by which he intends to be governed. Such professions are, however, rather general than minute, and seldom go farther than a confession of political faith, that depends much more on received axioms than on any private opinions. Still, there was a simplicity in the air of the President, and in the forms of the ceremony, which irresistibly led to the belief you were listening to professions that were entitled to more credit than those which similar scenes elsewhere are wont to create. When the address was ended, the assembly intermingled; and after the congratulations and compliments proper to such an event, the multitude quietly dispersed. Immediately after, the Senators proceeded to their chamber, where the oath was administered to Mr. Calhoun, who then took the chair of that body, in virtue of his office of Vice-President of the United States. He made a short and pertinent address, and the Senate soon after adjourned. During the course of that, or the succeeding day, Mr. Adams nominated Mr. Clay, the late Speaker of the House of Representatives, to fill the vacancy (Secretary of State) occasioned by his own election to the chair of the chief magistrate. Mr. Crawford, the Secretary of the Treasury, also retired; and Mr. Rush, who had recently been minister in England, was selected to fill the situation. The place of Mr. Calhoun was supplied by a gentleman from Virginia (Mr. Barbour.) With these changes the new cabinet was complete, the other incumbents retaining office. I understand it is a practice for every member of the cabinet to tender his resignation on the election of a new President, which gives the latter an opportunity of making such alterations as he may deem expedient, in the most delicate manner possible. Two of the vacancies, in the present instance, were the results of promotions; and it is understood that Mr. Adams would have gladly retained Mr. Crawford, had that gentleman been disposed to serve.

I confess I have been struck with the imposing simplicity of such a quiet transfer of power. The office of President of the United States is one of great dignity and high trust, and its duties have always been discharged with singular moderation and real. The present incumbent is a prudent and zealous patriot, and there is no reason to distrust his intelligence or intentions.

It is a necessary consequence of an European education, that we should subject all things to the rules that are known to govern life in our quarter of the world. Under these impressions, a thousand absurd and childish theories have been urged among us, concerning the probable influence of such an officer, as the one whose inauguration I have just described. It would teach some of us moderation, though it did not teach us wisdom, did we thoroughly understand the fact, that it is quite as unintelligible to the mass of the Americans how we contrive to get on under our systems, as it is to us how they manage to get on with theirs.

I have already endeavoured to convey some idea of the nature of the private intercourse which the President holds with his fellow-citizens. He is uniformly treated with personal respect, but never with adulation. The tone of the manners of the country is so much opposed to the practices of courts, that artifice itself requires that some sacrifice should be made to simplicity. Whenever the President appears in his official character, he is received with the quiet deference that is due to his office; but whenever he chooses to appear as a private citizen, he does it without exciting more attention than is naturally bestowed on an individual who occupies an elevated and responsible station. The late President (Mr. Monroe) made tours of observation through all the States, and along the whole line of the national frontier. His journey was rather of a public nature, and his receptions, in the towns and States, wore a good deal of a public character. The ceremonies through which he passed were a species of homage paid, in remote quarters of the confederation, to the unity of the nation in his person, though, in no instance, did

they exceed the compliments of the governed to the
man who filled a station to which he had been elected by the public will. When, on the other hand,
the President chooses to leave the seat of government on his private affairs, he passes through the
States like any other citizen, though it is not possible to separate the man entirely from the consideration, or, indeed, from the actual power which attends the office. He journeys, on these occasions,
like other people, in the steam-boats and public
coaches; and his passages through the towns are
distinguished by no other marks of attention than the
visits of compliment that he, or any other man of eminence, would naturally receive.

The constitutional power of the President is not
trifling, though it is always rigidly subordinate to the
law. He is commander-in-chief of the army; but
while it might prove some palliation to plead an illegal order issuing from this source, as an excuse for
violating any law, it would not be the slightest justi-
fication. The only supreme authority in this republic is the law: and the President, not in words, but
in fact, is just as much its subject as the meanest cor-
poral in the line. Should he venture to order a
subaltern to do an illegal act, the young man might
refuse to obey; and should he order him to be punished for his disobedience, there is an authority in
the country that would quietly take the supposed
offender out of his hands. Now this is not a naked
theory, but a rigid fact; and the consequence is just
what it should be. Those who wield the public
power for the time being, take all possible care never
to be legally in the wrong; for they well know, that
neither influence, nor situation, nor fear, nor any
other cause, can save the offender from open accusation before the nation. It is easy to say that such a
system must give rise to insubordination and tumult,
and a thousand other evils; but where is the proof?

The discipline of the army and navy of the United States is as good as those in other services, though submission to arbitrary power is far from being as common. All the authority is here, though it is not in the same hands as elsewhere.

I have mentioned this fact to show you, that while there exists here the right to command for all legal purposes, there exists no authority to intimidate inferiors into a dangerous submission. These people are born and educated in a state of society, which inculcates deep and settled respect for the laws, without any respect for individuals. The President of the United States is commander-in-chief, it is true; but he could have no security for obedience beyond the point where his views should become doubtful.

The risk is too certain, and the success too remote and doubtful, to leave any temptation before the President to abuse his power. Four years is not time enough to mature a plan that would be dangerous to liberty, especially as the agency of a majority of those who would be the losers by the change, must be employed to insure success. I do not believe you are silly enough to think that ten millions of people, who are excessively impatient of any of the forms of despotism, are likely to be subdued by a four-years' monarch, though he should happen to be another Napoleon; more especially when he can neither obtain, feed, clothe, arm, nor pay his troops, without begging money annually of those whom he would fain crush. If there shall ever be any great alteration in the principles of this government, rely on it, it will proceed directly from a conviction, in the mass of the people themselves, that such a change is necessary to their happiness.

Though the patronage of the President is great, it is subject to all the division of political support. In most cases, he is glad to get rid of the responsibility of appointments, since they oftener endanger, than

aid his popularity. He serves, therefore, rather as a
check on vicious recommendations, than as an active
source of emoluments and honour. On all high and
dignified appointments, he of course exercises a direct
influence, because he is supposed to know their duties
familiarly, and he ought to know the qualifications of
those he wishes to discharge them. But should he
be disposed to go wrong, the Senate would not ratify
his nominations, and then his power is just nothing.
Let us suppose a desire of usurpation.

An unprincipled individual finds himself in the
chair of the presidency. He wishes to become a
king. He has but two ways of effecting this object;
force or persuasion. If he has art enough to effect
the latter, he is just as likely to succeed here as the
King of England, for instance, would be likely to become absolute by the same means. If he be a man
of common discretion, he will know that he must
make a party, or his force will amount to just nothing
at all. We will suppose him to have blinded the
nation as to his real character, and views, and to have
selected and secured his agents; two pretty difficult
tasks, in the first place, you must allow. He has then
got to place these agents in offices of trust, or they
are no better than other men. In order to do this,
he must deceive, or corrupt, the Senate. But even
this difficult task must be done in two years, since
one-third of that body go out of office every other
year. Well, he has bribed a majority of the Senate,
and he gets his tools into power. He then goes to
work with the lower house, and soon brings two hundred men, who have been accustomed all their lives
to lock on him as an equal, to become his dependants.
The two houses then give him an army, and vote
money freely, in order to bribe that army; for it is out
of the question to think that men who have been
nursed in liberty, will serve despotism for nothing.
Now, we have him, in the short space of two years,

in possession of the two houses, of the treasury, and provided with an army. It is high time he should make a bold demonstration, or a new Congress will require new bribes. He takes the field with a hundred thousand men, and finds himself opposed to a million and a half of citizens unaccustomed to be controlled illegally, and who are bent on resistance. The odds are a little against him, you will allow, even supposing all the traitors he has gained to continue honest men, because they are in his service. I will leave him to fight this second battle of Armageddon, under the auspices of those wise heads, who think they see signs in the clouds, and portents in the air.

The legislative authority of the President is entirely negative. In this respect, he possesses much power to do good, and none to do evil. His signature is necessary to make a law, perhaps; but, if two-thirds of both houses vote in its favour, he dare not withhold it. He has, therefore, rather more of a voice than any one, or any twenty members, without, in truth, forming a separate estate. As he acts under a higher responsibility, and it is supposed, with a greater familiarity with the interests and policy of the country, than the ordinary legislator, his influence should be greater without putting it in his power to defeat the intentions of Congress. It is easy to suppose cases in which the President can do much good. We will take one that is the most obvious. The confederation is nearly equally divided into slave-owning, and what are called free States. These happen to be, just now, eleven of the former, and thirteen of the latter. In a few years more, the numbers will probably stand thirteen to fourteen. Now each of these States has two votes in the Senate, without whose concurrence no law can be enacted. The superiority of the representation of the free States, in the popular branch, can effect nothing on any question that may

be supposed to touch the delicate interests of slav ƒ,
without obtaining the acquiescence of the Senate. It
is not easy to imagine a case when, at least, two of
the northern Senators would not be inclined to moderate views, should a contest arise that seriously involved any of the more important interests of the
Union, and which was likely to divide men into sectional parties. But should parties in Congress ever
proceed so far as to produce, by a trifling majority,
(it could not be a large one without materially uniting
northern to southern men, or *vice versa*,) a law that
should threaten serious danger to the harmony of the
confederation, the President has power to send it
back, and to demand that a question of this magnitude
should receive the assent of a number, that must, of necessity, include a concesssion on one side or the other;
and concession, as you well know, is a great step towards harmony. It is just as likely that the President,
in the first place, should be a southern man, as a
northern man; and then he is expected to be, and,
in point of fact, is, commonly, above all the ordinary
excitements of legislative contests. The nation which,
rarely, I may say, never, enters very blindly into the
party heat which affects all legislative bodies, would
expect moderation in the President, and would support him in it. That such a case has not arisen,
proves nothing but the difficulty of obtaining even a
legislative majority on irritating and alarming questions; for it is certain that in one instance, at least,
such a question has been agitated. I mean the law
for the admission of the State of Missouri, (with the
privilege of holding slaves.) Had Congress passed
that law, and had the President good reason to think
that it would seriously endanger the harmony of the
confederation, he must have been an impotent man
indeed, not to have insisted that it should receive
the support of an unequivocal majority. I do not believe that a refusal to admit Missouri to the Union,

(with the privilege of holding slaves,) would have produced any other immediate result than applications to Congress to change their resolution; and time would therefore be given for the executive, (as well as the nation,) to estimate and weigh the consequences, even in the event of indecision on the part of the President; and it is scarcely possible to conceive a case, in which executive influence, and evident danger to the confederation united, could not produce a change of two votes, especially as the constant changes in the members themselves, admit of such an interference without involving personal vacillation.

This is one among a hundred similar familiar means, by which any great danger that is likely to arrive to this confederation, may, and would be avoided.

The President also possesses the power of referring a question to Congress, in order to demand a majority of two-thirds on any question of general policy. That public opinion will prevent the abuse of this power, through vexatious interferences with legislation, is known by experience, since it is difficult to conceive a case, unless of extraordinary magnitude, in which an officer so directly amenable to and dependent on public opinion, not only for his authority, but for his comfort, would dare to offend. The long neglect of the prerogative in England, is sufficient evidence of what public opinion can do in a case like this. But the neglect of the prerogative in England does not infer a necessary neglect of the salutary power of the President, since there is no *jealousy* of the exercise of the latter, the person who holds it being so shortly to be brought back into the bosom of the nation as a private citizen. In short, this is a power only to be resorted to in cases in which the moderate and the wiser majority of the whole people would be of one mind; and it is one that it might then be more injurious to neglect than to use.

The President commissions all the officers of the general government, except those, who, by law, receive their appointments from other functionaries. The judges of the United States' courts hold their offices during good behaviour.* With these exceptions, all other officers of the United States' government can be removed by the President. There are a great many officers of this government whose commissions are given but for four years; and though they are commonly recommissioned, it is in the power of the President to pass them by if he should please. You remember, of course, that in all cases which Congress has not named, by a law that can at any time be repealed, the assent of the Senate is necessary to an appointment.

In the army and navy, a regular system of promotion has been necessarily adopted; and as the Senate, without a good reason, would not confirm any irregular nomination, preferment, in those two branches of the public service, is always in due course, except in cases where character is implicated. So admirable is the practice of checks and balances throughout all the departments of this government, and so powerful and certain is the agency of public opinion, that no political management, except in cases that, by common consent, are thought to come fairly within the scope of political manœuvrings, can easily be exercised. The most commendable impartiality is observed in those appointments, which, in their nature,

---

* The judges of the State courts hold their offices by different tenures. Some are during good behaviour; others can be removed by the governors on a presentation by two-thirds of the two legislative bodies (which is, perhaps, the wisest provision of all;) others serve until sixty years of age, as in New-York; and some until seventy, as in Connecticut. All are, of course, liable to impeachment.

should be kept superior to party influence. The President cannot advance his son a step in either of the two services named, unless the Senate consents; and the Senate would not consent, unless the young man had clearly done something to merit the reward.

A case occurred a few years since, which goes to prove the truth of what I tell you. A meritorious lieutenant of the navy, who was entirely destitute of the influence of connexions, came under the displeasure of some of the powers about the department under which he served. His name was omitted in the nominations to the Senate, and juniors were promoted over his head. Unprotected, and supported only by the truth, this gentleman went to Washington, and laid his case before the Senators. He convinced them that justice had not been done him; and the executive, in order to get other nominations confirmed, was obliged not only to promote this gentleman, but to give him a commission that restored the rank he had lost. Here was a clear case of justice, in opposition to influence; for if the officer had been guilty of any offence, he was subject to a code of laws that, Heaven knows, is severe enough. If any man believes that such a system destroys discipline, let him go on board an American man-of-war, and examine for himself. In my opinion, it has a contrary effect, by placing inferiors less in the power of their immediate superiors, and by consequently rendering both parties equally watchful.

In relation to the more ordinary civil appointments, the executive of the United States adopts a sufficiently discreet and useful course. The situations are, in general, well filled, and such a thing as a sinecure does not exist in the whole government. The President is, in fact, so far removed from the familiar and personal interests of society, that it is not difficult for him, even in a country as democratic as this, to preserve a dignified moderation. One hears a great deal said, in the United States, of management and intrigue; but it is necessary to remember, that intrigue here, even when successful, does no more than a downright dogged power does elsewhere: and then it is always necessary to recollect, that the Americans, in complaining, compare themselves with the abstract right, and not with other people. Should one-tenth part of the executive abuses exist here that exist elsewhere, the world would ring with clamour.

You may form some idea of the truth of this opinion, by an anecdote I shall mention. A New-York merchant gravely assured me, that his countrymen were in a bad way; that corruption had made great strides among them; and that he saw the downfall of the nation in its advances. I begged he would mention a fact. Leading me into a corner, he solemnly assured me, in a half whisper, that he *knew*, of his own observation, that one of the clerks of the custom-house of that city was in the habit of taking fees that the law did not sanction. You may depend on it, Jules, I gave him a sharp look, to see that the fellow had no double meaning; and then, convinced of his sincerity, I thought it no more than humane to offer the consolation of assuring him that these things sometimes happened elsewhere. Now, is all this owing to simplicity, and a new state of society? It is a pity, then, it does not exist all over this continent. The President possesses the right to fill all vacancies that occur, during the recess of the Senate, by commissions that shall be valid until the termination of the next session, unless full appointments shall be sooner made. This power is in no danger of abuse, since the President himself can be removed with nearly the same ease as any other incumbent.

The authority of the President over the army and navy, though that of a general or an admiral, as well as of a civil magistrate, is always exercised by deputy.

The Secretaries of the two departments are his organs, and they sign the orders with their own names. Washington took the field, as President, to suppress the Pennsylvania insurrection; and, to his everlasting honour be it said, he effected his object without shedding one drop of human blood.

The President has a full, unequivocal power to pardon all criminals, except in cases of impeachment. It has been said (by Blackstone and Montesquieu) that this power is incompatible with the nature of a democratic government. I know no better answer to an argument than a fact, and the fact undeniably is, that the most democratic communities of the world exercise it with perfect safety. The mistake of these two writers only shows how very easy it is for the most acute minds to get so enveloped in prejudice, as in some measure to impair the faculties. The essence of the difference between a democracy and a despotism is not so much in the amount of the power wielded, as in the manner in which it is created.*

I believe I have now given you a hurried outline of the authority and office of the President of the

---

* It is surprising what vague and obstinate notions of government people acquire by habit. In America, the writer was several times asked how it was possible that one man could control the interests of a whole community; and in Europe, he has often been pressed to say whether there is any authority in the United States to repress the most common evils. If these worthy thinkers on civil polity would take the trouble to tax their intellects a little, they would see that necessity is a judicious legislator, and that no country can exist long, without such a state of things as shall render society reasonable, quiet, and secure. The great point of difference is in the forms by which its objects are effected. There is no doubt that one people can do things that would be fatal to the order of another (for a time at least) and it is quite certain that they who can get all that government aims at, in the cheapest and simplest manner, are the best off. The great desideratum is, to add security to freedom of personal efforts; and this is a point that varies in different situations of the world, just as much as intellect and intelligence themselves vary.

United States. He possesses a reasonable portion of power, but its exercise is balanced by a number of constitutional checks, and, what is not less available in the present state of the world, by the watchfulness and force of public opinion. Society must materially recede before this high functionary can easily abuse his trust; and when that happens, the Americans, in common with the rest of the world, must be content to return to the political condition from which all our ancestors emerged. It is important, also, to remember that the character, qualifications, and usefulness of a President, are pretty generally sifted to the bottom, before the individual reaches the station at all.

TO THE ABBATE GIROMACHI,

&c. &c.

Washington, ——

You inquire concerning the state of religion in the United States. I presume you ask the question in reference to its outward and visible signs, since it is not to be supposed that a layman, like myself, is sufficiently versed in its mysteries to go deeper than that which is apparent.

You know there is no establishment. Congress is prohibited by the constitution from creating one, and most (I believe all) of the State constitutions have the same provision. In point of fact, there is none whatever. The clergy, and all that pertains, therefore, to religion, are supported by voluntary contributions, or by endowments that have been made by devises, gifts, and other private means.

The first point to be considered, is the number and the nature of the sects. If the Presbyterians and Congregationalists, between whom there exist mere shades of difference in discipline and opinion, shall be considered as forming one sect, they are certainly the most numerous. It is computed that they posssess near three thousand congregations. The Baptists are known to have more than two thousand. Perhaps the Methodists rank next in numbers. The Protestant Episcopal church is greatly on the increase. I find, by the Ecclesiastical Register, that it contains ten bishops, and three hundred and ninety-four clergymen.* Most of the latter are settled, and many have two or three congregations under their charge. There are a good many Friends (Quakers)

---

* It may be interesting to those of a similar faith in England, to understand the constitution of this church in the United States. Where there are Episcopalians enough, the diocese is confined to a single State. But, as there are ten bishops, and twenty-four States, it is plain that several of the States are contained in one diocese. There are, in point of fact, however, eleven dioceses, that of Delaware being vacant. The highest spiritual authority known is, of course, a bishop. Priests and deacons being all the orders named in the Bible, are all the other orders known or used in America. The highest authority is exercised by the general convention. The general convention is composed of two bodies, a house of bishops, and a house of lay delegates. Each diocese has a convention for the regulation of its own affairs. The general convention consists of the bishops, who form the house of bishops, and of laymen, who are sent as delegates from the State convention. The object of this body is to promote harmony and uniformity of doctrine in the whole church. The State conventions contain the clergy of the diocese, and a lay delegation from each church. In both conventions, the clergy (or bishops, as the case may be) and the laymen vote separately, a majority of each being necessary to an ordinance. Clergymen are presented by their congregations, and bishops are elected by the conventions of the diocese, and are approved of by the house of bishops. There is no salary yet given to any bishop, though provisions to a reasonable amount are making for that object. At present, they are all rectors of churches. The oldest bishop for the time being, is called the presiding bishop, though he enjoys no exclusive authority. There have been, in all, twenty-one bishops of this church in the United States, and they hold their ordination

in Pennsylvania, New-Jersey, and New-York. The
two former States were originally settled by religionists of this persuasion. The Roman Catholics are
the most numerous in Maryland and Louisiana. The
first was a Roman Catholic colony, and the latter
has, as you know, been both French and Spanish.
The Floridas must also contain some Catholics.
Many of the Irish who come to this country, and
who are settled in the more northern States, are
also Catholics ; but, including all, I should not think
they rank higher, in point of numbers, than the sixth
or seventh sect, after allowing for all the subdivisions
among the Protestants themselves. There are some
Lutherans and Moravians, and a great variety of less
numerous or local sects.

The most important point that is proved by the
condition of this country, is the fact that religion can,
and does, exist as well without as with the aid of
government. The experiment has been tried here,
for two centuries, and it is completely successful. So
far from competition (if I may use so irreverent a
term on so grave a subject) weakening, it increases
its influence, by keeping zeal alive. While the Episcopalian clergyman sees the Presbyterian priest existing in his neighbourhood, and enjoying all the advantages that he himself enjoys, he is clearly obliged to
do one of two things ; either to abandon the race, or
to contend with watchfulness and care. Now, this
is exactly what is done here. The clergy are as
chary as women of their characters, for they are certain of being proved, not by tests of their own establishing, but by those established by their competitors.

from the archbishops of Canterbury and York, and from the
non-juring bishops of the Episcopal church of Scotland, jointly.

The law recognises these authorities to a certain extent, as
it does the authorities of all other churches. The Catholics
have their archbishops and bishops, the Methodists their bishops,
and the Presbyterians, Baptists, &c. &c., their own particular
forms of government.

You may be inclined to ask if such a rivalry does not lead to strife and ill blood? Just the contrary. Each party knows that he is to gain, or to lose influence, precisely as he manifests the practice of the doctrines he teaches: and that, I apprehend, so far as Christianity is concerned, is charity and forbearance. At all events, with now and then an insulated and rare exception, great apparent good-will and cordiality exist among the clergy of the different sects; and, I fancy, it is precisely for the reason that there is nothing to be gained, and a good deal to be lost, by a different line of conduct. This is considering the question solely on its temporal side, but you know I commenced with professing ignorance of the spiritualities.

Freedom of thought on matters of religion, is so completely a consequence of intellectual advancement, that it is impossible to prevent men who think much from doing one of two things; they either choose their own course, in secret, or they become indifferent to the subject altogether. I have always been of opinion that sects carry their articles of faith too far, since it is next to impossible to get two intellectual men to view any long series of metaphysical propositions in precisely the same light; and it would be better to leave them to the dictates of their own consciences, and to the lights of their own intelligence in lesser matters, after they are once fairly of a mind on the more material truths of their creed. This desirable object is obtained in the United States, to a certain degree, though not entirely, by allowing every man to choose his church, without attracting comment or censure. Charity is a consequence of such a state of things, at least that charity which manifests itself outwardly. The true object of religion is, to teach men the path to heaven, and that is an affair more affecting the individual than any body else. The moment society ceases to take the abso-

U 2

lute direction of the matter into its own hands, individuals interest themselves rather than lose the object; and, unless they do interest themselves, under any system, I believe we are taught to think that establishments will do them no great good.

Still society has a worldly interest in the existence of religion—granted. But if it can obtain its object without an establishment, of what use is the latter? It is true, one does not see as many churches in a given number of square miles in America, as in a given number of square miles in France or England: nor are there as many people to use them. In order to institute a fair comparison, all things must be considered. In the first place, I am of opinion that the Americans have more places of worship than twelve millions of people in any other country of the globe; and if the peculiar condition of the new States be considered, I believe they have, in point of moral truth, twice as many. I am quite willing to admit that the cheapness of construction, the freedom of opinion, and necessity itself, may all contribute to produce such a result, but I cannot see how this negative proof is to demonstrate that religion suffers from the want of an establishment. Let us examine the progress of the sects in a parish.

Ten miles square of wilderness is laid out in a township. Settlers come into it from all quarters, and of all denominations. The State has reserved a few hundred acres of land, perhaps, for the support of religion. The first thing commonly done, is to erect a shop for a blacksmith, and there is generally an inn near it, both being, of course, established in some convenient place. The school-house, or three or four of them, soon follow, and then people begin to think of a church. During the time that force for so important an object has been collecting, itinerant teachers, missionaries, &c., sent from the older parts of the country, have been in the habit of collecting the people in the school-houses, barns, or some other building, in order to keep alive the remembrance of holy things. I think it may be taken as a rule, that few settlements, in the more flourishing parts of the country, exist fifteen years without reaching the church-building age. Some do it much sooner, and others, certainly, require more time to mature their efforts. But the church (the building) must have a faith, as well as its builders? Not necessarily. Churches are frequently built and kept in abeyance for a maturity of opinions, though nineteen times in twenty the very disposition to erect a church pre-supposes an understanding as to the denomination it is to serve. In coming to this understanding, the minority are, of course, obliged to yield, which is precisely what they would have to do if there were an establishment. But an establishment would keep men from error. Let us see how the truth lies on this point. How do the establishments of Scotland, England, Denmark, France, and Turkey, for instance, agree? It is quite plain, I think, that establishments have nothing to do with truth; and is it not equally plain, by the example of this country, that they are not necessary to the existence of religion? But America was settled by religionists, and the spirit they infused in the country is not yet extinct! Admitted. Is there any more likelihood, had the ancestors of the Americans been Atheists, that the present generation would create an establishment, than that it would receive religion in sects? Did the apostles come into favour under an establishment? Or would not a country be more likely to receive religion in forms to suit tastes and opinions, than in any one form that could not suit all faculties, or appease all judgments? Here then, I think, we have some reason to believe that establishments neither introduce nor keep religion in a country. But let us go back to our settlement.

The church is built. and as the Presbyterians have given the most money, and are far the most numerous, the priest who is called is of their persuasion. Those who are firm in their own particular faith, cherish it in secret; and when the proper time comes, they join a congregation of their own people. They could do no more, if the church was built under an establishment. Those who are not very rigid in their faith, most probably drop quietly into the communion of the church they find so convenient. An establishment would compel them to do precisely the same thing. In the course of a few years more, however, the people begin to separate, or rather to follow their own opinions ; and then every thing settles down as quietly as men choose their wives, or make any other important selection that they have reason to think is particularly interesting to their individual happiness. But does not all this intermingling and indistinctness produce disorder and confusion ? Just the contrary. While society is in its infancy it produces harmony, by inducing mutual support; and it weakens prejudice, and is fatal to superstition, by bringing the former in subjection to all it wants to destroy it—familiarity : and by rendering the other obnoxious to the ridicule and exposed to the reason of competitors. It is a known fact, that a century ago, the American religionists were among the most bigoted of their respective sects ; and it is just as true now, that they have immensely improved, and that they are daily growing still more reasonable, as familiarity with each other teaches them how very little better any one man is than the rest of his fellow-creatures.

But it will become necessary, in time, to make some use of the land which has been reserved for the support of the gospel. How is this to be done in such a manner as not to give offence to the minority? You will recollect that this fund has been created in the most insensible manner, and not by the aid of any imposition that is felt by the citizen. It is not so much a measure of general policy, as one that is intended to aid, to a reasonable extent, the wishes of the majority. Were there Jews or Mahomedans enough in the land, to make such a measure necessary, I take it for granted, they would get their share. It is the great merit of this government, that it does not aim so much to satisfy theories as to produce wholesome practical results. It is the great fault of its enemies, that instead of looking at it as a government should be viewed, in its worldly and positive aspects, they are for ever endeavouring to find some inconsistency in theory which shall appease a sense of secret uneasiness, that is beginning to get a little too prevalent for their complacency, that it is a more enviable state of society than they wish to believe.

As respects the matter in question, the people of New-York (for it is altogether an affair of the individual States,) have seen they must do nothing, under the most favourable circumstances for doing a great deal for the support of religion, or they must incur the risk of invading some perfectly dormant principle of a bald theory. They give land, which is of no value at the time, leaving the people to dispose of it when it does become of value. We will suppose this reservation now to be worth a division. The inhabitants of the town are then required to make their election. Every congregation, which is in truth a congregation, gets its share, and there the business is disposed of. The infidel, or the man of indifference, or perhaps a solitary Catholic, gets nothing, it is true, for he does not want it. You will at once see that this sort of provision is of use only to those who go through the hardship of settling a town, since their successors may have different religious persuasions; but it is meant for the encouragement and consolation of those who do undergo the

privations incident to such a service. The best possible proof of the wisdom of the measure is, that it
does good, without doing the least harm to any body.
I can readily understand that they who have been
long accustomed to quarrel, and to see others quarrel
about the temporalities of churches, will find a thousand difficulties in disposing of such a grant as this I
have named; but fact is daily proving here that it
can be done, when men are once accustomed to meet
on such occasions in a spirit of amity, without any
difficulty at all.

I remember to have held a conversation with an
innkeeper, who resided within a few yards of an
edifice that was then in the course of erection as a
place of public worship. I asked him the denomination of the people to whom it belonged. His answer was, " The Presbyterians." " And you, you
are a Presbyterian, no doubt?" " No, I was baptized in the Episcopal church, and I must say, I like
it best after all." " Ah, then you have nothing to do
with the cost of building this house?" " I have paid
my share." " But how is this, you pay for the support of a church to which you do not belong?" " I
do as I please, and I please to help my neighbours,
who will help me in some other way, if not in this;
besides, they are Christians as well as myself: and
I mean to have a pew, and go and hear their parson
till I can hear one of my own church." " But you
may be converted?" " Well," he said, smiling, " then
I shall be a Presbyterian, and my wife and myself
will be of the same mind; we are not afraid of looking the truth in the face in America, let it come out
of what pulpit it may."

In fact, the utmost harmony and good-will prevails
among the different sects. Controversy is but little
known, though I have been present at a dispute of a
very remarkable character. The parties were a Baptist and an Universalist. They met in a field at an

appointed hour, and the ceremonial of the rencontre was arranged with as much precision as if they had met for a less pacific interview. They were to be placed so many feet asunder, in order that their voices should be audible. They were to speak alternately, and by the watch, so many minutes at a time; and each was to confine himself, according to an established protocol, to a certain set of opinions, during particular hours. The audience stood around as silent listeners.

It was a remarkable, and not an uninteresting scene. As you may suppose, the learning brought into the combat was none of the deepest, but the zeal and native shrewdness were great, and the discretion was admirable. I left the mooted point in as much doubt as I found it, though a great deal of absurdity was disposed of in the controversy, in a rough but sensible manner. This exhibition was, of course, as much of a novelty to the people of the country as it was to me.

I witnessed other scenes, that were alike impressive and beautiful. The Methodists have, at stated periods, what are called camp meetings. They assemble in thousands in some wood, and hold their religious festivals in a manner that is as striking by its peculiar simplicity, as it is touching by the interest and evident enjoyment they experience.

It is a fashion to ridicule and condemn these meetings, on the plea that they lead to excesses and encourage superstition. As to the former, the abuse is enormously exaggerated; though, beyond a doubt, there are individuals who attend them that would seek any other crowd to shield their vices; and as to the latter, the facts show, that while new and awakened zeal, in ignorant persons, frequently breaks out in extravagance and folly, they pass away with the exciting cause, and leave behind them tender consciences and a chastened practice. What are the

weaknesses of these men, to those that are exhibited
in countries where faith is fettered by the law? Or,
if you maintain an establishment, and let men follow
their private opinions, in what does America differ
from other countries, except in things that are entirely
dependent on the peculiar temporal condition of the
republic, and which could not be avoided, if the citizens were all in full communion with the church of
Rome itself?

It is a mistake to believe that the liberality on religious subjects, which certainly exists to so eminent
a degree in this country, is the effect of there being
no establishment. On the contrary, the fact that
there is no establishment is owing to the liberal institutions, and to the sentiments of the people. You
will remember, that the same political right to create
establishments is to be found in the State governments,
here, as is to be found any where else. *All* power
that can belong to governments, and which has not
been ceded to the United States, is the property of
the States themselves, in their corporate capacities.
It is true that most of them have decreed, in their
constitutions, that no religious tests shall be known;
but it is necessary to remember who have framed
these imperative and paramount ordinances. The
powers, too, that decreed these limitations can change
them. But let us examine into the actual state of the
law on this interesting subject.

The provision contained in the constitution of the
United States is altogether prohibitory. It goes to
say, that the government of the confederacy shall pass
no law to create a religious establishment, or to pro-
hibit the free exercise of religion. It is contained in
an amendment, and is embodied in a paragraph which
exposes rather a declaration of the limits of congres-
sional power, than any concession of power itself.
The object of this amendment was unquestionably to
afford a clearer evidence of the public mind, and to

set at rest for ever any questions which, by constructions of any previously-conceded rights, might by
possibility arise on matters of such importance. Still
the declaration that Congress shall not have power
to do this or that thing, only leaves the individual
States more unequivocally in possession of the right
to do it, since they possess all the rights of government except those conceded to the Union.

New-England was settled by the Puritans. Whatever might have been the other good qualities of these
zealots, religious liberality was not one of their vir-
tues. It argues a somewhat superficial knowledge
of the subject to contend that the Americans owe all
their mental advancement, and freedom from prejudices, to the circumstance that they came into the
country as reformers. It would be more true to say,
that they came as dissentients; but though dissent
may, it does not necessarily, infer liberality. The fact
is, that no country ever possessed a more odious and
bigoted set of laws, on the subject of conscience, than
those first enacted by the Puritans. Independently
of the little favour that was extended to witchcraft,
it was made death for a Quaker to enter several of
their colonies! This spirit, which they brought with
them from England, was part of that noble and much-
vaunted mental gift that the Americans received from
the mother country. Fortunately, they had wisdom
enough left to establish schools and colleges; and
although it is quite probable that many worthy sectarians, who aided in this labour, thought they were
merely fortifying their exclusive doctrines, the result
has shown that they then took the very measure that
was likely to introduce liberality and promote Christian charity in their land.

The Quakers themselves, though less sanguinary,
for they did not deal in death at all, were not much
more disposed to the intercourse than their eastern
brethren. The Catholics in Maryland enacted the

laws that Catholics are fond of adopting, and, in short, genuine, religious liberality was only to be found in those colonies where the subject was thought to be of so little interest as not to invite bigotry. Out of this state of things the present rational, just, charitable, novel, and, so far as man can judge, religious, condition of society, has grown.

The unavoidable collision of sects has no doubt contributed to the result. It was not in nature to embitter life by personal and useless conflicts, and collected force did not exist in situations to produce combined oppositions. The Puritans had it all in their own way in New-England, until time had been given for reason to gather force: and, in the other colonies, adventitious circumstances aided to smother discussions. Liberality in politics, in some degree, drew religious freedom in its train; and when the separation from England occurred, the public mind was prepared to admit of great equality of rights in all things. Slavery, which was certainly retained, was retained much more from necessity than from any other cause.

Still the advancement of thought in America was rather gradual than sudden. Many of the original provisions of the States, on the subject of religion, imply a timid and undecided policy. In New-Jersey no *Protestant can be denied* any civil right on account of religion. This is clearly a defensive enactment. In Pennsylvania, Mississippi, and Tennessee, a belief in God, and a future state of rewards and punishments, is necessary to hold office. In North Carolina, no person who *denies the truth* of the *Protestant religion*, or the divine authority of the Old and New Testament, was capable of holding office. Many of these provisions have been changed, though some of them still remain. There is scarcely a year passes, in which some law, that has been a dead letter, is not repealed in some one of the States, in order to bring the theory of the government more in unison with the practice. I believe I have quoted, above, all the States in which any thing approaching to religious tests has existed, within the last ten years. Massachusetts has certainly altered its constitution since that period; and a law disfranchising the Jews has just been repealed in the State of Maryland, which you know was originally a Catholic colony.

In New-Hampshire, the constitution *authorizes* the legislature to make provision for the support of *Protestant* ministers; and in Massachusetts, the same duty is *enjoined.* The practice is simply this. An assessment is laid on all the inhabitants according to their estates. It is, like all other assessments in this country, exceedingly light, as its amount is regulated by the people themselves, through their immediate representatives. If a Baptist, for instance, resides in a parish where there is no Baptist church, he is at liberty to prove that he has paid the assessment to a Baptist church any where else; but should he not be disposed to take this trouble, the money is paid to the town collector, who gives it to the church nearest his place of residence, I believe. A similar practice prevailed not long since in Connecticut; but, as I have already said, gradual changes are making, and it is a little difficult to get at the precise conditions of the laws of so many different communities, that are fearlessly adapting their institutions to the spirit of the age.

In Maryland, Virginia, North Carolina, and Tennessee, ministers of the gospel are not eligible to the State legislatures. In South Carolina, Kentucky, and Mississippi, they can be neither governors nor legislators. In Missouri, they can fill no other civil office, but that of justices of the peace. In New-York, Delaware, and Louisiana, they can hold no civil offices at all. The constitution of the United States, and of all the other States, I believe, are silent on the matter; and, of course, clergymen can serve in any situation to which they may happen to be called. In all cases, I understand, the construction put on these regulations is applicable only to men in the actual exercise of clerical functions. The opinions of the whole nation are directly opposed to the union of civil and religious duties in the same person.

I have already told you, and I wish to repeat it, as an important fact that is always to be remembered, that, considering their scattered condition and circumstances, the people of this country manifest great zeal and interest in behalf of religion: I honestly think more than any other nation I know, and I believe it is simply because they are obliged to depend solely on themselves for its comforts and security. Perhaps the activity of the nation has its influence on this as on other things. Mind, I do not say that we see spires and holy places as often here as in Europe: if we did, America would contain twenty times as many places of worship as the largest empire we have, being, Russia excepted, twenty times as large; and the State of New-York alone, with 1,750,000 souls, (1828) would possess two-thirds as many churches as England with her twelve or fourteen millions of people.

English writers have not been ashamed to dwell on the comparative scarcity of churches in this country, compared with those in their own, as if the circumstance afforded any argument of a want of religion in the people. They might just as well quote the fact that there were not as many tombstones, to prove the same thing; or the American might make the circumstance that this country possesses more trees than England, a matter of moral exultation.

You would be astonished to witness the perfect liberality between the sects, which has grown up under this state of things. In the first place, there is nothing temporal to quarrel about, and the clergy are driven to their bibles for their influence and power. I have asked several members of Congress how many Catholics there were in that body, and nobody knew. I once asked an individual, in the interior of New-York (and in a thriving and beautiful village,) to what denomination a certain person we had just left belonged. "He is an Episcopalian," was the answer. This was disputed by a third person present. Proof was then adduced to show which was right. All parties agreed that the individual in question was a strictly religious man. One insisted that he had seen him commune the preceding Sunday in the Episcopal church. "What of that?" returned the other; "and I have seen his wife commune among the Presbyterians; and every body knows that she and all her family are Episcopalians." But every body did not know any such thing, for the other disputant maintained exactly the converse of the proposition. An umpire was chosen in the street. This worthy citizen "really did not know, but he thought that man and wife were very pious people! Stop," he continued, as he was coolly walking away, "you are right, John; Mr. —— is a Presbyterian, for I paid him the pew money last fall myself; and he would not have collected for the Episcopalians." But even *this* was disputed, and so, determined to settle the point, I went and asked the individual himself. He was a Presbyterian. "But you sometimes commune with the Episcopalians?" "Often." "And your wife?" "Is an Episcopalian." "And your children?" "We endeavour to make them Christians, without saying much of sects; when they are old enough, they will choose for themselves." "But which church do they go to?" "Sometimes to one, and sometimes to the other." "But they are baptized?" "Certainly." "And by which clergyman?" "By the Episcopalian; because my church does not deny the validity of his ordination, though my wife's church disputes a little

X 2

the validity of the ordination of the Presbyterian."
"And your wife, what does she think about it herself?" "I believe she is of opinion that there is a
good deal more said about it than is necessary." And
there the matter rested. Now this may, according to
some people's opinion, be dangerous intercourse, but,
on the whole, I am inclined to think Christianity is
the gainer.

Religion is kept as distinct as possible from the
State. It is known that Mr. Adams, the President
just elected, is an Unitarian; a persuasion that is
repugnant to most Christian sects, and yet you see
that he is in the chair. People at a distance would
infer indifference to the subject of religion from such
an excess of liberality, but the fact is, the most zealous religionist in this country knows that the salvation of Mr. Adams' soul is a matter of more moment
to himself than to any body else, and that if he be in
error, it is misfortune enough, without condemning
him to a worldly persecution. Besides, they have
sagacity enough to know that there is no more infallible way to give strength to any party that cannot be
positively crushed, than by giving it importance and
energy by resistance.

The sheriff of the city of New-York, an officer
elected by the people, was, a few years ago, a Jew!
Now all the Jews in New-York united, would not
probably make three hundred voters. Some kind-
hearted people got up a society to convert the Jews
there, a short time since; and a notice soon appeared
in a paper inviting the Jews to meet to concert
means of converting the Christians.

Notwithstanding all this, the country is as much,
or more, a Protestant and Christian country than any
other nation on earth. I merely state a simple fact,
on which you are at liberty to reason at pleasure.
The sects are about as numerous as they are in the
mother country, and all that one hears concerning

Thumpers and Dunkers, and other enthusiasts, is grossly caricatured. They exist, when they do exist at all, as insulated and meagre exceptions; and it is odd enough, that perhaps half of these fantastical sects have been got up by emigrants from disciplined Europe, instead of being the natural offspring of the liberal institutions of the country itself. There is no doubt that many people come from our side of the ocean with strange notions of liberty and equality, and that they either quarrel with the Americans for not being as big fools as themselves, and then set to work, in order to raise up creeds and political doctrines that they fondly hope will elevate man far above any thing heretofore known. In the mean time, the natives go on in their common sense and practical way, and say as little as possible about liberty, equality, or bigotry, and contrive to be the freest and the happiest, as they will shortly be, in my poor opinion, the wealthiest and most powerful nation of the globe, let other people like the prediction as they may.

I shall close this letter with giving you an account of one sect, that is as remarkable for its faith as for its practices. I mean the Shaking Quakers. I have been at three of the establishments of these people, viz. Hancock (in Massachusetts,) and Lebanon and Niskayuna (in New-York.) I believe there is still another establishment, in one of the south-western States. The whole number of the sectarians is, however, far from great, nor is it likely to increase, since their doctrine denies the legitimacy of matrimony, or any of its results. There may be a thousand or fifteen hundred of them altogether.

The temporalities of the Shakers are held in common. They are not an incorporated company, but confidence is reposed in certain trustees, who are selected as managers and guardians of all their real estates, goods and chattels. They are an orderly, industrious sect, and models of decency, cleanliness, and of morality too, so far as the human eye can penetrate. I have never seen, in any country, villages so neat, and so perfectly beautiful, as to order and arrangement, without, however, being picturesque or ornamented, as those of the Shakers. At Hancock, the gate-posts of the fences are made of white marble, hewn into shape and proportions. They are manufacturers of various things, and they drive a considerable trade with the cities of New-York, Albany, and Boston. They are renowned retailers of garden-seeds, brushes, farming utensils, &c. &c.

Though men and women, who, while living in the world, were man and wife, are often to be found as members of these communities, the sexes live apart from each other. They have separate dormitories, separate tables, and even separate doors by which to enter the temple.

But it is to the singular mode of worship of these deluded fanatics, that I wish to direct your attention. You know, already, that no small portion of their worship consists in what they term the "labour of dancing." Their founder has contrived to lay his finger on one or two verses of the Old Testament, in which allusion is made to the custom of the Jews in dancing before the ark : and, I believe, they also place particular stress on the declaration of Solomon, when he says, "there is a time for all things," among which, dancing is enumerated. It is scarcely necessary to say, that none but the most ignorant, and, perhaps, the weakest-minded men, can join such a sect from motives of conscience. I saw several negroes among them.

I went to attend their worship at Niskayuna. It was natural to suppose that their dancing was a sort of imitation of that of the dervishes, in which enthusiasm is the commencement, and exhaustion the close. On the contrary, it was quite a matter of grave preparation. The congregation (the Shakers) entered the meeting by different doors at the same time, the elders of the two sexes leading the advance, and one following the other in what is called single file. The men arranged themselves on one side of the room, and the women on the other. Their attire was rigidly simple, and fastidiously neat. It was made nearly in the fashion of the highly respectable sect of Friends, though less rich in material. When silence was obtained, after the movement of the *entrée*, the whole group, who were formed in regular lines, commenced singing certain spiritual songs of their own composition (I believe) to lively tunes, and with a most villanous nasal cadency. These songs were accompanied by a constant swinging of the bodies; and, from this commencement, I expected the access of the infatuated worship would grow by a regular increase of excitement. On the contrary, the songs were ended tranquilly, and others were sung, and always with the same quiet termination. At length, one of the elders gravely said, " Let us labour," just as you hear priests say from their desks, " Let us pray." The men then proceeded with gravity to take off their coats, and to suspend them from pegs; after which they arranged themselves in rows on one side of the room, the women occupying the other in the same order. Those who did not join the sets, lined the walls, and performed the duties of musicians with their voices. At the commencement of the song, the dancers moved forward, in a body, about three feet each, turned, shuffled, and kept repeating the same evolutions during the whole time of this remarkable service. It is scarcely possible to conceive any thing more ludicrous, and yet more lamentable. I felt disposed to laugh, and yet I could scarcely restrain my tears. I think, after the surprise of the ludicrous had subsided, that the sight of so much miserable infatuation left a deep and melancholy regret on the mind.

They appear to have an idea that a certain amount of this labour is requisite to salvation, for I learned that many of the elders had reached perfection, and that they had long since ceased to strive to reach heaven by pirouetting.

Now the laws of the different States where the small fragments of this sect exist, are far too wise and too humane to give their deluded followers any trouble. They are inoffensive and industrious citizens, and, in one or two instances, the courts have interpreted the laws as humanely in their favour as circumstances would reasonably allow. It is plain that the true bond of their union is the effect which concerted action and strict domestic government produce on the comforts of the grossly ignorant; but as the class of the very ignorant is quite limited in this country, and is daily getting to be comparatively still less numerous, there is no fear that this, or any other religious sect that is founded altogether on fanaticism and folly, will ever arrive to the smallest importance.

TO THE PROFESSOR CHRISTIAN JANSEN,

&c. &c.

Washington, ——

—You know not what you ask! I have already sent you an imperfect account (I, must confess) of the jurisprudence of the United States, and now you ask me for what you are pleased to call an outline of its civil and criminal law. Do you know there are four-and-twenty States, one district, and four territories in this country, and that each of them has its own laws, varying in some particulars of form and of policy from those of all the rest? My answer shall, therefore, be very short; nor should it be given at all, did I not know that various absurdities are circulated in Europe, on this very matter, by men who travel here, and who rarely possess a knowledge of, or give themselves the trouble to inquire into, the true condition of the society, whether considered in reference to its conventional tone, or to its positive institutions.

The criminal law of the United States is more sanguinary than that of any particular State. Piracy, treason, murder, robberies of the mail, in which the life of the person in charge is jeoparded, and a few ther offences, are punished with death. Crimes committed on the high seas, in certain reservations, such as forts, light-houses, &c., are also punished by the laws of the confederation. Smaller offences are punished by fines, or imprisonment, or by both. Some of the States inflict death for a variety of offences, especially the slave-holding communities; others again are very tender of human life. In New-York, murder, arson, if the building be an inhabited dwelling, and treason, can be punished with death. All crimes that are exclusively military, are punished by the military code of the general government.

The great fault in the exercise of the criminal law, in most, if not all, of the States of America, is a false humanity. The people have heard a great deal, and a great deal justly, of the useless severity of the laws in many European countries, and they very naturally turn with horror from a system, that they are fond of thinking is unnecessary to a nation in their own condition. I cannot say I agree with them. As there is less temptation to crime in the United States, than in any other country, and, as more care is taken to prevent it by the use of education, and the entire absence of legal monopolies, it is as unwise as it is unnecessary to reject those means of preserving the order of society which the experience of all ages has shown to be salutary.

The first and great duty of every government is to remove, as far as possible, all temptations to crime. This is to be done by the admission of equal rights, and by as general a diffusion, as possible, of moral influences. But after these solemn and imperative duties are performed, little can be said against a stern and wholesome exercise of justice. Punishment, in order to be impressive, should be prompt and infallible. The indiscreet use of the prerogative of mercy is one of the great errors of American criminal policy; though it is said that necessity often compels its exercise, as the public penitentiaries cannot hold the convicts that are accumulated by time, and which embrace crimes that elsewhere would sweep the offender from the earth. I should think this argument must prove some fault in the criminal code. It is true, that an immense proportion of the convicts are foreigners, or of the unfortunate race of blacks: but still it is necessary to legislate for things as they are; and if rogues can emigrate from Europe, and a class of ignorant and hapless wretches exist in the State to swell the amount of crime, I should think both policy and justice require that a suitable provision should be made to meet the evil.

I was particularly struck with the fact, that a report of the superintendents of the New-York State Prison, commenced with premises like this: "As the object of all punishment is the reformation of the offender;" now I take it, that the object of the punishments which communities inflict, is for no such purpose. Society punishes for its own protection, though reformation *may*, and when practicable without losing sight of the great and principal cause of legal punishments, it *should* ever be considered as a collateral good, to be effected by the same means. But it is dangerous, indeed, to assume that punishment has no other motive than reformation. If this be true, why do we execute for murder, or why are so many people taught to believe that He who holds the destinies of the universe has decreed that sinners shall expiate their offences in a lasting condemnation? It is very true, that as we can understand only our relations to the Deity, without comprehending the relations which the Deity holds to us, it may be dangerous, or even impious, to pretend to deduce any reasoning from the great laws of God, which shall be strictly applicable to the obligations which man owes to his fellows. But we all know that the world does not graduate punishments of offences against society for the purpose of amending the criminal, though we may all feel that an object so humane should not be neglected when good opportunities for effecting it are afforded.

America is peculiarly placed as respects crime. It is a young, vigorous, abundant, and a highly commercial country, in which moveable property abounds, and in which it is remarkably exposed to be pilfered by the absence of a rigid police; a sort of protection that is not very suitable to the habits and opinions of its people. The great and increasing intercourse with an old nation, in which crime abounds to an extraordinary degree, and the prodigious facilities of a communication which every day is rendering still more easy, tempt rogues from the mother country to shift their scene of action. Thus, while the country has been acting on a criminal law that is adapted, perhaps well enough, to the degree of temptation which exists in the nation itself, its cities are beginning to swarm with fugitive felons from England, who, under favour of a common language, not only practise all their artifices with equal dexterity as at home, but, what is far worse, who bring corruption into the land, and lead hundreds of youths into the paths of vice. But this is an evil that will correct itself, though I think the good people, especially of the large towns, are little aware that their excessive lenity is not only mistaken on abstract principles, but that it is peculiarly wrong in a nation, that, however it may go to the root of crime by diminishing temptation as much as possible, must still, for a long time, be exposed to a prodigious importation of vice.

The law of real property, in the United States, is a good deal the same as that of England. Entails are, however, destroyed every where, and the doctrine of descent has, in many of the States, been roughly handled. In New-York—I quote this State oftenest, as the most populous and the most important, though you are to understand that the laws of New-York are strictly applicable only to itself, while they are commonly founded on principles that are general—in New-York, the *father* is the next heir of a child who leaves no issue. This is a wise, a humane, and a natural departure from the dictum of the common law, and it does much good in a country like this. The next of kin inherit, after the father, in equal portions, without distinction of age or sex. The widow is entitled to one-third of the personal estate of the husband, and to the use of one-third of the real estate during life. The husband is owner of all the personals of the wife, and he is the tenant by the courtesy of her real estate, according to the provisions of the English common law. There is, however, a good deal of difference in the rights of husbands and wives in the different States. In some, the property of the woman is much more respected than in others.

The party in possession of property in fee, can devise it, without restriction, to whom he pleases. This is, I think, a wiser provision than the law of France, which renders natural descent, to a certain extent, unavoidable; but the law of France I take to be an enactment that is intended to do away with the custom of entails, which had gotten such deep root in Europe. Rich men, here, often give more to their sons than to their daughters; though it is very common for men of small fortunes to make the daughters independent at the expense of the sons. Of course, any irregularity or alienation of property from the descent (or *ascent*) prescribed by the law, must be made by will.*

Marriage is, of course, altogether a civil contract. Its forms are, however, more or less artificial, according to the policy of particular States. In some, bans are necessary; in others, evidence that would establish any other contract would establish that of marriage. As a breach of the marriage contract is always criminal, the law requires, in cases of indictments for bigamy, rather more positive testimony than would be required in those of inheritance and legitimacy. Thus, a child would be considered born in wedlock, in many States, under the reputation of matrimony, though a man would scarcely be punished for bigamy, without direct evidence of the two contracts. The policy of the different States, however, varies so much, to suit the particular conditions of society, that no general rule can be laid down. In portions of the country recently settled, it is the practice to make the contract before a justice of the peace, as in many parts of New-York; but then, a justice of peace has no more power to celebrate a marriage than any other man. It is thought that his testimony, as

---

* The writer is hourly acquiring evidence of the gross ignorance concerning the United States, which travellers are importing into Europe, where, Heaven knows, enough has long existed. He has lately read a book, written by an Englishman, in a sufficiently amicable spirit, which says that a gentleman of New-York, who is the proprietor of a large estate (40,000 acres) is obliged by law to let it pass to his nephews and nieces! It is possible that, in the case in question, a reversionary interest might have been given by some former owner in fee, to certain nephews and nieces; but any owner in fee (of mature age) can devise to whom he pleases. The law allows devises to go as far as all people actually living, and to twenty-one years after, by fixing age, sex, or any other qualification by which the party to inherit can be accurately distinguished.

a public officer, is more imposing than that of a private individual, and these people always attach high importance to legal rank.   People of any condition are always (unless in extraordinary exceptions) married by clergymen.

I can tell you little more that is distinctive in American law, without dealing in exceptions ; since, though the governing principles are always the same, the policy of one State differs so much from that of another.

TO SIR EDWARD WALLER, BART.

&c. &c.

New-York, ——

It is an age since I wrote to any of the club. But though my pen has been necessarily quiet, the intervening time has not been unemployed. In the interval, I have run over an immense surface in the southern and western States. It would be idle to attempt to describe all I have seen, and there would be the constant danger of leading you astray by exceptions, should I descend into detail. Still, as there is a great deal that is distinctive, I shall endeavour to convey to you some general ideas on the subject.

The first, and by far the most important feature, which distinguishes these States from their northern sisters, is slavery. Climate and productions induce some other immaterial differences. The laws, usages, institutions, and political opinions, with such exceptions as unavoidably grow out of states of society marked by such distinctions as the use or the absence of domestic slaves, are essentially the same.

There is a broad, upland region, extending through the interior of Virginia, the two Carolinas, and Georgia, where slaves are used, more as they were formerly used in New-York and in the eastern States, than as they are now used in the other sections of the States named. That is to say, the farmer is the master of three or four labourers, and works in the field at their sides, instead of being a planter, who keeps a driver, and what are called gangs. Tennessee, and Kentucky also, with some exceptions, employ the negroes in a similar manner; while on the Mississippi, the Gulf of Mexico, and along the coast of the Atlantic, as far north as the Chesapeake, slavery exists much in the same forms as it is found in the English West India islands.

The country, on the whole coast of the United States, until one gets far northward and eastward, is low and champaign. It is healthy, or not, according to the degrees of latitude, and to local situation. The uplands are invariably salubrious. There is no region on earth more beautiful, or more fertile, than large parts of Virginia, Kentucky, and Tennessee. There is also much barren, or otherwise little valuable land, in the former State, as there is in the neighbouring States of North and South Carolina.

South Carolina and Louisiana are the only two States which, at the census of 1820, contained more blacks than whites. The former had 231,812 white inhabitants, and 258,497 blacks; leaving a balance of 26,685 in favour of the latter. Of the blacks, 251,783 were slaves, being 19,971 more slaves than whites. Louisiana had, at the same time, 73,383 whites, and 79,540 blacks; of the latter, 69,064 were slaves, being rather fewer slaves than whites. All people having black blood are enumerated as blacks. Georgia is the next considerable community, which has so large a proportion of blacks. It had, in 1820, 189,566 whites, and 151,439 blacks. Vir-

ginia had 603,008 whites, and 462,042 blacks; and
North Carolina, 419,200 whites, and 219,629 blacks,
or nearly two whites to one black. In Kentucky
there were 434,644 whites to 129,491 blacks; and
in Tennessee, which is much disposed to the habits
of a free State, there were 339,727 whites to 82,826
blacks; a proportion of the latter not greater than
what formerly existed in New-York and New-Jersey.
Most of the blacks, in all these States, are slaves.

In 1790, there were 757,208 blacks in the United
States; in 1800, 1,001,729; in 1810, 1,377,810; in
1820, 1,764,836. By making premises of these facts,
and taking the past rate of increase as a rule for the
future, it would be found that there are now (1828)
about 2,000,000 of blacks in the United States. In
1820, there were 233,400 *free* blacks in the United
States. As the free blacks do not increase at the
same rate as the slaves, this number cannot have
accumulated in a full proportion, by natural causes.
But emancipation has been busy since. New-York,
alone, has liberated more than 10,000 slaves since
1820. We will therefore assume that natural increase and emancipation have kept the free blacks
up to the level of the increase of the whole number.
This would leave us something like 1,750,000 for the
whole amount of slaves in the country, at the present moment (1828.) This result is probably not far
from the truth. You will see, however, that my
premises are a little faulty, because the increase of
blacks between the years 1800 and 1810 was a good
deal greater, in comparison with whole numbers, than
between 1810 and 1820. This fact is owing to the abo-
lition of the slave trade, which occurred between the
two censuses of 1800 and of 1810, and which being
known by a prospective law, induced extraordinary
importations. Thus the increase between 1800 and
1810 was 376,581, whereas between 1810 and 1820
it was only 387,026, although there was so much

larger a stock to increase from. Still, I think the amount of slaves cannot be much short of the number I have named. The white population, in the whole country, is now about 10,000,000. Of this number, however, at least 6,000,000, and probably a great many more, are in the free States. If we put the entire white population of the slave-holding States at 3,500,000, we shall probably give them quite as many as they possess. This would be making two whites to one slave in those States, and it is probably as near the truth as one can get at this distance of time from the census. But it has already been seen, that in many of these States the proportion of blacks is much larger than in others; South Carolina actually possessing more slaves than whites; and Tennessee having four whites to one black. There are, again, districts in these very States, in which the proportion of the whites to the blacks, and of the blacks to the whites, is even still greater.

In addition to these facts, it may be well to state that the whole white population of the country is known to have increased faster than that of the coloured, though the black population of the southern, or slave-holding States, is thought to have increased a little faster than that of the whites.

In considering the question of slavery, as now existing in the United States, the subject naturally divides itself into the past, the present, and the future. It has been often said, that a people, claiming to be the freest of the earth, ought to have brought their practice more in conformity with their professions, and to have abolished slavery at the time they declared their independence. There are many unanswerable reasons to this allegation; or reasons that will be deemed unanswerable, by that portion of mankind who regard life as it actually exists, in its practical aspects and influences. There is not now, nor has there ever been since the separation of the colonies from the mother country, any power to emancipate the slaves, except that which belongs to their masters. This reason might satisfy most practical men of the impossibility of instantly achieving so desirable an object. That sort of humanity, which regards the evils of a distant and alien people, and which, at the same time, turns a cold eye on the sufferings of those at hand, is, to say the least, as useless as it is suspicious. There is scarcely a nation in Europe, if, indeed, there be one, that has not a proportion of its population, that is quite equal to the proportion the slaves of America bear to the whites, which is not quite as low in moral debasement, the name of liberty alone excepted, and which, as a whole, endure much more of physical suffering than the negroes of America.

The condition of the American slave varies, of course, with circumstances. In some few portions of the country, he is ill dealt by. In most districts his labour is sufficiently light, his clothing is adapted to the climate, and his food is, I believe, every where abundant. The strongest evidence, after all, which can be given, that the amount of animal suffering among the American slaves is not great, (there are exceptions, of course,) is the fact that they are a lighthearted and a laughing race. I am very ready to grant that ignorance, and absence of care, are apt to produce hilarity, and that some of the most degraded and least intellectual people of the earth, are among the gayest; but I believe that it is a rule in nature, that where there is much animal suffering there is an animal exhibition of its existence.

There is still a higher, and a very numerous class of American slaves, who are far better instructed, better clothed, and better fed, and who are altogether a superior race to the lowest class of the European peasants. I mean the domestic servants, and those who labour as mechanics and artisans.

While on this branch of the subject, I shall take occasion to say, that yearly meliorations in the condition of the slaves (and of the blacks generally,) are taking place in some one part of the country or other. Several unjust and exceedingly oppressive laws, that were the fruits of colonial policy, have been repealed, or greatly qualified; and public opinion is making a steady advance to the general improvement, and, I think, to the final liberation of the race. Although these changes are not as rapid as they might be, even with a due regard to policy, and far less rapid than most good men could wish, it is a course that is more likely to be attended with less positive injury to the race of beings that true philanthropy would so gladly serve, than one as headlong and as ill-advised as mere declaimers and pretenders would dictate.

I think no candid man will deny the difficulty of making two or three millions of people, under any circumstances, strip themselves, generally of half their possessions, and, in many instances, of all. There are few nations in Europe, at this hour, in which the poorer classes would not be relieved from serious pressure, would they, who have the means, tax themselves to discharge the debts which are the causes of so much of the heavy impositions of their respective governments. Now, this would be a measure that would do good to millions, great and almost inconceivable good, and harm to none but to them that paid; whereas, a sudden, or any very violent emancipation of the slaves of America, would ruin those who did it, and scarcely do less than ruin half, or even more, of those in whose behalf the charitable act would be performed. Let me be understood. I do not mean to say that much more than is done might not be done, prudently, and with safety; nor do I mean to say that most of those who find themselves in possession of a species of property, that they have been educated to think a natural and just acquisition, think much of the matter at all; but what I would wish to express is, that they who do think calmly and sincerely on the subject, see and feel all these difficulties, and that they weaken efforts that would otherwise produce an effect more visible than the sentiment which I think is silently working its way throughout the whole of this nation.

In considering the question of American slavery, in reference to the past, it is plain that Europe has been an equal participator in all that there is of shame, or sin, in the transaction. There can be no charge more vapid and unjust, than for an European to reproach the American with the existence of slavery in his country. That the American is in the enjoyment of greater power to do natural justice than the European, is just as true, as that, in most things, he does it. That slavery is an evil of which the great majority of the Americans themselves, who have no present agency in its existence, would gladly be rid of, is manifest, since they have abolished it in so many States already; but that it is an evil not to be shaken off by sounding declarations, and fine sentiments, any man, who looks calmly into the subject, must see. But so far as a comparison between Europe and America is concerned, let us, for an instant, examine the exceedingly negative merit of the former. Is it not a fact that the policy of all America was for more than a century controlled by Europe, and was not this scourge introduced under that policy? Has that policy, in Europe, been yet abandoned? Let us take the two most prominent nations boldly to task at once; does England or France, for instance, at this moment, own a foot of land on earth, where black slaves can be profitable, and where they do not use them?* It is absurd for France, or for England, to

---

* It is well known that a negro would be next to nothing in the Canadas, &c.

say, we have no slaves in our respective kingdoms, properly so called, when every body knows that the one is at this moment filled with white beggars, and the other with paupers who are supported by the public purse, and both for the simple reason that they are overflowing with population. It is true, that two centuries ago, when they had more room, they did not import negroes from Guinea; but it is, also, just as true, that they sent their ships to convey them to colonies which are situated in climates where they might repay them for their trouble. It is as puerile as it is unjust, therefore, for these two countries, (most others might be included,) to pretend to any exclusive exemption from the sin or the shame of slavery.

The merit of Christendom on the subject of the wrongs of Africa, is, at the best, but equivocal. Yet, such as it is, the meed is better due to the United States than to any other nation. They were the first to abolish the trade in human flesh, though the nation, of all others, that might most have reaped that short-sighted, but alluring profit, which tempted men to the original wrong. Had not the Congress of the United States abolished this trade, there is no doubt millions of acres might have sooner been brought into lucrative cultivation, and the present generation at least would have been millions the richer. The whole body of the whites might have become a set of taskmasters to gather wealth from the labour of the blacks. No doubt true policy dictated the course they have taken, and they have but a very negative merit in pursuing it: still it should always be remembered, that what has been done, was done by those who might have profited in security by a different course, and by those, too, who had been educated in the shackles of a deeply-rooted prejudice on the subject.

In reproaching the Americans with incongruity

between their practices and their professions, two or three points are very necessary to be remember-ed. In the first place, it is not true, as respects near 7,000,000 of the ten that comprise their population; for *they* have given freedom and (essentially) equal rights to those blacks who remain among them. The very condensation of the interests of slavery adds, however, to the difficulty of the subject, since it makes the loss fall on a comparatively reduced num-ber. The northern men had to do one of two things; to separate their fortunes from a portion of their countrymen, to whom they were bound by the ties of fellowship, blood, common interests, and common descent, or submit to be parties to an union in which some of the other parties were slave-holders. They were, in fact, slave-holders themselves, at the time of the compact, so that it would have been absurd to be very fastidious in the matter; and there would have been but little wisdom in rejecting so much positive good, in order to assert an abstract principle, that could be attended with no single practical benefit. The southern States would have held their slaves, had the northern refused to have joined them to make one nation; and, so far as humanity is concerned, the negroes would not have been so well off, since they now feel the influence of northern policy, while war and bloodshed, and all the evils of a dangerous rivalry that would have arisen between men whom nature had made friends and brothers, are avoided. In short, this is a reproach against the northern man, that is more likely to be made by those who view the Union, and the continued harmony which pervades these vast regions, with unquiet jealousy, than by any reasoning and practical philanthropist.

As to the southern man himself, he is placed, like so many nations of other quarters of the globe, in an unfortunate predicament, that time and society, and all the multiplied interests of life, render so difficult

to change. The profession of the southern man is unquestionably that of equal rights ; and it is undeniable
that he holds the black in slavery : but this does not
involve quite so great an absurdity as one would at
first imagine. The slave-holders of the present day
(viewed as a body) are just as innocent of the creation of slavery, as their fellow-citizens of New-York
or Connecticut; and the citizens of New-York or
Connecticut are just as innocent of the creation of
slavery as the citizens of London or Paris. But the
citizens of the two former States have a merit in the
matter, that the citizens of neither of the towns named
can claim, since they have stripped themselves of
property to give freedom to their blacks, while those
who were parties to the original wrong have contributed nothing to the measure they so much urge. But
is it not possible to assert a principle under acknowledged limitations ? The black man in the southern
States of this Union is not considered a citizen at all.
It would not be safe to consider him a citizen, in a
country of equal political rights, since he is far too
ignorant, and must, for a generation at least, remain
too ignorant, to exercise, with sufficient discretion,
the privileges of a citizen in a free government. It
would, if any thing, be more prudent for the Virginian
and Carolinian to admit boys of twelve years of age
to vote and to legislate, than to admit their blacks, in
their present moral condition, without having any
reference to the danger of a personal dissension.
Equal rights do not, in any part of America, imply a
broad, general, and unequivocal equality. It is the
glory of the institutions of this country, that they have
never run into practical excesses, in order to satisfy
craving theories. By equal rights, the citizen of Connecticut, (and, I believe, no man doubts his rational
and unlimited freedom,) understands that all who have
reached a certain standard of qualification, shall be
equal in power and that all others shall be equal in

protection. He does not give political power to the pauper, nor to females, nor to minors, nor to idiots, nor yet even to his priests. All he aims at is justice; and in order to do justice, he gives political rights to all those who, he thinks, can use them without abuse. He would be culpable only, if any class existed in his community, who might, with a little care, freely enjoy these rights, did he neglect to resort to that care. He therefore excludes only those who, on great, general, and lasting principles, are disqualified from exercising political power. The situation of the Carolinian is different, but his principle is quite the same: he excludes more; for, unhappily, when he arrived at the knowledge and the practice of a liberal policy himself, he found a numerous class of human beings existing within his borders, who were not competent to its exercise. He had but a choice between a seeming inconsistency, or the entire abandonment of what he thought a great good. He chose to make all equal, who could bear equality; and in that, he has done exactly what his northern countryman has done, and no more. Should he unnecessarily neglect, however, to qualify these exceptions to enjoy a better state of being, he then becomes inconsistent.

I think these considerations must lead us to the conclusion, that most of the merits of this question lie in the fact of how much has been done and is now doing, towards effecting a change in what is admitted to be a prodigious evil. I feel confident that no discreet father, or husband, or brother, could ask a Carolinian, who was existing in a state of highly polished society, and who enjoyed all the advantages of great moral improvement, to admit, at once, a body of men who had been nurtured in the habits of slavery, with all their ignorance and animal qualities, and who are numerically superior, to a participation of equal political rights. Such a measure would induce an absolute abandonment of their country and property on the part of the whites, or it would involve a degradation, and abuses that are horrible to reflect on. Individuals may and have parted with their means of personal indulgence to give liberty to their slaves; but it is too much to expect it from communities: nor would discreet individuals do it, if it were to be a general act, since a disorganization of society would be an inevitable consequence.

The true question, and that in which the friends of humanity should feel the deepest interest, is that connected with the steps that are taken to lead to the general emancipation, which must sooner or later arrive.

At the period of the declaration of the independence of the United States, slavery existed in all the British colonies. The blacks were not numerous in the northern provinces, for, there, the white was the better labourer. Still there were slaves in every one of the thirteen original States of this Union. The proportion of slaves in some of the middle States was nearly equal to what it now is in some of the southern. Massachusetts (which in 1790 had 5,463 blacks,) put such a construction on its own bill of rights as abolished slavery. This was the first measure of the sort that was ever taken on the American continent, I presume. The example has been successively followed, at different periods, by all the northern and middle States, until slavery is either abolished in fact, or by laws that have a prospective operation, in nine out of the fourteen States that adopted the present constitution in 1789. You may form some idea of the difficulty of getting rid of such an evil as slavery, by observing the caution with which these comparatively little encumbered States have approached the subject. Perhaps twenty years are necessary to effect the object humanely, even after the policy of a community is perfectly decided,

Numberless influences have, at the same time, been at work, however, to extend the limits in which slavery might exist. Alabama and Mississippi formed parts of Georgia; Kentucky and Tennessee were within the ancient limits of Virginia; and Louisiana, and Missouri, and the Floridas, were acquired by purchase. The people of Virginia and Georgia, in ceding their territory, were not disposed to cede the right of emigration, with the privilege of carrying their wealth with them; and slavery, in consequence, became extended over the four States named. Slaves were found in the two others, and in the Floridas. In this manner the eleven present slave-holding States came into existence. In the meanwhile, the States of Ohio, Indiana, and Illinois, were organized off what was once called the north-western territory. These, added to the nine States that had abolished the policy of slavery, and by the subsequent acquisition of Maine, brought their whole number up to thirteen.

I think that the influence of free opinions, if I may so express it, is steadily on the increase. It is not the smallest evil of slavery, that it begets in the master an indifference to its existence, and that it gives birth and durability to cruel and lasting prejudices. That these prejudices must be rooted out of the majority of the citizens of the southern States themselves, ere slavery shall cease to exist, is indisputable, since no power but their own can extinguish it. But my friend assures me, that within his recollection, an immense change has taken place in this particular. Twenty years ago, even in New-York, a general and deep prejudice existed against this unfortunate class of human beings. It is rapidly disappearing. It is true, that the sort of commingling of the races, which a certain class of philanthropists are much fonder of proclaiming than they would be fond of practising, does not occur, nor is it likely very soon to occur in this country. Still there is every disposition to do

the blacks justice, though there is none whatever to
mingle the blood. I have heard of instances in which
human beings of peculiar colour and form were
esteemed in Europe as curiosities; but I fancy, if
they abounded in any country, there would be found
the same natural desire, in that portion of its inhabitants who believed themselves to possess the
physical advantage, to retain it, as is now found here.
It is odd enough, that Europe, which, for so many
centuries, has been making patents of nobility obstacles to matrimony, should decry so loudly against a
people who hesitate a little at intermingling colours.

But there will still be a greater objection against
this mingling of the races, for at least a long time to
come. With few exceptions, the blacks of America
belong to an ill-educated and inferior class. When
free, they are left, like other men, to look after their
own interests; and most of those, who have character and talent enough to rise above the condition of
menials, push their fortunes in countries where they
are not daily and hourly offended by the degradation
of their caste. I think this circumstance must long
keep them in a station which will prevent intermar-
riages. You will admit, too, that matrimony is very
much an affair of taste; and, although there well
may be, and there are, portions of the world where
white colour is not greatly admired, such is not the
case here. The deep reluctance to see one's posterity exhibiting a hue different from one's own, is to
be overcome, ere any extensive intercourse can occur between the blacks and the whites.

The probable future fate of the blacks of America, is a subject of deep and painful interest. I confess, however, I am not one of those who see any
great danger to the whites in their increasing numbers. While they remain ignorant, their efforts must
always be feeble and divided, and, as they become
enlightened, they must see the utter impossibility of

any continued success in a rising against a force numerically and morally so superior.   Although the
distances in America seem very great on the map,
the inhabitants have contrived the means of bringing
themselves wonderfully near to each other.   The
whites in the whole country increase faster than the
blacks ; and I think it will be found, that as emanci-
pations multiply, the disproportion in numbers will
be still greater, and always in favour of the former.
It would not only be the duty of the northern men,
but it would be a duty readily performed, to fly, in
case of need, to the assistance of their southern neighbours.   It is not easy to suppose circumstances in
which the white population of the southern States,
already (as a whole) two to one against the slaves,
armed, intelligent, organized, and possessing the immense moral superiority of their domestic relations,
should not be sufficient of themselves to protect their
persons and property against a rising.   The only
circumstances in which the danger could be very im-
minent or extensive, would be in the event of a foreign
war ; and then their common country would be a
party, and the aid of States that will shortly number
of themselves twenty or thirty milllions, could be
commanded in their defence.

But the danger of slavery, so far as it is connected
with numbers, has its own cure.   No man will keep
a negro after he ceases to be profitable, any more
than he will keep an extra supply of other animal
force.   If Carolina can bear 500,000 slaves, Carolina
will probably accumulate that number ; but after she
has reached the point where policy says she must
stop, instead of resorting to laws to retain her negroes, she will have recourse to laws to get rid of
them.   This, to an European, and particularly to an
Englishman, who knows that excessive population is
the greatest burthen of his own country, may seem
difficult ; but in order to form a correct opinion of a

question purely American, it is necessary to consider the actual state of things on this side of the Atlantic.

The already vast, and constantly increasing coasting trade of the United States, offers an easy, natural, and perfectly practicable drain, to the black population of the south. The blacks furnish, already, thousands of sailors, and quite useful sailors too, and they constitute a very important material of the supply of seamen, in considering the future commercial and nautical power of this confederation. The demand for domestics at the north, too, will, for many years, continue beyond the probability of a white supply. You will remember that experience has shown that the free blacks have very little natural increase, and both these growing demands must therefore meet with most of their supplies from the slave-holding States. Then, again, the proximity of the West Indies, of Mexico, and of the South American States, in which a commingled population already exists, offers facilities for emigration, that Europe does not present. The slave population of the United States may reach 4 or 5,000,000, but (after a very short time) at a diminishing rate of increase,* and then I think it will be found that new means will be taken to get rid of them.

In forming these conjectures, I have not regarded the narrowing of the limits of slavery by the constant advancement of opinion. It is true, that the surface on which slavery, in fact, exists, has, on the whole,

---

* At present the slave-holder has a motive for increasing his slaves, since he can sell them in the new States; but this demand will, of course, cease as the new States get full. Louisiana has recently passed a law, prohibiting the importation of slaves; a fact which the writer thinks proves the truth of his theory. The reader will always recollect that slaves cannot be *imported* into the United States, but that they can be *transported* from one State to another, unless prohibitions are made by the States themselves. This was part of the original compact, without which the southern States would not have consented to the present constitution

been rather enlarged than otherwise, since the existence of the confederation ; but we should not lose sight of the circumstances under which this extension of the slave region has been effected.

It has spread with the diffusion of population, over districts that were originally the property of the slave-holders; and in no respect, except in mere territorial division, has there been any virtual enlargement of its political limits, unless one can thus call the enlargement of the borders of society. It is true, that when Missouri was admitted to the Union, an effort was made by the friends of the blacks (I use the term technically) to abolish slavery in that State. Had they succeeded, it would have been an inroad on the ancient limits; but their defeat ought not to be deemed an extension of the surface occupied by slaves, since slaves were there before. It was a sort of attempt to turn the flank of slavery, or to get into its rear ; whereas I think it manifest that the great victory over habits and prejudices, which true policy will be sure to gain in time, is to be gained by pressing steadily on, in an open, manly, but cautious and conciliating manner, in its front. Ardent and steady a friend of universal liberty as you know me to be, I am by no means sure, that, had I been a member of that Congress, I would have given so violent an alarm to the slave-holders of the south, as to have contributed to attempt to carry that law.

It is only necessary to witness the immense superiority that free labour possesses over slave labour, and to examine the different conditions of society in a State without slaves, and in one with, to see that a close contact must be destructive to the principles of slavery. The friends of emancipation have now a noble front, extending from the Atlantic to the Mississippi. I even think that accident has contributed to throw those communities most in advance, which are the least likely to retard the progress of emanci-

pation. The honest and affluent, but quiet population of Pennsylvania, for instance, is much less suited
to give the alarm to their neighbours of Maryland,
than would be done by the more restless, ever-busy
people of New-England; while their example is left
to produce its undiminished effect. If I have been
correctly informed, public opinion and sounder views
of policy are making great progress in the latter State.
The inhabitants begin to see that they would be richer
and more powerful without their slaves than with
them. This is the true entering wedge of argument;
and juster views of moral truth will be sure to follow
convictions of interest, as they have followed, and
are still following, emancipation further north.

The first and surest sign of a disposition to give
freedom to the slaves, is the accumulation of the free
blacks, since they are not only a positive proof that
emancipation exists, but they argue an indifference
to slavery in the whole community. In Maryland,
there were 145,429 blacks in 1810, and 147,128 in
1820. During the same time, the whites increased
from 235,117 to 260,222. Emigration retarded the
increase of the two races, no doubt; and yet, you
see, contrary to the law of increase in most of the
slave-holding States, the whites grew faster than the
blacks. Now, of this number of 147,128 blacks,
39,730 were free. This is a very large proportion,
and I hail it as a most auspicious omen. In point of
fact, there were 4,109 fewer slaves in Maryland in
1820, than in 1810; while the whites had increased
25,105. Indeed, I heard very many enlightened and
respectable men in Maryland regret that slavery existed among them at all; and the opinion is getting
to be quite common, that free labour is the most
profitable. Even in Virginia, the whites have increased 51,474, during the same ten years, while the
blacks have increased only 38,954. It is true, the
emigration renders these results a little doubtful; but

the fact that there were, in 1820, 36,889 free blacks in Virginia, proves something. It is also of importance, that there exist, in so many of the slave-holding States, large bodies of their respective communities, who have very little interest in the perpetuation of the evil, except as their own personal welfare is connected with that of society. Although the latter influence is one of moment, it is also one that may influence a man both ways, since he may be as likely to believe that the interests of society call for some relief against the evil, as to think he ought to support it.

I have endeavoured to lay this important subject before you in a practical form. It has been done rapidly, and, I am quite certain, very imperfectly. It is proper to understand, there is so much of intimate detail necessary to view the state of American slavery with discretion, that it is highly probable I may have fallen into error; but I still think you will find the views I have taken of it not without some plausibility. I shall sum them up, together with the leading facts, in as few words as possible.

I think liberal sentiments towards the blacks are rapidly gaining ground in most of the southern States.* Positive, political freedom is granted, or is in the course of being granted to them, in thirteen of the twenty-four communities of the confederation. Emancipation, geographically speaking, has now reached a formidable point of resistance (on account of the numbers of the slaves,) but it is steadily advancing through the powerful agency of public opinion. When it has passed this point, its subsequent march will, I think, be easier and more rapid. Tennessee and Kentucky, the States that flank Virginia, have by no means as deep an interest in the maintenance of

---

* The writer does not mean that every man becomes in some degree sensible of the evil, but that a vast number do, and of men, too, who are likely to have an effect on legislation.

slavery, as the States further south; and I think it is not chimerical to hope that, by the aid of prospective laws, many are now living who may see slavery limited to the shores of the Atlantic, and to the Gulf of Mexico, with perhaps a belt for a little distance on each side of the Mississippi. In the mean time, the advance of opinion is steady and great. Unless the Christian world recedes, its final success is inevitable. I shall not incur the charge of empiricism by pretending to predict the precise period.

I do not think that slavery, under any circumstances, can entail very serious danger to the dominion of the whites in this country, for at least a century or two. Districts might be ravaged, beyond a doubt; but the prodigious superiority of the whites, in every thing that constitutes force, is the pledge of their power.

I am of opinion that the number of the slaves will be limited, as a matter of course, by necessity. There is a point beyond which they would be a burden. Nor is that point so distant as we commonly imagine. Perhaps it has been already obtained in some of the older States.

I think that the free black population (except in the way of emancipation) does not increase, or, at least, not materially; and that the proportion between the whites and the blacks is steadily growing in favour of the former; that, in future, it will even grow faster; that emigration, the navy, commerce, and unsettled habits, will tend to repress the increase of the blacks, and to consume their numbers; and that the time of the intermingling of the races to any great extent is still remote.

Though there is much in these views to excite the regrets of a man of pure philanthropy, it appears to me that the cause of emancipation is far from being as bad as it is generally supposed to be in Europe.

Impatience is a characteristic of zeal. But impa
tience, though creditable to the feelings of the European, sometimes leads him, on this subject, into
assertions that might provoke comparisons which
would not be so honourable to his own society, perhaps, as he is apt to fancy. Impatience, however,
on the part of the American, may even do worse; it
may retard the very consummation he wishes. Mild-
ness, candour, and conciliation, are his weapons; and
I think they will be irresistible. Although an ardent
wisher of the happy moment of general emancipation,
I always turn with disgust from those cold and heart-
less paragraphs which occasionally appear in the
northern journals of this country, and which, under
a superficial pretension to humanity, trifle with the
safety and happiness of two of their fellow-citizens,
in order to give an affected aid to the undoubtedly
righteous cause of one black man. If this species of
irritating language did good, if it did no harm by
hardening men in their opinions, it would be disagreeable; but under the actual state of things, it is
far worse than useless. The general tone of the
press, however, is sufficiently amicable; and all those
who understand the difference between argumentation and judgment, have reason to hope it may long
continue so.

But physical suffering, especially in a country like
this, is not the prominent grievance of slavery. It is
the deep moral degradation, which no man has a
right to entail on another, that forms the essence of
its shame. God has planted in all our spirits secret
but lasting aspirations after a state of existence
higher than that which we enjoy, and no one has a
right to say that such are the limits beyond which
your reason, and, consequently, your mental being,
shall not pass. That men, equally degraded, exist
under systems that do not openly avow the principle

of domestic slavery, is no excuse for the perpetuation of such a scourge, though circumstances and necessity may urge a great deal in extenuation of its present existence.

TO SIR EDWARD WALLER, BART.

&c. &c.

New-York, ———

THE next subject of interest, after the unfortunate descendants of the Africans, that has been brought into my notice by this southern tour, is the remnant of the original possessors of these regions. By far the most numerous, and the most important of the native tribes, which still continue in the immediate vicinity of the whites, are those which occupy reservations in Georgia, the Floridas, Alabama, Mississippi, and Tennessee. The lingering fragments of a hundred tribes are certainly seen scattered over the immense surface of this country, living on greater or less tracts that had been secured to them, or dwelling by sufferance in the woods; but the only people now residing east of the Mississippi who can aspire to the names of nations, are the Creeks, the Choctaws, the Chickasaws, the Cherokees, and the Seminoles, all of whom dwell in the portion of country I have named.

As a rule, the red man disappears before the superior moral and physical influence of the white, just as I believe the black man will eventually do the same thing, unless he shall seek shelter in some other region. In nine cases in ten, the tribes have gradually removed west; and there is now a confused assemblage of nations and languages collected on the immense hunting grounds of the Prairies.

It is impossible to say any thing of the numbers of the Indians, except by conjecture, since they are not considered as coming properly within the computations of the censuses. Perhaps the five nations named may contain not far from twenty thousand souls. It is not probable that all the Indians that live within the boundaries of the United States, stretching from the Atlantic to the Pacific, materially exceed 120,000, if indeed they reach that amount. Still I do not pretend to any great accuracy in my estimates. Their numbers, in this quarter of America, have always been exaggerated; and the sounding terms of nations and tribes have contributed to the extension of a mistaken idea of their importance.

The ordinary manner of the disappearance of the Indian, is by a removal deeper into the forest. Still, many linger near the graves of their fathers, to which their superstitions, no less than a fine natural feeling, lend a deeper interest. The fate of the latter is inevitable; they become victims to the abuses of civilization, without ever attaining to any of its moral elevation.

As might be supposed, numberless divisions of these people, when the country was discovered, were found in possession of districts along the coast, and deriving a principal means of support from the ocean. They were fishermen rather than hunters, though the savage state ordinarily infers a resort to both pursuits. Most of these people, too, retired reluctantly from a view of " the great salt lake," but some were environed by the whites before they were properly aware of the blighting influence of the communion; and, getting gradually accustomed to their presence, they preferred remaining near the places where they had first drawn breath. Trifling districts of territory have been, in every instance in which they were sufficiently numerous to make such a provision desirable, secured to them, and on these little tracts of land many of them still remain. I have visited one or two of their establishments.

In point of civilization, comforts, and character, the Indians, who remain near the coasts, are about on a level with the lowest classes of European peasantry. Perhaps they are somewhat below the English, but I think not below the Irish peasants. They are much below the condition of the mass of the slaves. It is but another proof of the wayward vanity of man, that the latter always hold the Indians in contempt, though it is some proof that they feel their own condition to be physically better: morally, in one sense, it certainly is not.

Many of these Atlantic Indians go to sea. They are quite often found in the whalers, and, in some instances, in the vessels of war. An officer in the navy has told me that he once knew a Montauk Indian who was a captain of the main-top in a sloop of war; and in another instance, a flag officer had his gig manned by Indians. They make active and very obedient seamen, but are never remarkable for strength. The whole number of them who now go to sea, does not, however, probably exceed a hundred or two.*

---

* The writer, while in America, heard an anecdote which may give some idea of the notions of retributive justice which linger so long in the philosophy of an Indian, and which is, probably, the basis of his desire for revenge, since he is well known to be as eminently grateful as he is vindictive. The whalers always take their reward in a portion of the profits of the voyage. An Indian made several voyages in succession, in the same ship; he found, at his return, that bad luck, advances, and the supplies of an extravagant family at home, left him always in debt. " What shall I do?" was the question put to his owner, as each unfortunate balance was exhibited. "You must go to sea." To sea he went, and, as stated, for four or five years, always with the same result. At length, good fortune, with a proper amount of preventive castigation on his im-

I accompanied Cadwallader on a visit to a connexion, who lives within forty miles of New-York,
on the adjacent island of Nassau (Long Island.)
The uncle of my friend was a man of an extensive
hereditary estate, on which there might have been
a reservation of a few thousand acres of woods.
While shooting over this forest, one day, the proprietor asked me if I felt any desire to see an Indian
king. Surprised at such a question, in such a place,
an explanation was requested. He told me that an
Indian, who claimed to be a descendant of the ancient
Sachems, then held his court in his woods, and that
a walk of fifteen minutes would bring us into the
presence of King Peter. We went.

I found this Indian, dwelling with his family, in a
wigwam of a most primitive construction. It was in
the form of a bee-hive, or rather of a very high dome.
The covering was made of a long, tough grass, that
grows near the sea, and the texture was fine and even
beautiful. A post in the centre supported the fabric,
which was shaped by delicate curving poles. A hole
in the top admitted the light, and allowed the smoke
to pass out; and the fire was near enough to the up-
right post to permit a kettle to be suspended from
one of its knots (or cut branches) near enough to feel
the influence of the heat. The door was a covering
of mats, and the furniture consisted of a few rude
chairs, baskets, and a bed, that was neither savage,
nor yet such as marks the civilized man. The attire
of the family was partly that of the one condition, and
partly that of the other. The man himself was a
full-blooded Indian, but his manner had that species

---

provident wife, before he sailed, brought the balance on his side.
The money was of course tendered; but for a long time he refused to receive it, insisting that justice required that his owners
should now go to sea, where it would seem he had not enjoyed
himself quite as much as he believed the other party to the
contract had done on shore.

of sullen deportment that betrays the disposition without the boldness of the savage. He complained that "basket stuff" was getting scarce, and spoke of an intention of removing his wigwam shortly to some other estate.

The manufacture of baskets and brooms is a common employment of all the Indians who reside near the settlements. They feed on game, and, sometimes, like the gypsies, they make free with poultry, though in common they are rigidly honest; nearly always so, unless corrupted by much intercourse with the whites. With the proceeds of their labour they purchase blankets, powder, and such other indulgences as exceed their art to manufacture. King Peter, I was told, claimed a right, in virtue of his royal descent, to cut saplings to supply his materials, on any estate in the island. He was permitted to enjoy this species of feudal privilege in quiet, it being well understood that he was not to exceed a certain discretion in its exercise.

In the more interior parts of the country, I frequently met families of the Indians, either travelling, or proceeding to some village, with their wares. They were all alike, a stunted, dirty, and degraded race. Sometimes they encamped in the forests, lighted their fires, and remained for weeks in a place; and at others, they kept roaming daily, until the time arrived when they should return to their reservations.

The reservations in the old States, and with tribes that cannot aspire to the dignity of nations, are managed on a sufficiently humane principle. The laws of the State, or of the United States, have jurisdiction there, in all matters between white men, or between a white man and an Indian; but the Indians themselves are commonly permitted to control the whole of their own internal policy. Bargains, exceeding certain amounts, are not valid between them and the whites, who cannot, for instance, purchase their lands. Schools are usually provided, in the more important tribes, by the general government, and in the less, by charity. Religious instruction is also furnished by the latter means.

I saw reservations in which no mean advances had been made in civilization. Farms were imperfectly tilled, and cattle were seen grazing in the fields. Still, civilization advances slowly among a people who consider labour a degradation, in addition to the bodily dislike that all men have to its occupations.

There are many of these tribes, however, who fill a far more important, and altogether a remarkable position. There is certainly no portion of country within the admitted boundaries of the United States, in which their laws are not paramount, if they choose to exert them. Still, savage communities do exist within these limits, with whom they make treaties, against whom they wage open war, and with whom they make solemn peace. As a treaty is, by the constitution, the paramount law of the land, the several States are obliged to respect their legal provisions.

That neither the United States, nor any individual State, has ever taken possession of any land that, by usage or construction, might be decreed the property of the Indians, without a treaty and a purchase, is, I believe, certain. How far an equivalent is given, is another question : though I fancy that these bargains are quite as just as any that are ever driven between the weak and the strong, the intelligent and the ignorant. It is not pretended that the value of the territory gained is paid for ; but the purchase is rather a deference to general principles of justice and humanity, than a concession to a right in the Indians, which itself might admit of a thousand legal quibbles. The treaties are sufficiently humane, and, although certain borderers, who possess the power of the white man with the disposition of the savage, do sometimes violate their conditions, there is no just reason to distrust the intentions or the conduct of the government. But you may desire to know something of the detail of the intercourse.

You have seen that the expenses of the war department of this government, for the year 1826, was 6,243,236 dollars. Among other charges, I find the following items included in the gross amount. The sums are all in dollars. Civilization of Indians, 14,914; pay of Indian agents, 29,860; sub-ditto, 12,131; presents to Indians, 16,387; contingencies of Indian department, 130,542; general councils with Indians on Lake Superior, 270,000; relief of the Florida Indians, 7,249; treaties with ditto, 3,218; Creek treaties, 109,471; Choctaw treaty, 2,056; Choctaw schools, 2,804; treaties with Choctaws and Chickasaws, 15,000; other Indian treaties, 183,568; annuities to Indians, 243,542, &c. &c.

The annuities are sums paid for grants of land. At the treaties, presents are always made to the tribes, and the agents and sub-agents are men employed to maintain the influence of the government, and at the same time, to see that the rights of the Indians are respected.

There is a bureau of the war department that is called the " office of the Indian affairs." A humane and discreet individual is at its head, and a good deal is endeavoured to be done in mitigating the sufferings and in meliorating the condition of the Indians, though, owing to the peculiar habits and opinions of these people, but little, I fear, is effected. I see by the report of the current year, (1827) that, in nine months, requisitions towards the support of the objects of this bureau, were made to the amount of 759,116 dollars, or at the rate of a little more than a million of dollars a year. This, you will remember, is one-tenth of the current expenditure of the whole government, and nearly as much as is paid for the support of the whole civil list, strictly speaking.

The manner in which the money is appropriated, can be seen in the extracts already quoted for the year 1826.

The government, it would appear by the reports, puts the utmost latitude on the construction of their constitutional powers, by even paying money for the support of missionaries among the Indians. I believe, however, that the alleged and legal object of this charge, is for general instruction, though in point of fact, the teachers are missionaries. They are of all sects, Protestant and Catholic, the question of creed being never discussed at all. I see by the reports, that (in 1827) there were 1291 scholars in the different schools that come under the superintendence of the government. It is not probable that all the Indians belonging to the tribes that receive this instruction, much exceed, if indeed they reach, the total number of 30,000. I think it is therefore apparent, that quite as good provision for elementary instruction is made in behalf of the Indians, as is commonly made for the people of any country, except those of the United States themselves. There is no reason to suppose that all the children who present themselves, are not taught; and there is much reason for believing that efforts are constantly making to induce all to come. The number of teachers is 293, which is quite enough to instruct ten times the number. You are not to suppose, however, that all these teachers are men hired expressly for that purpose. They are the missionaries, their wives and families, and some of them are for the purpose of instructing in the arts of life, as well as in reading and writing. Much of the expense is defrayed by charitable associations. The sum actually paid by the government for the express object of instruction, is 7,150 dollars, or enough to maintain rather more than forty teachers at stipends of 150 dollars each. It is probable that

some receive more, and some less. It is said that the
schools are generally in a flourishing condition.

Where there is much intercourse between the]
very strong and very weak, there is always a tendency in the human mind to suspect abuses of power.
I shall not descend into the secret impulses that give
rise to these suspicions: but in this stage of the world,
there is no necessity for suspecting a nation like this
of any unprovoked wrongs against a people like the
savages. The inroad of the whites of the United
States has never been marked by the gross injustice
and brutality that have distinguished similar inroads
elsewhere. The Indians have never been slain except in battle, unless by lawless individuals; never
hunted by blood-hounds, or in any manner aggriev-
ed, except in the general, and, perhaps, in some degree, justifiable invasion of a territory that they did
not want, nor could not use. If the government of
the United States was poor and necessitous, one
might suspect it of an unjust propensity; but not
only the facts, but the premises, would teach us to
believe the reverse.

A great, humane, and, I think, rational project, is
now in operation to bring the Indians within the pale
of civilization. I shall furnish you with its outline
as it is detailed in a recent report of the head of the
Indian office.

Most, if not all of the Indians who reside east of
the Mississippi, live within the jurisdiction of some
State or of some territory. In most cases they are left
to the quiet enjoyment of the scanty rights which
they retain; but the people of their vicinity commonly wish to get rid of neighbours that retard civilization, and who are so often troublesome. The
policy of States is sometimes adverse to their continuance. Though there is no power, except that of
the United States, which can effect their removal
without their own consent, the State authorities can

greatly embarrass the control of the general government. A question of policy, and, perhaps, of jurisdiction, lately. arose on this subject between Georgia and the general government. In the course of its disposal, the United States, in order to secure the rights of the Indians more effectually, and to prevent any future question of this sort, appear to have hit on the following plan.

West of the Mississippi they still hold large regions that belong to no State or territory. They propose to several tribes (Choctaws, Chickasaws, Cherokees, &c.) to sell their present possessions, improvements, houses, fences, stock, &c., and to receive, in return, acre for acre, with the same amount of stock, fences, and every other auxiliary of civilization they now possess. The inducements to make this exchange are as follow:—Perpetuity to their establishments, since a pledge is given that no title shall ever be granted that may raise a pretext for another removal; an organization of a republican, or, as it is termed, a territorial government for them, such as now exist in Florida, Arkansas, and Michigan; protection, by the presence of troops; and a right to send delegates to Congress, similar to that now enjoyed by the other territories.

If the plan can be effected, there is reason to think that the constant diminution in the numbers of the Indians will be checked, and that a race, about whom there is so much that is poetic and fine in recollection, will be preserved. Indeed, some of the southern tribes have already endured the collision with the white man, and are still slowly on the increase. As one of these tribes, at least, (the Chickasaws,) is included in this plan, there is just ground to hope that the dangerous point of communication has been passed, and that they may continue to advance in civilization to maturity. The chief of the bureau on Indian affairs gives it as his opinion that they (the

Chickasaws) have increased about ten per cent.
within six years. Their whole number is computed
at four thousand souls.

Should such a territory be formed, a nucleus will
be created, around which all the savages of the west,
who have any yearnings for a more meliorated state
of existence, can rally. As there is little reluctance
to mingle the white and red blood, (for the physical
difference is far less than in the case of the blacks,
and the Indians have never been menial slaves,) I
think an amalgamation of the two races would in
time occur. Those families of America who are
thought to have any of the Indian blood, are rather
proud of their descent, and it is a matter of boast
among many of the most considerable persons of
Virginia, that they are descended from the renowned
Pocahontas.

The character of the American Indian has been
too often faithfully described to need any repetition
here. The majority of them, in or near the settlements, are an humbled and much degraded race. As
you recede from the Mississippi, the finer traits of
savage life become visible ; and, although most of the
natives of the Prairies, even there, are far from being
the interesting and romantic heroes that poets love
to paint, there are specimens of loftiness of spirit, of
bearing, and of savage heroism, to be found among
the chiefs, that might embarrass the fertility of the
richest invention to equal. I met one of those heroes of the desert, and a finer physical and moral
man, allowing for peculiarity of condition, it has
rarely been my good fortune to encounter.

Peterlasharroo, or the young knife chief of the
Pawnees, when I saw him, was a man of some six or
seven-and-twenty years. He had already gained renown as a warrior, and he had won the confidence
of his tribe by repeated exhibitions of wisdom and
moderation. He had been signally useful in destroy-

ing a baneful superstition, which would have made a
sacrifice of a female prisoner, whose life he saved by
admirable energy, and a fearless exposure of his own.
The reputation of even this remote and savage hero
had spread beyond the narrow limits of his own
country; and, when we met, I was prepared to yield
him esteem and admiration. But the impression produced by his grave and haughty, though still courteous mien, the restless, but often steady, and bold
glance of his dark, keen eye, and the quiet dignity of
his air, are still present to my recollection.   With a
view to propitiate so powerful a chief, I had prepared a present of peacock's feathers, which were
so arranged as to produce as much effect as the fine
plumage of that noble bird will allow.   He received
my offering with a quiet smile, and regarded the boon
with a complacency that seemed to find more of its
motive in a wish to be grateful, than in any selfish
gratification.   The gift was then laid aside, nor was
it regarded again, during the whole of a long and interesting interview.   You may judge of my surprise,
when I afterwards learned that this simple child of
the plains considered my gift in some such light as
a courtier would esteem a brilliant. The interpreter
assured me that I had made him able to purchase
thirty horses, a species of property that constitutes
the chief wealth of his tribe.   But, notwithstanding
my unintentional liberality, no sign of pleasure, beyond that which I have related, was suffered to escape him, in the presence of a white man.

TO SIR EDWARD WALLER, BART.

&c. &c.

Washington, ———

You can scarcely expect a very minute description of what I have seen in my southern tour. Still I may put a few general facts before your eyes, in a new, and, perhaps, not uninteresting manner.

The eleven slave-holding States of this confederation contain about 489,000 square miles of territory. If Arkansas and the Floridas (not yet States) shall be included, they will swell the amount to about 600,000, or something less than double the extent of the whole thirteen northern, or free States, including Michigan, which, together, cover a surface of 334,000 square miles. Thus, you see, that about one-half of the whole computed territory of the United States is so far settled, as to have arrived at the point of establishing the State or territorial governments. But there is no probability that any other community will be speedily formed, on this side of the Rocky Mountains, of sufficient importance to aspire to the possession of a separate government. The Prairies, and the deserts of the west, present natural obstacles to the further progress of the population in that quarter; and climate opposes a serious reason to the comfortable existence of man towards the north-west. That all these regions will, in time, come to have a population of their own, is certain; but, in a country where there is still so much room for the employment of men, that day is necessarily distant.

I have estimated the whole white population, who are now in possession of these 600,000 square miles, at 3,500,000, and the blacks at less than 1,900,000, of which number, as you know, I think something like 1,750,000 may be slaves. The free blacks in the *free* States, in 1820, amounted to 112,281; 10 or 12,000 have been manumitted since, by the operation of the laws. The estimate of the whole number of blacks in the United States, must materially exceed 2,000,000, or I have given quite enough to the southern States. Supposing these estimates to be near the truth, (it is impossible that they should be exact,) the whole of the 600,000 square miles are occupied by 5,400,000 souls, exclusive of Indians; or at the rate of nine inhabitants to the square mile. But the remark which I have made concerning the districts of country, entirely uninhabited, to the north, is also applicable to similar regions to the south. There are also fewer villages to the south than to the north. The same is true with respect to towns of all sizes. Baltimore, the largest city in the slave-holding States, contains, perhaps, about half as many inhabitants as Philadelphia; and New-Orleans, and Charleston, and Richmond, the only other three towns of any magnitude, are not, all together, as large as Boston. After the places just named, there is no town that reaches 10,000 inhabitants, and few that come up to half that number. There are, however, one or two new thriving places on the bays of the Gulf of Mexico, where cities will probably be formed, though, I think, there is scarcely a town now in existence, except Baltimore, New-Orleans, Charleston, and Richmond, in the whole of this immense region, that contains 10,000 souls.

In forming an idea of the appearance of a country thus inhabited, in addition to the general fact of districts that are entirely untenanted, you are to call into view the peculiar division of property which occurs on nearly all the coast. Extensive plantations, on which none but the best land is worked, make fearful interruptions in the agricultural character of the country: and the vast pine barrens that occur along the Atlantic, and even on the Gulf, leave wide spaces of unoccupied ground, even in the longest settled parts of these States.

But there are States, or parts of States, that present a very different picture. Some of the counties of Maryland and Virginia are in a high degree beautiful; and the uplands of the Carolinas and Georgia are of an entirely different character from the coasts. Tennessee has not only a fine climate and a fertile soil, but a population that, in common, might vie with the population of any country for all the best attributes of man.

You will see that the great physical force of this nation, however, lies in the more northern States. If we except Kentucky, Tennessee, and the uplands generally, I think this must long continue to be the fact. The arts of life are more cultivated there than to the south; and as they get still more into use, men will cling to their indulgence with all the tenacity of acquired habits. Emigration to the south-western States has been chiefly fed by Virginia, Georgia, and the two Carolinas. These four States contained, in 1790, 1,463,982, and in 1820, 2,535,493. Emigration to the new northern States has been chiefly fed by New-England. In 1790, New-England had 1,009,522 souls; and in 1820, 1,659,864. Here you see that the rate of increase is rather in favour of the latter; but if we look into the increase of the States that have been fed by this emigration, it will be found to be still more in favour of the northern portion of the country. In 1790, all the free States had 2,033,248 inhabitants, and in 1820, 5,225,117. In 1790, all the slave-holding States contained 1,890,030 souls; and in 1820, 4,400,617. Here you see that, notwithstanding the vast superiority of the southern States over the northern in extent, the increase of population in the latter is in a ratio considerably in their favour.

In 1790, the slave-holding States had 137,168 fewer
inhabitants than their northern sisters; whereas, in
1820, the northern States had 824,500 the most.
After allowing for the difference of *capital*, the excess
is nearly 400,000 too many for the regular proportion
of the increase.   It is also known that many adventurers go from the northern States into the southern,
while comparatively few southern men come north,
though it is certainly done. If we take 6,500,000 as
the present population of the northern States, (and
I believe it is within bounds,) there will remain
5,500,000 for the southern.   This will show again
that the southern States are beginning to maintain
their own; but their present growth is more owing
to the vast regions of fertile land that have lately been
opened for sale at the south, than to natural increase,
since every man who emigrates counts two in the
amount of comparative numbers.

The inducements that carry the northern man far
south, must be exceedingly strong to overcome the
effects of climate, and the repugnance he is apt to
feel to slavery. Still these inducements do exist, and
in some parts of the country the climate itself is among
the reasons for emigration. It is the coast, chiefly,
which is unhealthy; and even on the coast, there are
found many delightful and salubrious situations, where
northern men gladly resort for the purposes of trade.
It is quite natural that the northern population, having
occupied most of their own best lands, should begin
to find their way into the southern, and particularly
into the south-western States.

There is a considerable difference of character
between the people of the northern, and between
some of the people of the southern States of this
Union. I do not allude to the distinctive traits which
form the habits of a border man, and a man of the
towns; for these exist between the frontier inhabitant
of New-York and the inhabitant of the city of that

name. But slavery itself, and the dispersed establishments of the whites, which are a consequence of
slavery, have a direct effect on the manners of the
southern inhabitants.

The owner of slaves, whatever may be his correla-
tive standing with men of his own colour, is a species
of aristocrat, so far as manners are concerned.   He
is kept, in his own person, from the pursuits and employments that are commonly thought to degrade
men, and of course he acquires the opinions of a superior caste.   Where opportunity of sufficient association is allowed, he gets the habits, also, of this
caste.   I am of opinion, that in proportion to the
population, there are more men who belong to what
is termed the class of gentlemen, in the old southern
States of America than in any other country of the
world.   So far as pride in themselves, a courteous
air, and a general intelligence, are concerned, they
are, perhaps, quite on a level with the gentry of any
other country, though their intelligence must necessarily be chiefly of that sort which is obtained by the
use of books, rather than of extensive familiarity with
the world.   In respect to conventional manners, they
are not so generally finished as the upper classes of
other countries, or even of some classes in their own;
though I do not know where to find gentlemen of
better air or better breeding throughout, than most
of those I have met in the southern *Atlantic* States.

The American who has had the advantage of early
association with men of breeding, and who possesses
the advantages of fortune and education, occupies a
station in society that the gentleman, or nobleman, of
no country of different political institutions can ever
fill.   He sees, and knows that he exists without a superior.   He has wealth, and manner, and education,
and beyond this, neither he nor any of his countrymen can go.   No man can, in truth, go beyond them
any where; though artificial distinctions may have the

effect to reduce men *below* the consideration that these advantages should produce. So long as society shall be governed by its ordinary and natural feelings, it is not possible to deprive money, intelligence, and manners, of their influence ; but it is quite possible to give an artificial importance to other causes of distinction, to which society must bend by its own ordinances. It is true, that in some countries, actual power is connected with nominal rank ; but it is just as true, that actual power is to be attained in America, though by different means. Thus, the English gentleman may become a peer, and the American gentleman may become a Senator ; and, although the former is certain of transmitting his rank to his posterity, still it is a rank which, while it has many inferiors, has some superiors. The American who sees himself in possession of the three great requisites of an elevated condition, meets the President as an equal, who is intrusted for a time, with honourable powers, but who merely fills a station that he himself may one day occupy,

It is the fashion of Europe to talk a great deal of the levelling institutions of the United States. I have elsewhere said, that elevating would be a better word. It is difficult to conceive how institutions that admit of the strongest temptations for every man to aspire, can have the effect of placing a nation below the level of other communities. All rational theory, and what is of far more importance, the facts, prove exactly the reverse. I would defy any nation on earth to produce as many men (and women too) as the United States, allowing for their opportunities and their numbers, who have reached a creditable moral elevation of character. I include manners, no less than principles, intelligence, and other requisites. That this class will increase, both in quality and quantity, as the population becomes more dense, is,

I think, unavoidable; and then we shall have a new
face put upon certain ancient theories.

Let us suppose these States inhabited by one hundred millions of people. It is, for our present purpose,
a matter of indifference whether they shall live under
one government, or under twenty. Their men of
fortune, breeding, and education, have reached the
acme of human elevation, (of course no allusion is intended to religion,) for a patent of nobility does nothing towards raising the qualifications of its possessor,
however it may serve to depress his inferiors. We
will suppose some four or five millions of these men
acknowledging, and actually possessing no earthly
superior, in full communion with the rest of the world.
What do you think will be their effect on the condition of society? They will claim to be equal to ranks
that are admitted to be superior to the immense majorities of other nations. Nor do I see how their claim
is well to be denied. They will be quite equal in
manners, in wealth, in general elevation of character,
(even admitting that they shall be subdivided again
and again as States in political power,) and they will
insist on being equal, in society, to the highest ranks
of other countries. Now, my dear Somersetshire
baronet, what are we to do in order to maintain our
present unquestionable superiority over these gentry,
who are contriving to get above us by their levelling
institutions. We cannot pistol them down, for, unhappily, a democrat can shoot as well as an aristocrat,
and in point of numbers, they will be ten to one; we
cannot laugh them down, for the joke will be on their
side; we cannot look them down, for they will have
a full share of the substantials, and by present symptoms, I think they will have more; nor can we send
them to Coventry, for, independently of getting so
many motley nations as Europe contains, to be exactly of one mind, they will care less about the
association than we.

I have been led into this train of reflections, by studying the character of the better classes of these people, more especially as I have found them in the southern States. Their conventional manners vary, of course, according to circumstances; but that high and manly principle of fearless independence, which is almost peculiar to this country, forms a conspicuous feature in their characters. I very well know, that where manners are wanting, this bold quality may make men exacting and coarse; but where manners do prevail, and, considering the circumstances, they prevail here to an extraordinary degree, it makes men truly noble.

Slavery is not favourable to the milder qualities in the master. It may polish, but it never subdues his manner. But he who governs many human beings, without having much intercourse with his equals, is apt to acquire habits of impatience and self-will. That these qualities exist in a much greater degree in the southern than in the northern States of America, is, I believe, undeniable; though I do not think they exist to the degree that the theory would lead us to suppose.

The accounts of the violence and vindictive tempers of the people of the southern States of America are, I am quite satisfied, grossly exaggerated, not only in Europe, but in America itself. It is commonly sufficient that rare exceptions of any thing extraordinary should occur, any where, to give circulation to reports that such things are distinctive of national character. I recollect to have seen a caricature, in the Palais Royal, of an Englishman leading his wife to be sold with a halter round her neck; and I make no doubt, that to thousands of the spectators it conveyed an idea of a common national usage, if not of a law. When I descended the Ohio and the Mississippi, it was not done without some terror for my eyes; but I cannot say that I saw any body gouged

during the whole journey. Sundry marvellous tales
were told me; but, like all other marvellous exploits,
they would not endure examination. Such things
must have occurred, or the rumour would not have
been raised; but, if it were ever common, the practice is certainly getting into disuse. That rude and
violent men should have navigated these endless
rivers when their banks were nearly untenanted, is
quite probable; but the manners of the boatmen now
are about as good as those of boatmen in Europe; in
many things, they are much better.

I have elsewhere alluded to the duels of America,
and as they may properly be introduced here, we
will endeavour to discuss the subject. Personal combats are, beyond a doubt, the relics of an age when
man had the desires of high civilization, without any
other means of attaining them than by appeals to
force. The principle on which they are grounded,
says, that a man is willing to prove that he cares less
for his life than he does for his reputation. I fear,
too, that more or less of a desire to punish aggression,
or of personal feelings, are mingled with the sentiment; but as it is a chivalrous subject, we will give
it its most chivalrous construction. In the eastern
States of America, in New-York, (the city of that
name excepted,) and in parts of Ohio and Pennsylvania, duels are less frequent than, perhaps, in any
other civilized country, especially in a country where
men have as high a respect for themselves as they
have in this. My friend, who has known the more
western counties of New-York intimately for thirty
years, assures me that he does not recollect but one
duel in all that time, and that was fought full five-
and-twenty years ago. He does not pretend that this
combat stands alone; but he thinks that he should
have heard of them had there been many more. He
also excepts those meetings which took place between officers while the troops and seamen were

serving within the districts named. A duel in New-England is exceedingly rare. He accounts for this fact on his favourite principle of common sense. Religious education may do a great deal, but then common sense has something to do with religion. There are many instances in which English clergymen have been engaged in duels: and I fancy that it is not an uncommon circumstance for men who are in full communion with their respective churches, in Europe, to meet in private combats. Such a thing could scarcely occur in the United States, the reason of the people being much too exacting to allow of so broad a contradiction between profession and practice. Cadwallader thinks, and my own observation confirms his opinion, there is a greater proportion of men (in high situations of life too) in the United States, who dare, and who would, refuse, and who have refused to fight duels, on the ground of the absurdity of the practice, than in any other nation he has visited. I must say that this is the only people among whom I have found gentleman-like men who have openly laughed at the gross folly of the usage, and who, it was understood, considered themselves as too rational to be guilty of so great an act of folly. It must be admitted that common sense has done all it can do with these individuals.

Next to this class, which is very numerous in the portions of country named, come those who live in the great towns, and all the rest of the middle States. Duelling is about as common in this portion of the country, as it is in France or in England. Perhaps the older parts of Virginia and the two Carolinas may be included in this division; though, as it is thought, and I believe justly, that men in warm climates have quicker and more sensitive passions than men in colder, it is possible they may be rather more frequent.

The whole of the remainder of the Union may be

included, with certain exceptions, in another division, in which duels are probably, considering the amount of the white population, as at least four to one, compared with Europe, or even in a higher rate of disproportion.

It is necessary, however, to bear in mind one circumstance which has had a great influence in obtaining a character for the Americans, not only as duellists, but as a semi-barbarous people, in Europe. Nothing occurs the least out of the ordinary course of events, and in which the law is offended, that does not go the rounds of their thousand journals. It is also fair to suppose that the ingenuity of an editor on a remote frontier is often at a loss to give interest to his sheet, and that when an opportunity does occur, he suffers none of the more interesting, which is always the exciting, portion of the incidents to be kept in shadow.

A century ago, men met in detachments of five and six on a side, to settle some trifling point of honour between two. After this, it was thought that every man might purge himself of disgrace in his own person. Swords were used, until common sense began to teach men that it was folly to pre-suppose the same degree of strength and personal activity and skill in any two men. Then came pistols. For a long time (the practice still exists in some places) the injured party was to call out the offender, and to stand up and be shot at, before he could with propriety get a chance to redress his wrongs. This practice can surely only be accounted for by supposing that the object of the challenger was to purge himself of disgrace by risking his life.

As I understand the matter, the rough, steady, unaccommodating fashion, which the Americans have of viewing things, had long induced them to chafe under these equivocal practices. Common sense did its work thoroughly on a great proportion of the nation, who said plainly, we shall not do so ridiculous a thing as to let a man shoot at us because he has done us a wrong; and as for revenge, we think it nobler to forgive. But common sense did not go so far with, perhaps, a moderate majority. They continued to fight in the European fashion. About five-and-twenty years ago, there was a great intellectual crisis in this nation. They began to cut up certain antiquated opinions, freely, and to talk with more boldness than before, of all things connected with government, morals, and customs. When two men went into the field and both returned unharmed, the non-combatants were apt to ask, with a sneer, for what did you go there? This sort of language, which was used openly, and with something of the air of contempt, compelled the combatants to give some proof that they had been in a little jeopardy, and, in short, it set common sense at work on their side of the question. They were not sufficiently under its influence to join the non-combatants, but they had too much directness of thought not to make the practice consistent with itself. When they looked at their pistols, which were fixed with hair-triggers, and which bore a most bloody aspect, and which, by the bye, underwent all these preparations in Europe, whence they were imported, they were induced to inquire into the object of so much arrangement. The result was, that in addition to the absurdity of fighting at all, they had incurred the absurdity of fighting with so little danger, as to make the practice doubly ridiculous in the eyes of those who determined to look at the naked truth. So they began to take aim, and to practise, and to get skill, until they reached the present honourable standard.

This system of stripping a thing, that is foolish in itself, of all its inconsistent folly, has brought the custom under a certain set of rules. The true object of every duel is, or it ought to be, to exhibit courage.

A shall not injure B without incurring a certain risk; and he shall, at least, be driven to prove that he has spirit to meet that risk. It is true, that the world admits a degree of vengeance into the custom, since it says, that certain offences require two shots, and certain others may be expiated by one. But I think, on the whole, that even this extraordinary bloody-mindedness takes the aspect of an additional purgation to the man who has received the wrong. That courage which is willing to endure the pain of a wound, but which shrinks from the danger of death, say the American duellists, (in their practice) is, like the courage of a boxer, of a very inferior quality. They, therefore, deal in that which is thought to be superior.

It is quite plain that fighting is a serious thing, and serious things become a little absurd, unless done in a serious manner. But it is plain, that there must be a medium in the serious character of a duel, or men might put the pistols into each other's mouths at once, and then absurdity on the other side, would be gained, and a practice, that is sufficiently foolish in itself, is obliged to get as near the true medium as possible, or it could not exist in a common sense nation. This little prelude brings us to the field of battle.

The American brings on the ground, just as much skill with the weapon as he is to use, as he can; which, you will see, is just what the swordsman did, or the great masters of the art, the ancient chivalry of Europe. When confronted to his antagonist, he finds himself thrown on the severest possible trial of his steadiness and nerves, or on the very quality whose prepossession he came thus to prove. He knows that his life is the penalty of a blunder, just as a false guard would have been fatal with the other weapon. The result is, certainly, that, perhaps, in every two or three duels, one man falls, and, in almost all, some-body is hurt. The usual forms are much as they are in Europe. As, however, skill is deemed not only fair, but necessary, when there is reason to suspect that either party is inferior to the other in the use of the weapon, his second takes care to propose some alteration in the distance, which destroys skill, and throws the combatants more completely on their nerves. In some few instances, rifles and muskets have been used, to produce this equality, especially among border men, who have been most used to these weapons. This, is, clearly, no more than another change like that from the lance and the casque to the small-sword, and from the small-sword to the pistol. And still, so completely do we get to be the slaves of custom, that we shudder at hearing of a duel with a rifle, while we think nothing of a duel with a pistol! Surely the change from the small-sword to the pistol, was greater than the change from the pistol to the rifle. For my own part, I wish they would introduce artillery; for I feel perfectly convinced, that so long as men can maintain a reputation for spirit, at a rate so cheap as one life in ten or twelve duels, the barbarous custom will continue. It will go out of use in something like an explosion of a magazine. It is a pity that the friends of humanity had not hit on some less suspicious plan of furthering their views, than one so very equivocal as that which teaches us to believe, that this sort of honour can be maintained at the least possible danger.

With respect to the causes of the frequency of the American duels, a great deal can be said. The military and naval men have fought more duels than they would otherwise have done, on account of their long peace. Swords get impatient of quiet, and courage is a quality so vital to a soldier, that he is often uneasy until he has had an opportunity of proving its existence. They are said to be much less frequent now than formerly; especially, when the increased number of the officers is remembered.

Duels of mere manners are, if any thing, (out of the two services,) less common here than in Europe. The Doctors' Commons heals no breaches in the United States. The offence is rare, but the pistol is always the proctor. I am inclined to think that the political institutions of the nation, by bringing men of different breeding and education, more in contact than they are found in other countries, give rise to many duels.

The frequent recurrence of the elections, while they render the polls more quiet than they would be under any other system, produce a greater proportion of grave political quarrels than elections do, for instance, in England. Then the dispersed, secluded situation of the planters, in the southern States, has a tendency to foster morbid sensibility, while their habits bring them, frequently, into a species of irritating association.

The laws of England, and of most of the States of this country, are the same on the subject of duels. To kill a man in any violent rencontre, which can be readily avoided, is, by the common law, murder. Nor is it a legal plea, that mere honour was a sufficiently compulsory motive. Now, the same common sense and directness of thought, which, in some cases, makes the American refuse to fight at all, and induces him, in others, to fight in a reasonably dangerous manner, produces another difference in the practices of the mother and child, on this subject. In England, when a man is killed in a duel, the survivor is tried, and all things being found fair, he is acquitted according to opinion, and not according to law; whereas, in America, the direct and unaccommodating way these people have of considering matters, precludes such a result. The law is the same as in England, but their construction on it would be different. A man, who had killed another in a duel, would, most probably, be sentenced to be hanged, and the conventional opinion of society is, therefore, exhibited in not trying him at all. There is an occasional struggle between the combatants and the non-combatants to bring some particular case before a jury; but the former are always too wise to incur the risk; they therefore get out of the way. You may see, in this very fact, a striking difference in the manner in which thought is exercised in the two nations.

The people of this country have fought many duels with the English, while they scarcely ever fight with any other foreigners. This was, perhaps, for many reasons, to be expected. Their wars were irritating; their policy has often been conflicting; and the citizen of the young nation may have often been too sensitive, and the subject of the old nation may sometimes have been too exacting. I know no more of the matter than that the people of both nations think that their own countrymen have been right in these quarrels, and the foreigners wrong; which is only another proof that there is no great reason in any thing that appertains to the practice.

No hospitality, kindness, or courtesy, can exceed that of most of the planters of the southern States of this confederation. It was a practice, long in use, for a stranger to drive up to the door of a dwelling, of any pretension, and to ask food and lodging for the night. The custom is not entirely neglected, even now, though increased travelling, and the greater frequency of inns, have conspired to put a stop to it. This freedom of intercourse is, clearly, no more than a natural consequence of simplicity of manners, and of absence of suspicion. It is even practised in the northern States. I remember to have seen a country-house, which had the air of the residence of a man of fortune, while travelling in the interior of New-York. Cadwallader demanded its owner's name of a man by the road side. "It is near dinner-time," he then coolly said, "and we shall not fare well in these woods at the inn; let us try Mr. ————'s table." "Do you know him, then?" "Not at all; I know his family, and he must know mine." Of course I was anxious to see the result of such an interview. A servant was asked if Mr. ———— was at his residence? The answer was favourable. We were ushered into a genteel saloon, where we found a very gentleman-like man, a well-bred woman, and two or three charming daughters. "I am Mr. John Cadwallader, of Cadwallader, in ———— county," said my friend, "and I have taken the liberty to pay my respects to you in passing." Our host held out both hands, and expressed his satisfaction at the *compliment;* I was then introduced, and we found the dinner so abundant, and the wines so delicious (to say nothing of the young ladies) that we were induced to stay till next day for a second trial. In fifty other instances, have gentlemen who had heard of our presence in their neighbourhoods, ridden miles to meet us, and to invite us to their dwellings ; and I do firmly believe, that through Virginia and the Carolinas, and in several other States, we might have travelled without spending a sixpence, or eating, drinking, or sleeping in an inn. Indeed, I am persuaded that this hospitality is one reason why the inns are not better in the southern States, for, out of the towns, they are generally worse than they are found to be farther north.

From what I have written, you must have already gathered that the southern States are to be divided into two classes of society, or, rather, that in some instances, one State may, in itself, contain both. I allude to the material difference which exists between the small proprietors, who are, to all intents, capital farmers, with from four, or even from one, to twenty slaves, and the great planters, who own several hundreds. The former generally grow wheat, corn,

C c 2

(maize) and all the other articles of a divided husbandry; while the others produce tobacco, rice, cotton, or sugar. They are, however, beginning to grow tobacco in some of the free States, as in Ohio.

But I have not room, or knowledge enough, to enter into the endless details which such a state of society, and regions so vast, can produce. You will see some curious accounts of manners and customs in the "Letters from the South," a book that is ascribed to Mr. Paulding, an American writer, who stands among the highest of his countrymen for talent, and who, being a gentleman generally known to his countrymen, has had the best opportunities for observing their manners in those parts of the country that he has visited.

TO THE COUNT JULES DE BÉTHIZY,

&c. &c.

Boston, ——

I ARRIVED here about a fortnight since, in order to see the town, and to witness a ceremony that took place yesterday. Before attempting a description of the latter, I shall give a brief answer to your question concerning the movements of your countryman.

During my recent excursions to the south, I freruently met La Fayette, who has now been in nearly all, if not in every one, of the twenty-four States of this Union. So far from the warmth and cordiality of his reception having in the least abated, he is just as much the object of affectionate and sincere atten tion to-day as he was the hour he landed. We were in New-York together lately, when there was a constant succession of entertainments in his honour, and as earnest a desire manifested to press about his person as in the interviews I have so often related.

Among the different public exhibitions got up on this occasion, there was one which is worthy of being particularly mentioned, by its singularity. There is a great deal of wood used in the construction of most American houses. Until within the last twenty years a great many in New-York (more especially in the less pretending quarters of the town) were built of this material altogether. There are, consequently, an extraordinary number of fires in that city. Fires are infinitely more frequent in all parts of America than in Europe, from this very cause. In a city like New-York, it is also a consequence of frequent danger from such an enemy, that there exist admirable skill and preparation to subdue it. It is often said, and, from repeated observation I believe it to be true, that the firemen of New-York are more expert and adventurous than those of any other town in the world. When an alarm is given, the citizens, in general, give themselves no trouble in the matter, unless chance has placed them in the immediate vicinity of the danger. The cry is sounded by boys and repeated by the firemen themselves, for a minute or two, and then a few or more bells, according to the degree of the danger, ring the alarm. In the day these frequent cries produce no extraordinary sensation, but when they break in upon the stillness and security of the night, I scarcely know a more startling or disagreeable interruption to one's slumbers. There is a defect in this part of the arrangement, though it is difficult to see how it can be well remedied under the present system. The firemen are citizens; chiefly shop-keepers and mechanics, and they pursue their ordinary employments at all

times, except when required to meet to render aid,
or occasionally for the purpose of discipline. The
latter is little needed, however, in a place where
there is so much serious practice.

I remember to have been at one of these fires in
the night. A vast pile of pine boards, which filled
a lot adjoining a row of noble brick houses, was
in flames when I reached the place. Within fifty
feet, on the other side, there stood a small temporary
wooden building. The sheets of the element flashed
upwards against a battlement of brick, which they
even surmounted, and bending like the tongue of the
serpent, they wound themselves along the cornices
of the adjoining dwelling. It was too late to save
much of the lumber, and all the attention of the firemen was given to the buildings. Engine arrived after
engine, with great rapidity; and with the most beautiful accuracy, the captain of each machine took his
station in the place he was ordered to occupy. There
might have been two thousand persons collected at
the spot; but scarcely any other sound was heard
than the whizzing of the streams of water, the strokes
of the engines, and the crackling of the conflagration.
Water was thrown from one machine to another, by
means of conducting leathern tubes. One of those,
near which I stood, burst. I followed the man who
was sent on the errand that immediately succeeded
the discovery of the accident. He approached a
carriage loaded with the article he needed, and communicated the fact; " So many feet of hose," said
the person to whom he addressed himself, with perfect quiet; it was supplied, and the damage was repaired without the slightest confusion, and without
the least unnecessary delay. From time to time, the
flames were seen kindling on the roof of a small
wooden building, and then the engine nearest the
conflagration directed its stream, for an instant, to
the spot. No rifleman could have sent his deadly

messenger with surer aim, than the water fell upon
the little torch-like flame.

The families continued in the adjoining houses,
and the proprietor of the building next the lumber,
resolutely refused to open his doors for the removal
of the furniture, though his cornices were frequently
blazing. He was right; for the steadiness, activity,
and skill of the firemen, soon reduced the glaring
torrent of the elements to a pile of black smouldering
ruin.

The ceremony to which I alluded in the opening
of this letter, was a review of these firemen by La
Fayette. The engines, with their companies, were
all assembled in the little park (paddock would be a
better name,) in front of the City Hall. These engines
bear some such comparison to the engines of Europe,
as the English mail-coaches, on a birth-day, bear to
the ordinary French diligences in the provinces. No
nobleman's carriage is more glossy, neater, or, considering their respective objects, of more graceful
form. They are also a little larger than those we
see on our side of the Atlantic, though not in the
least clumsy. When La Fayette had passed in front
of these beautiful and exquisitely neat machines,
they formed themselves in a circle. At a signal the
engines were played, and forty limpid streams shot
upward, toward an imaginary point in the air. It
appeared to me that they all reached that point at
the same instant, and their water uniting, they formed
a *jet d'eau* that was as remarkable for its conceit as
for its beauty.

But the ceremony yesterday, was of a very different description. It was the anniversary of the battle
of Bunker's hill. Fifty years ago, the yeomanry of
New England first met the battalions of England, in
open and deadly conflict. The affair of Lexington
had occurred a few weeks earlier; but, though blood
was first drawn in that straggling contest, it neither

produced the important results, nor was it characterized by so many striking and memorable incidents as
the affair on the hill.

In the battle of Bunker's hill, the Americans had
no positive leader. A thousand men, chiefly youths
under the age of five-and-twenty, passed over in the
night from the adjacent country, into the peninsula
of Charlestown. It was intended to occupy a high
conical eminence called Bunker's hill, at the distance
of long cannon-shot from the batteries in the town
of Boston. By some mistake, the working party
advanced much nearer to the enemy, and took possession of a much lower ridge of land, that terminated suddenly at a short distance in their front, quite
near to the shore. The latter hill was, in fact, known
by the name of Breed's.* Here a small redoubt,
flanked by a low entrenchment, was thrown up. The
party who performed this labour, was led by a gentleman of the name of Prescott, who had seen some
service in the colonial wars, and who held the rank
of colonel in the levies of the province of Massachusetts Bay. You will remember that the affair occurred in the summer of 1775, and, as the independence of the colonies was not declared until July
1776, the appellation of *States* was then unknown.

There was an eminent physician in Boston, of the
name of Warren, who had acted a conspicuous part
in all the political measures that preceded the quarrel. This person was distinguished for his high moral
intrepidity. As he was a man in the vigour of life,
and of a daring mind, the provincial congress of Massachusetts had chosen him a major-general in their
levies, only the day before the battle.

General Warren appeared on Breed's hill in the

---

* Bunker and Breed are the names of two families of New-
England. Individuals of those names were, or had been, the
owners of the two hills in question.

morning, bearing a musket, though not with any desire to exercise his newly acquired military authority. Delicacy to his veteran countryman, and perhaps some incompleteness in the forms of his appointment; might have forbidden such an assumption of power. It is said that Mr. Prescott offered him the command, and that he declined assuming it. In the course of the movements that preceded the conflict, General Putnam, a well-known partisan officer of the adjoining province of Connecticut, led some small bodies into the peninsula, over whom, he of course exercised a species of authority. But the chief command, if it belonged to any one, was the right of Mr. Prescott, who constructed, and who held the half-finished redoubt. The result of the battle is well known; but, unhappily, at its close, Mr. Warren, or as he is usually called from the nature of his death, *General* Warren, fell, by a musket-ball which passed through his head.

The exceeding merit and unquestionable patriotism, no less than the high rank which this gentleman was destined by his countrymen to fill, induced them to consider his loss, and very justly, as the greatest calamity that befell them on that day. A small, unpretending monument, of very perishable materials, had, therefore, been erected to his memory, on the precise spot where he fell. But it is now intended to rear a column in granite, which shall be more worthy of the great occasion, and more in conformity with the augmented means of the State, to perpetuate an event which is deemed to be so creditable to their exertions in the conflict. The ceremony of yesterday was to lay the corner-stone of this monument.

I shall not pretend to enter into a detail of proceedings that were alike noble and affecting. Tens of thousands were on the hill, and Mr. Webster, a distinguished citizen of Boston, addressed his coun-

trymen from a stand where his words reached the
ears of a multitude. I saw La Fayette in the occu-
pancy of a high place, and when the orator spoke of
his particular services, there were a few minutes of
intense and delightful interest. There was also a little
group of gray-headed and tottering veterans, who,
fifty years before, had risked their lives, or shed their
blood, on the precise spot where so many people had
now assembled in prosperous and peaceful security.
Altogether it was one of the most interesting ceremonies I ever witnessed, and I regret that my limits absolutely forbid its description. Among other things,
there was an entertainment spread on the hill, of
near or quite four thousand covers.

Boston is a wealthy, a thriving, and decidedly a
picturesque town. It stands on an uneven surface,
and it occupies nearly the whole of a peninsula of
several miles in circuit. Large villages are rising
on the adjoining shores, at the different points where
the numerous bridges connect the town with what
may be called the main. The population, within a
circumference of twelve miles, must, I think, exceed
eighty thousand souls. The harbour is beautiful, and
dotted with islands. It is one of the most secure in
America, and would easily contain five or six hundred sail. But there is no fixing its limits, as it is
several miles to the open sea, and warehouses might
be erected to advantage on most of the islands, especially if a few breakwaters were constructed.

One of the best, and the oldest of the universities
of the United States, is within a few miles of Boston.
We visited this institution, as well as that of Yale, in
our journey to this place. We dined in the commons
of the latter, with one of the tutors. I was struck
with one circumstance on this occasion, which, as it
is in striking contrast with what occurs in the universities of the mother country, I shall mention.

Cadwallader has a kinsman at Yale, who is descended from one of the wealthiest and best known families of this country. The young man himself, who is a fine, gentleman-like and manly youth, is actually in possession (or will be on attaining his majority) of a fortune that would be deemed very large in most countries. He dined at a table within twenty feet of us. During the repast, which was exceedingly simple and without any beverage but water and cider, I observed one of the servants coolly seated by the side of, and in close conference with, the kinsman of my friend. In a few minutes the domestic arose to hand the bread to one of the young gentlemen. In the course of the evening, when we were at our inn, I ventured to ask the youth if the servants of the university were permitted to take such liberties. The face of the young man flushed, and he told me he did not understand me. I explained. · " Oh, that was ———— ; he is a class-mate: but he waits, during the meals, in order to pay his board: he is poor, and can do no better." " And you make a companion of him?" " Why not: is poverty a shame?" I was silenced, and when ———— had left us, the conversation was renewed between Cadwallader and myself.

" There is a singular but gross error prevalent in Europe," said my friend, " on the subject of the influence of wealth in America. Money is a positive good every where, since it buys not only necessaries, but commands, in a greater or less degree, the respect of those who wish to profit by it. But money is more within the reach of individuals here than any where else, at least, a sufficiency of money to leave men in the possession of those independent feelings which belong to nature, and which must be suppressed by some artificial cause, or they will be found in every bosom, inasmuch as they depend on the inherent qualities of pride and will. I think money of more importance in England, than in any country I

have ever visited. It is obviously necessary it should
be so, since, without it, men are reduced to scanty
means of subsistence, and to a straitened and often
miserable economy. I have seen people in England
with incomes of two or three hundred a year, existing in narrow lodgings, compelled to calculate closely
the amount of their daily consumption, and positively
enjoying no one exclusive advantage; when men of
the same income, in America, might dwell in houses
of three times their size, better furnished, and supplied in abundance with every necessary of life; indeed, in an abundance that is scarcely known in any
part of Europe. I know this fact from close observation. People may wish to dispute it; but the prices
of things are sufficient evidences of its truth. There
is scarcely a necessary of life, clothes and some few
manufactured articles excepted, that is not to be had
at about half the cost in America that it can be had
in England. But most of the exceptions are articles
to be purchased rarely: in the articles of luxury,
there is no comparison. It is, therefore, no more
than a natural consequence of such abundance, that
money should be less esteemed than where indulgences are dearer. Then our institutions, our habits,
and our opinions, give no artificial importance to
wealth. A man can neither buy preferment in church,
state, army, navy, nor in any thing else, with his dollars. He can give dinners, and he can educate his children, and give them manners, and, in this direct and
natural manner, advance his own or their importance;
but there the benefits of money cease. I do not
mean to say that society is not penetrated in America
by the use of money, for it is to be penetrated every
where by its agency; but it must be done here exactly as it is done in France, for instance; and it has
vastly less instrumentality in effecting that object than
it has in England. A rich widow cannot get precedency of her superiors, by giving her hand to any

possessor of a high title; nor can a seat in Congress be bought, and dollars be made the entering wedge of further advancement, except as people choose to yield to their influence in the shape of entertainments, extravagance, and show. In point of fact, money, without character, will do little here beyond what it can get in plain barter. But you have been at Oxford. There, young men can buy silk gowns, and, with silk gowns, consideration, and with consideration that is bought by money, they get exaggerated and unnatural ideas of its importance. You see young ———— never dreamt that his class-mate was poor, though he himself has more than twenty thousand a year. I affirm, for I have passed the ordeal, and I know it, that the thought of distinction from money never enters the head of an American schoolboy, unless, indeed, it may be the child of some exceedingly vulgar *parvenu.*

"Now, what can be more absurd than the fact that grave English writers are constantly affirming, that there is no other ground of distinction in America than money? This incessant habit of asserting so glaring a falsehood can only proceed from a consciousness of the exorbitant influence of wealth among themselves. There is no sort of doubt, that when money is united to merit and talent, in the United States, it can do more than when the latter qualities stand unsupported by so powerful an ally; but among all the unjust and ridiculous charges brought against us, there is not one more absurd than this, that money places men in power, or at the head of society, or high in the estimation of their fellow-citizens. With the exception of the Patroon, there is not a decidedly wealthy man in the whole representation of the State of New-York. Mr. Clinton is notoriously very poor. Of all the Presidents, only one could be called rich. There is not a man of any great fortune in any one of the higher offices of the general government; and it is not thought very reputable for a man of good estate to fill a situation of mere emolument. Indeed, his countrymen would not let him have it, for the simple reason that he had enough already, unless his peculiar talents were needed.

"As to society, it must always support that part of its influence which is dependent on show and expense, by money; but in large towns, where there is competition in wealth, as in other things, money does but little in this way, and it is every hour doing less. You scarcely saw a *parvenu*, unless he had merit, (and a large proportion of our *parvenus* have merit,) in the circle into which I introduced you, though you saw a vast number of men of breeding and character, who had very little money. It is impossible to prevent people who have money from riding in coaches and giving entertainments, and it is not possible to prevent people of grovelling minds from envying them these enjoyments; but it is possible for a community to be so constituted as to limit the superiority of mere money; and if such a community exists on the globe, it exists here. I dare say that men who have made their money, get purse-proud, in the United States, as they do in other places; but it must be proved that men who have not money are abject, and time-serving, and spiritless, before any thing is made out towards establishing that money does more in America than it does in France, or half as much as it does in England."

I must say, that my own observations confirm this opinion. There was a beautiful simplicity in the conduct of young ———, that denoted an entire absence of the coarser influence of money, and which spoke volumes in favour of the wise regulations of the institutions of his college. I am assured, and, so far as opportunity will allow me to speak, I have every where seen the most perfect and just equality in the treatment of the youths, in all the public schools I have visited. I am told that this was not always the case. In Harvard College, for instance, before the revolution, the aristocratic classification of the mother country prevailed, and boys were taught from earliest life, to consider the adventitious circumstances of wealth and birth as being things of primary good. As Cadwallader says, they who write of this country, should know more of the actual state of its society before they affirm so boldly that this or that influence controls society, on authority no better than the habits of those who live under systems so totally different. I have certainly seen sneers in the public journals, and heard them uttered too, against the sudden elevation of this or that individual, by means of his wealth; but I find, on examination, that his rise is little more than the style he can display, at the cost of money, and that the bottom of the complaints is generally envy. The boldness and distinctness with which these remarks themselves are made, are proofs that there is no overwhelming, since there is not even a silencing, influence attached to the possession of wealth.

TO THE COMTE JULES DE BETHIZY.

&c. &c.

Washington, ——

My pen grows weary, for I have seen so much, and written so little to the purpose, that I feel disposed to throw it away altogether. After making the tour of the coast of New-England, and seeing all its large towns, I have returned here to prepare for my departure. I cannot quit the country, however, without giving you a summary of the information I

D d 2

have gained, or without indulging a little in speculations to which that information must naturally give
rise.

The first reflection that is excited in the mind of
an intelligent foreigner, after visiting these States, is
an inquiry into the causes that have affected so much
with means so limited, and in a time so short. A
century ago, the whole of the 1,000,000 of square
miles that are now more or less occupied by these
people, did not contain a million of souls. So late
as the year 1776, the population was materially under
3,000,000; nor at the time did they actually cover
more than 200,000 square miles, if indeed they covered as much. But since the peace of 1783, activity,
enterprise, intelligence, and skill, appear to have been
contending with each other, and they have certainly
produced a result that the world has never before
witnessed. I have heard Europeans say, that when
they have heard that the Americans, of whom they
had been accustomed to think as dwellers in remote
and dark forests, possessed a million of tons of
shipping, they believed their neutral character had
made their flag a cloak for the enterprise and wealth
of other nations. No doubt their commerce was a
little unnaturally forced, and many frauds did exist;
but the motives for deception have ceased these dozen
years, and still America has a million and a half of
tonnage. Perhaps no one demonstration of the energy
of this population has excited in Europe the surprise
that has been created by the boldness and dexterity
with which they have constructed canals, that put to
shame all similar works any where else. We understand the nature and the expense of this description
of public works, and we know how to make a proper
estimate of the enterprise necessary to effect them.
But although the system of canals, which has broke
so suddenly into existence in the United States, within
the last ten years, argues an advanced and advancing

state of society, it manifests no new principle of energy. It may be a higher exhibition of the quality, since the stage of improvement demands a superior manifestation of skill; but, believe me, the spirit which has produced it has not been dormant an hour since the British colonies have achieved their independence.

Although circumstances have lessened the interest which Europe has felt in America, it may be well questioned, whether the United States do not, at this hour, enjoy a higher consideration, on our side of the Atlantic, than the political doctrines, formerly in fashion, would have given to a people so dispersed, so few in numbers, and so remote. Their vast and growing commerce, alone, makes them an object of the greatest attention; and the sure conviction that the child of that commerce, a marine, is likely soon to play its part in the great game of nations, gives additional interest to this republic. Still our anticipations are vague, founded on data but imperfectly understood, and, at all times, fettered by the prejudices and distinctive opinions of our own hemisphere.

In the first place, the influence of emigration on the growth of the United States has been usually overrated by Europeans. I have had occasion to say, already, that for thirty years it did not add many more than five thousand souls, annually, to the population. The fact is sufficiently known by the returns of the custom-houses, where all masters of vessels are obliged to report the number of their passengers. It is true, that thousands, who leave the mother country for the British provinces, find their way into the republic by land; but, perhaps, an equal number of natives have removed into the Canadas, the upper province of which is nearly, or quite half, peopled by emigrants from the States, or their descendants.

The first, the most important and the least understood, cause of the exceeding advance of the Ameri-

can States, is to be found in the character of their
population. The general diffusion of a respectable
degree of intelligence, would, of itself, produce an
effect that it might be difficult to estimate precisely,
but which may be always traced in its strongest point
of view, in the respective conditions of the savage
and of the civilized man. In addition to this general
and mighty cause, the actual necessities of society
supply an incentive to ingenuity and talent, that are
wanted elsewhere. Were the American an indolent
and contented being, nurtured in dulness, and kept
in ignorance of the incentives which prompt men to
exertion, this very state of necessity might serve to
depress him still lower in the scale of being. But
there is nothing more surprising in the country, than
the universal knowledge which exists of the condition
of Europe. Their wants, therefore, feed their desires, and, together, they give birth to all the thousand auxiliaries of exceeding ingenuity. A proof of
this fact is to be found in the manner in which the
first canal of any importance was constructed. As it
speaks volumes on the subject, I shall relate it.

Five-and-twenty years ago, engineers from Europe
began to make their appearance in America. They
brought with them the rules of science, and a competent knowledge of the estimates of force, and the
adaptation of principles to results; but they brought
them, all calculated to meet the contingencies of
the European man. Experience showed that they
neither knew how to allow for the difficulties
of a novel situation, nor for the excess of intellect
they were enabled to use. Their estimates were
always wild, uncertain, and fatal, in a country that
was still experimenting. But five-and-twenty years
ago was too soon for canals in America. It was wise
to wait for a political symptom in a country where
a natural impulse will always indicate the hour for
action. Though five-and-twenty, or twenty, or even

fifteen years, were too soon, still ten were not.   Ten
years ago, demonstrations had been made which enabled keen observers to detect that the time for extraordinary exertion had come.   The great western
canal of New-York was conceived and planned.   But
instead of seeking for European engineers, a few of
the common surveyors of the country were called to
the aid of those who were intrusted with the duty
of making the estimates; and men of practical knowledge, who understood the people with whom they
had to deal, and who had tutored their faculties in
the thousand collisions of active life, were brought
to the task as counsellors.   The result is worthy of
grave attention.   The work, in its fruits and in its
positive extent, exceeded any thing of a similar nature ever attempted in Christendom.   The authority
to whom responsibility was due, was more exacting
than any of our hemisphere.   Economy was incul-
cated to a degree little known in other nations ; and,
in short, greater accuracy than usual was required
under circumstances apparently the least favourable
to attain it.   Now, this canal was made (with such
means) at a materially less cost, in infinitely less
time, and with a boldness in the estimates, and an
accuracy in the results, that were next to marvellous.
There was not a man of any reputation for science
employed in the work.   But the utmost practical
knowledge of men and of things was manifested
in the whole of the affair.   The beginning of each
year brought its estimate of the expense, and of the
profits, and the close its returns, in wonderful conformity.   The labour is completed, and the benefit
is exceeding the hopes of the most sanguine.

   In this sketch of the circumstances under which
the New-York canal has been made, we may trace
the cause of the prodigious advance of this nation.
Some such work as this was necessary to demonstrate
to the world, that the qualities which are so exclu-

sively the fruits of liberty and of a diffused intelligence, have an existence elsewhere than in the desires of the good. Without it, it might have been said, the advance of America is deceptive; she is doing no more than our own population could do under circumstances that admitted of so much display; but she will find the difference between felling trees, and burning forests, and giving the finish which denotes the material progress of society. The mouths of such critics are now silenced. The American can point to his ploughs, to his ships, to his canals, to his bridges, and, in short, to every thing that is useful in his particular state of society, and demand, where a better or a cheaper has been produced, under any thing like circumstances of equality?

It is vain to deny the causes or the effects of the American system, dear Béthizy; nor should a man as philanthropic as yourself wish to deny them, since they rest on principles that favour the happiness and prosperity of the human race. We should not cavil about names, nor minor distinctions, in governments, if the great and moving principles are such as contemplate the improvement of the species in the mass, and not in exclusive and selfish exceptions.

The second great cause of the advancement of the United States is the abundance which is the consequence of room and of intelligence united, and which admits of so rapid an increase of its positive physical force. It is known that the population has doubled in about twenty-three years, though it is supposed that this rate of increase is gradually diminishing. It is probable that in the next fifty-five years, there will be two more duplications of the amount. Of this number, supposing that slavery continues in its present form, and under its present influences, (two things that cannot be rationally supposed,) seven millions will be slaves, and forty-three millions freemen. But slavery, though on the increase, as a whole, is known not to be on the increase in a ratio equal to that of the whites.

The third cause of the great progress of this country, and it is one intimately blended with all the other moral causes, is the perfect freedom of its civil and religious institutions, which give the utmost possible play to the energies, and the strongest possible inducements to the laudable ambition of man.

There is unquestionably a powerful action and reaction between all these influences, which produce a vast combined result. A rapid review of what has been done in the way of general improvement, in the nation, may serve to give some idea of their effects.

I shall not write here of the condition of the army, and navy, and militia, since enough has been already said to furnish a sufficiently accurate knowledge of those branches of the subject.

The finances of the United States, you know to be prosperous. The public debt, at the close of the last war, (1815,) amounted to about 120,000,000. On the first of October, 1827, it was 68,913,541 dollars. But as seven millions of this debt was created for the purchase of the bank stock so often named, the true debt should not be estimated at more than 61,913,541 dollars.* This debt pays an interest of 6, 5, 4½, and 3 per cent. On 13,296,247 dollars, an interest of 3 per cent. is paid; on 28,831,128, an interest of 6 per cent. is paid; on 15,993,972, an interest of 4½ per cent. is paid; on 5,792,000, an interest of 5 per cent. is paid. These sums make the amount named. The gradual diminution of the debt is taking place as fast as the terms of the loans will admit,

---

* On the first of January 1828, it was estimated to be 67,413,377 dollars; or, deducting the seven millions for bank stock, at 60,413,377. The writer has since seen it announced, that 5,000,000 of principal will be paid on the 1st of July, 1828, so that the debt of the United States, on that day, will be about 55,413,377 dollars, if the cost of the bank stock shall be deducted. (See next page.)

and on those portions which pay the highest rate of interest. The last *may* be redeemed in 1835, and probably *will* be redeemed, at the present rate of diminution, before the end of the next dozen years, unless some new causes for loans should occur. In addition to these facts, it must be remembered that a stock which pays but three per cent. is never worth par. Thus, if the 13,296,247 of the 3 per cents. can be bought for 80 dollars in the 100, this portion of the debt is also reduced in point of fact to 10,596,968 dollars. So that, all things considered, the whole actual debt of the United States cannot be considered as being more (on the 1st of July, 1828) than 52,714,098 dollars, or something less than 12,000,000 of pounds sterling.

In a country so united in interests, but so separated by distance, a system of extended and easy internal communication is of vital importance. Without it, neither commerce, nor political harmony, nor intelligence, could exist to the degree that is necessary to the objects of the confederation. It has therefore been effected at some cost, but in a manner that is already returning its reward in pecuniary profit, as well as in the other great essentials named. The subject naturally divides itself into three branches, viz. that of information, that of internal trade, and that of personal communication.

For the first, the general post-office, with its numberless dependencies, has been established. The diffusion of intelligence is justly considered by the American statesmen to be no less important to the preservation of their institutions, than to the general advancement of the character and power of the nation. There are in the country about 7000 post-offices, (1828,) and a nearly incalculable distance of post route. The chief of this department says, that there is now scarcely an inhabited district of any size in all these vast regions, to which the ramifications of these routes do not extend. The same admirable economy exists in the management of this department, as in all the others of the government. Although it is quite plain that comparatively little correspondence can exist to defray the expenses of routes so extended, yet the department not only pays for itself, but it is beginning to yield a small revenue to the country. One would think that, under such circumstances, the cost of letters and journals was greater here than elsewhere. You shall judge for yourself. A letter for less than thirty miles pays six cents ; for less than eighty, and over thirty, ten cents ; for less than one hundred and fifty miles, and over eighty, twelve and a half cents ; for all distances over four hundred miles, twenty-five cents. A cent is one hundredth part of a dollar, or about an English half-penny : thus a letter will be transferred fifteen hundred miles, for a shilling sterling. Double letters pay double, until they attain a certain weight, when they begin to pay by the ounce. Printed sheets, journals, or any thing else, pay one cent, for less than one hundred miles, per sheet, and one cent and a half for all distances over. The editors of public journals receive all their printed sheets gratis. The mail is carried in coaches a great proportion of the distance, in sulkies in other portions, and on horseback the rest.

The personal communication is effected by means of stage-coaches and steam-boats. The vast rivers, and the prodigious facilities that are offered by means of the bays, enable passengers to travel with astonishing ease, rapidity and cheapness. The traveller may leave Boston by land ; a ride of forty-five miles brings him to Providence ; here he embarks for New-York, 200 miles further, by the way of the sound of Long Island ; the Raritan carries him to Brunswick ; a few miles more of land carriage takes him to the Delaware ; the river and bay of that name bring him to New-castle ; three hours by land, and he is on the waters of the Chesapeake ; from the bay he may ascend half a dozen rivers, or proceed along the coast. At Norfolk, he enters a canal, and by means of sounds, bays, and trifling land carriage, it is quite possible to reach the southern limits of Georgia. Most of this route is travelled in the manner I have described, and the rest of it is daily getting to be more so.

The internal commerce of America exists with the least possible encumbrance. It is conducted chiefly by water, and an immense deal of it is done coastwise, by means of the rivers, that are so many arteries penetrating the country in every direction. A license costs a few dollars, (two I believe,) and when a vessel is provided with such a document, there is no impediment to its passage into any of the public waters of the country. The whole confederation is unqualifiedly one nation in respect to commerce.

The government of the United States is also making certain military roads that are intended to intersect the country in those directions in which water does not flow. In addition to these improvements, States and chartered companies are effecting a vast deal more in the same way, that I have neither the room nor the knowledge necessary to communicate. As the debt is discharged, and larger sums come into the disposal of Congress, it is to be presumed that they will increase the expenditures, by advancing the improvement of the country in all things that properly belong to their power.

In manufactures, the Americans have made immense progress, since their separation from the mother country. The great Lord Chatham declared it should be the policy of England to prevent her colonies from manufacturing even a hobnail; and this plan of monopolizing wealth was tolerably successful, so long as the Americans were dependent on England, and even for many years afterwards. But, although the importations of this country, for home consumption, are greater now than they ever have been, its own manufactures have increased fifty-fold.

The question of protecting manufactures by legislative enactments, is the one which involves more political warmth, at the present time, than any other question of mere policy. Indeed, it may be said to be the only one. The disputants are chiefly men that are immediately interested in the result, though it is certain, that a few leading politicians adopt the opposite sides on policy or on principle. The only real point in dispute is, whether America has reached the period when it has become her interest to encourage her manufactures, at some little expense to her commerce, or rather at some little expense and loss to those who are engaged in particular branches of commerce, since it is obvious that nothing can have a greater tendency to increase the trade between different sections of a country like this, than increasing its objects. A vast deal is said, pro and con, on this subject. One party contends that it will destroy the shipping, and prove fatal to the revenue. If this reasoning be true, then the time is inevitable when the shipping and revenue of the United States must disappear, for nothing is more certain than that the time will come, when a vast proportion of their population will find that no great community can exist in prosperity, without a division of employment. But it is plain that these partisans utter absurdities, since it is a matter of perfect indifference to the citizen to whom or by what process he pays the dollar of duty that he is now obliged to pay for his coat. If the collector of some port does not receive it, some other collector can and will. But this dollar will be paid on an increased price, since the American manufacturer cannot put his goods in the market as cheap as the foreign manufacturer, or he would not ask for protection. This may be true at the moment, and I am of opinion, that, with the exception of articles that are deemed important to defence, and perhaps to certain articles that require some little time to give them the perfection necessary to competition, no laws will be passed immediately on the subject. The question of manufactures is, however, clearly one of interest. Of their usefulness, and of their being one of the most active agents of wealth, as well as of the comfort of society, there can be no doubt. It is therefore like so many other questions in America, purely one of time. Although it may not accord with her policy this year, to encourage them, or for her citizens to embark in them, the result is inevitable. A nation that lives as fast as this, does not compute time by ordinary calculations. Fifty years ago, they manufactured next to nothing. They now manufacture almost every article of familiar use, and very many of them, much better than the articles that are imported. They even begin to export. The coarse cotton goods of this country are already sent to South America, and I am told that they are preferred to the British. Importations of coarse cottons from India have entirely ceased; and indeed I was assured that their coarse cottons were greatly preferred in their own markets to any other.

The American manufacturer has to contend with one difficulty, that is not known to the manufacturers of other countries. The unobstructed commerce of the United States admits of importations from all quarters, and of course the consumer is accustomed to gratify his taste with the best articles. A French duke might be content to use a French knife or a French lock; but an American merchant would reject both: he knows that the English are better. On the other hand, an English duchess (unless she could smuggle a little) might be content with an English silk; but an American lady would openly dress herself in silk manufactured at Lyons. The same is true of hundreds of other articles. The American manufacturer is therefore compelled to start into existence full grown, or nearly so, in order to command success. I think this peculiarity will have, and has had, the effect to retard the appearance of articles manufactured in the country, though it will make their final success as sure as their appearance will be sudden.

It is impossible to speak with certainty on the details of a question so complicated. A thousand articles are manufactured already, and may be considered as established. Twenty years ago, the Americans imported all their good hats; fifteen years ago, they imported most of their coarse cottons; and ten years ago, they imported most, if not all, of their fine glass and ornamental hardware, such as fire-grates, &c. A vast deal of these importations have ceased, and I am told that, considering the increase of the consumers, they are diminishing daily.

Though the particular matter that is now in dispute may be one of deep interest to certain merchants and manufacturers, it is clearly not the main question. Manufacturing is a pursuit so natural, and one so evidently necessary to all extended communities, that its adoption is inevitable at some day or other. The policy of the Americans wisely leaves them, in all cases except those of extraordinary necessity, (which become exceptions of course,) to the operation of natural influences. Policy will, nineteen times in twenty, indicate its own wants. If it be admitted that a people, who possess the raw materials in abundance, who enjoy the fruits of the earth to an excess that renders their cultivation little profitable, must have recourse to their ingenuity, and to their industry, to find new employments and different sources of wealth, then the Americans must become manufacturers. When the true hour shall arrive, it will be vain to utter speculative reasons, for the wants of the nation will work out their own cure.

If restrictive laws shall be necessary to effect it, the people will allow of a lesser evil to get rid of a greater. When the manufacturers of America have once got fairly established, so that practice has given them skill, and capital has accumulated a little, there will be no fear of foreign competition. The exceeding ingenuity and wonderful aptitude of these people will give them the same superiority in the fabrication of a button or of a yard of cloth, as they now possess in the construction of a ship, or as they have manifested that they possess in the construction of a canal. A sufficient motive is all that is necessary to induce exertion. They have taken the infallible measure to insure success, in bringing the greatest possible number of competitors into action, by diffusing intelligence so widely, and to an extent so creditable. I think that most questions of manufacturing will be settled practically in the next five-and-twenty years.

The vast extent of the United States affords all the means of wealth and comfort that climate, mines, and other natural facilities, can supply. They are known to possess lead, copper, gold, iron, salt, and coal. The lead mines of Missouri are very extensive, and, with little or no skill, are already productive. The gold of Carolina is probably quite as abundant as is desirable. Copper is found in many places, but it is not yet much wrought. Iron is abundant, much worked, and some of it is more esteemed than any imported. Salt abounds, and could easily supply the whole country, or even furnish the article for exportation. It is not mined for yet, since the springs are found so saturated with the mineral as to render the process of boiling and evaporation more profitable. Coal exists in various parts of the country. It is procured, however, chiefly in Virginia, Pennsylvania, and Rhode Island. It is of various kinds, and of different degrees of excellence. That most in use is of the class *an thracite.* Of this species there are several gradations of quality. That of Pennsylvania is said to be the best. Mountains of coal exist in that State, and the people of the growing manufacturing town of Pittsburgh cut it out of the hills with as much facility as they would bring away an equal weight of dirt. Canals and railways are made to several of the coal mines, or rather coal *mountains*, and domestic coal is getting into very general use. The coal of eastern Pennsylvania is most fortunately placed. It lies within sixty or seventy miles of Philadelphia, to which place it is already conveyed by water. Philadelphia has a large capital, is now a great manufacturing town, and will probably be one of the largest in the world in the course of half a century. When at Philadelphia, coal, or any thing else, can be carried by water to any part of the country which has a water communication with the ocean.

The cultivation of the vine has commenced. Wine is already made; though, as time is absolutely necessary to produce excellence in the quality of the grape, and as capital is still easily convertible to so many lucrative uses, it is possible that half a century may elapse before the United States shall export their liquors. That they will sooner or later do so, is, I think, beyond a doubt. The silk-worm is also beginning to attract attention, and plantations of the olive are coming daily more into fashion. In short, there are no means of comfort, indulgence, or wealth, that the Americans, in some one part of their country, cannot command; and it would be as weak, as it will unquestionably be false, to suppose that a people so sagacious and so active will neglect them beyond the moment when circumstances shall render their adoption profitable or convenient.

The construction of canals, on a practical scale, the mining for coal, the exportation of cotton goods, and numberless other improvements, which argue an advancing state of society, have all sprung into existence within the last dozen years.* It is a knowledge of these facts, with a clear and sagacious understanding of their immense results, coupled with the exciting moral causes, that render the American sanguine, aspiring, and confident in his anticipations. He sees that his nation lives centuries in an age, and he feels no disposition to consider himself a child, because other people, in their dotage, choose to remember the hour of his birth.

How pitiful do the paltry criticisms on an inn, or the idle, and, half the time, vulgar comments on the vulgarity of a *parvenu*, become, when objects and facts like these are pressing themselves on the mind! I have heard it said, that there are European authors who feel a diffidence of contracting acquaintances with American gentlemen, because they feel a consciousness of having turned the United States into ridicule! I can tell these unfortunate subjects of a precipitate opinion, that they may lay aside their scruples. No American of any character, or knowledge of his own country, can feel any thing but commiseration for the man who has attempted to throw ridicule on a nation like this. The contest is too unequal to admit of any doubt as to the result, and the wiser way will be for these Quixotes in literature to say and think as little as possible about their American tilting match, in order that the world may not liken their lances to that used by the hero of La Mancha, and their helmets to barbers' basins.

---

* Forty years ago, no cotton was raised in the United States

TO SIR EDWARD WALLER, BART.

&c. &c.

Washington, ——

HAVING given so much of our attention to the subject of the sources of the national importance possessed by the Americans, it may not be without its use to devote an hour to the consideration of the manner in which they will probably be used. The points of main interest are, whether the present republican institutions of the country will endure, and whether the States will long continue to act as one people, or will submit to be divided into two or more confederacies.

The first fact that strikes an intelligent man, in considering the structure of this government, and the state of society that exists under it, is its perfectly natural formation. It is scarcely possible, I am not sure that it is possible, to conceive of a community which has attained the advantages of high civilization, that is less artificial.

In order that individual efforts should be excited (without which nations must inevitably become sluggish, and finally barbarous, though dwelling in any abundance,) the rights of property are respected. Beyond this the law leaves every man (the slaves in the southern States excepted) on grounds of perfect equality. This equality is, however, an equality of rights only; since talents, money, and enterprise, being left to their natural influences, produce their natural effects, and no more.

In respect to the continuation of the present republican institutions of this country, every fact, every symptom, and all reasoning, is, I think, in their favour. In the first place, they have, in substance, continued for nearly, and in some instances for quite, two centuries. The habits of the people, their education, their feelings, and their interests, unite to preserve them. It is true, there are not many instances in the world, of governments on an extended scale, existing for any great length of time, in forms nearly resembling those of the United States; but there are examples enough to prove that governments have endured for centuries on *principles* that will make this endure, though policy were less active than it is in contributing to its preservation. We will endeavour to find some of them. The government of England is representative, and to a great degree it is free; that is to say, it is a government of laws, instead of being a government of will, which I take it constitutes the essential difference between liberty and despotism. Now, the main point of difference between the government of England, and that of the United States, is in the bodies that are the respective repositories of power. In the former country, the power is in the aristocracy; in the latter country, it is in the people. That the latter is more natural, is sufficiently evident, from the fact that England itself has been quietly tending towards the same result, during two centuries, under circumstances that have been calculated to bring natural influences into play. It is true, that the power still rests in the aristocracy, but it is not an aristocracy that is exclusive. To speak of the *governing* aristocracy of England, as a class of nobles, is absurd; it is the aristocracy of wealth, of talents, and of enterprise, that rules Great Britain. Were the avenues to political power closed against the approach of new aspirants, the government of Great Britain would be overturned in a dozen years. It is not in the power of art to repress the energy of natural influences, when they have once gathered head. The

effect of vast commerce, of intelligence diffused to a
certain degree, and of individual enterprise, has been
to wrest the power from the crown, to curtail its influence in the lords, and to repose most of its exercise
in the commons.   Now, all that democracy can do
without recourse to violence in England, is here
done, because it is obeying a natural law.   But the
very difficulty which is found in effecting a final triumph, (as by compelling the lords to acquiesce at
all times in the wishes of the commons,) proves the
difficulty of completely wresting power from those
who hold it, though they may happen to be the few.
So far it is an argument in favour of the perpetuity
of the American democracies, for they, too, are used
to the authority of the people.   Still, public opinion,
which is no more than popular law, is so triumphant,
that it is difficult to conceive a question on which
a clear majority of the people of England should be
decidedly united, that the three estates would incur
the risk of opposing.   Let us turn the picture to the
side of America.

Here we have a government in which the people
are the sources of power.   The state of society is
precisely that (though in a still higher degree) which
in England has wrought a change from absolute monarchy to a species of qualified aristocracy.   Instead
of waiting for the march of natural events, circumstances permitted that they should be anticipated.
They have been anticipated, and so far from a reaction being the result, greater harmony is daily occur-
ring between causes and effects, as the government
gets more adapted to practical objects.

I see but one possible manner in which the people
of the United States can ever lose any of their liberty.
They may enact laws of a more rigid character as
the advancement or corruption of society shall require them, and they may possibly be driven to some
slight curtailments of the franchise for the same

reason; but this will, in no degree, change the principle of their government. By losing their intelligence, the people of the United States may lose the consciousness of their rights, and with it their enjoyment. But all experience goes to show how difficult it is to wrest vested rights from communities.

But the vulgar argument against the perpetuity of the American government, is the impossibility that the rich should not govern the poor, and the intellectual the weak of mind. The continuation of property in families, and its consequent accumulation in individuals, by entails, is a provision of aristocracy in order to secure its power. The very provision itself argues a consciousness of natural weakness. It is evident, that it is as unjust, as it is opposed to our common affections, to make one child affluent at the expense of half a dozen others. No man, left to the operation of natural feeling, would do so cruel an act. This fact is sufficiently proved by the example of the Americans themselves, who have a perfect right to do this injustice if they please, by simply making those in existence, and who have a natural hold on their affections, the subjects of the wrong. Still no man does it. It is true that the father of an only son might create a sort of short entail, that should work injustice to descendants he could not know; or a father who was educated under an artificial system, where advantages are actually established from the practice, might do the same thing; but we have proof in the United States, that the father will not do it, under the operation of natural causes. Now, the Americans have taken care that this artificial state of things shall not occur, for strict entails cannot be made; and if one father should be so obdurate and unnatural as to do a wrong, in order to rob parties who were strangers to him, of their natural rights to his estate, he has no pledge that his son will be as absurd as himself.

There is no truth more certain, than that property will regulate itself when left to itself. It will change hands often, and become the reward of industry, talent, and enterprise. But we have no need of speculating in order to know what effect money will produce on the institutions of America. There are thousands of rich men here, and of very rich men too, and there is not a class of the community that has less political power. There are many reasons why it should be so.

Wealth gives no direct influence in politics. Seats in Congress are not bought and sold. Then the owners of great wealth are two-thirds of the time more agreeably employed in its increase, than in courting popularity, without which, nothing political can be done; and there is also a reluctance to give men, who have much money, places of much profit at all. But it is plain, that wealth, even supposing it could be brought to act in concert throughout a country like this, can never work a change in its institutions, until it can be accumulated for generations; and that is a result the institutions themselves forbid. Indeed, so little do I think a danger that is so often named is to be dreaded, that I think there would be vastly more danger, that the people of a nation like this would find means to strip any given set of men of exorbitant wealth, than the set of men themselves would find means to strip the nation of its liberties. Neither case is likely to occur, however, since the danger is scarcely within the bounds of a reasonable probability.

Talents may unite to destroy the rights of the people. I take it, that talents are just as likely to regulate themselves, and to produce an equality, as money. It is not in nature, that any great number of talented men should conspire to overturn the government, since, in the first place, it would require an improbable unanimity of talent, and, in the second place, a

majority of the conspirators would be literally selling their birthrights for messes of pottage. If there be
a country in the world where talent has already a
certain and manly road to preferment, it is in this.
Under the present system, each man can work for
himself, whereas, by changing it to a monarchy, the
many would have to toil for the advantage of the
few. As to those inducements which are known to
influence men in Enrope, such as titles, and decorations, they are entirely artificial; and I know, from
observation, that it would be a difficult matter to get,
even now, a vast proportion of the Americans to consent to use them. We are completely the creatures
of habit in all these matters, and it is the habit of
the American to look on distinctions of this nature
with a cold eye. This peculiarity of opinion is gaining ground daily, for there was, for a time, on precisely the same principle of habit, a lingering of the
ancient prejudices. We should never forget that the
moral influence of this nation is beginning to manifest itself in stronger colours every hour. The time,
I think, is near, when the American gentleman will
pride himself as much on his peculiar simplicity, as
gentlemen of other nations take pride in their quar-
terings and titles. The strength of this feeling will
keep even pace with the power of the nation, until
it will become difficult indeed, to persuade a man
that glories in having no worldly superior, to submit
to a division of society, that, by an artificial arrangement, shall place him beneath so many others. You
will remember, that the great difference between this
government and most others, is the important fact,
that the Americans began at the bottom to raise their
superstructure, whereas we have, in nearly every instance, began at the top to work downwards. Men
have been elevated towards the throne in our systems; but in what manner are you to elevate a man
who finds himself already at the summit? It is true,

that if a hundred, or a thousand Americans could monopolize the honours and emoluments of a change of government, that number might conspire to keep their present elevation, and force the rest of the nation below them. But a thousand, nor ten thousand men of the highest talent, could not persuade a million to give up rights that they are educated to believe inherent, even if these ten thousand could agree among themselves as to the gradations of their own rewards. A nobleman of France, or of England, cannot understand the sort of veneration that a vizier feels for the Grand Turk; and any attempt on the part of the sovereigns of these two countries, to bring the peers into the abject submission that is practised in the seraglio, would induce a singular commotion. Now, to the American it is just as inconceivable how one man can yield precedency, or respect, or submission to another, merely because he happens to be born an eldest son. You see all this is artificial, and the fact of its long existence in the world establishes nothing, but the opinions of the world. Opinions that are the nearest to nature, are the least liable to change. The world thought that the sun moved round the earth until quite lately, and yet the fact, I believe, is not so. We will sum up this argument in a very few words. Ten centuries ago, one century since, nay, twenty years since, very different opinions existed in Europe on the subject of governments from those that are now getting into fashion. The tendency is to natural rights, at the expense of artificial institutions. In some few instances, change has been attempted by revolution; but revolution is a dangerous remedy. The Americans had no revolution, strictly speaking; they have only preceded the rest of Christendom in their reforms, because circumstances permitted it. If they have gone farther than it may be wise for other nations to follow, it is no reason that they are not safe themselves. So has

England gone farther than France, and France farther than Sweden, and Sweden farther than Russia. There is no danger of reaction in America, for there has been no blow to produce the rebound. The progress has been steady and natural; and there must be a gradual return to the ignorance of the thirteenth and fourteenth centuries, to effect any material change. It is odd enough, that in an age when even despotism is fettered by public opinion, men should affect to believe that a people who feel its influence more than any other, who have fortified their institutions by law, by habit, and by common sense, are liable to be affected by causes that are hourly losing their ascendancy in every other country.

I shall state one more simple fact, leaving you to reason on it for yourself. So far from increasing familiarity and intercourse with the system of Europe producing any desire for imitation on the part of those Americans who are brought in contact with our privileged orders, it is notorious, that it produces quite a contrary effect.

But the question of infinitely the most interest is that which touches the durability of the confederation. It is the only one of the two that is worthy of grave comment.

If we fix the habitable territory of the United States, east of the Rocky Mountains, at 1,000,000 of square miles, we shall not exceed the truth. By giving a population of 150 to the square mile, we get a gross amount of 150,000,000 for the population of this republic. In 1850, the population will probably be 24,000,000; in 1880, 48,000,000; and in 1920, near, or quite, 100,000,000. I do not think there are sufficient reasons to distrust the increase so far as the period named. If any thing, I believe I am materially within bounds.

Now the first impression that strikes the mind, is the impossibility that 100,000,000 of people should consent to live quietly under the same government. It is quite certain that such vast masses of intelligent men could not be controlled by force; but it remains to be proved that they cannot be kept together by interest. Let us examine how far the latter agent will be active.

The people of the United States can, under no other arrangement, enjoy protection against foreign wars at so cheap a rate. Aggression on their rights will be out of the question, should they remain united. Should they separate, they would make rivals, and of course enemies, at their own doors. Nature has adapted these vast regions to profit by internal trade. This species of commerce can never be conducted on terms so favourable as those offered by the Union. Should they separate, a thousand irritating and embarrassing questions about the right to navigate the rivers and bays, would unavoidably occur, which now are unknown. They are a people of peculiar institutions, and vast political weight is necessary to secure the proud and manly population of this country, the respect they claim in foreign countries. They have felt the degradation of being contemned; they are beginning to know the privileges of being respected; and they will shortly enjoy the advantages of being feared. It is not in nature to suppose that men will wilfully and blindly throw away their superiority. I think there will also be an outward pressure that will tend to unite them still closer.

The confederated government of the United States has not power enough to make itself dangerous to the rights of the States. In the first place, it is no more than a representation of the people in another form; and there is little probability that any decidedly unpopular policy can long continue, if, indeed, it could be adopted at all. Each hour lessens the danger of particular States receding from the Union, by lessening their relative importance. Even New-York, with ten millions of inhabitants, would be embarrassed, surrounded by a powerful rival of fifty or sixty millions. The great communities would be safer, and more important, by exercising their natural influence in the confederation, and the smaller could not exist separately. But it may be thought that the separation will take place in such a manner as to divide the present Union into two great nations. That these expectations are vague, and founded on a general reasoning that may be false when applied to a particular case, is evident by the fact that men are divided on the grounds of this separation. Some say that the slave-holders will separate from their northern brethren; and some think that the line will be drawn north and south. Now, in point of fact, there is no solid reason in either of these opinions, except as they have a general reference to the difficulty of keeping such masses of men together. My own opinion is, that the United States are now passing, or, in fact, have in a great measure passed, the ordeal of the durability of the Union.

As to grave shakings of the head, and general assertions, they prove nothing, unless, as they often do, they prove ignorance. Forty years ago, unbelievers would have shaken their heads, had they been told that a constitutional government would now exist in France. We must look at plain, direct, and natural causes, for the influences that are to support, or to destroy, this confederation. We can easily see the advantages of the connexion, now let us endeavour to seek the disadvantages.

The first objection that presents itself is distance. But distance is an object that has more force now, when roads and communication by water are in their infancy, than it can ever have hereafter. Existing facts, therefore, not only show that the United States are sufficiently near to each other for all practical and desirable purposes of general government, but that in truth the empire might still be extended without material inconvenience.

The next objection is the question of slaves and of freedom. The control of the slaves is a matter left entirely to the States who hold them; and, so far as they have any direct influence on the durability of the Union, it is, I think, in its favour, by adding an additional motive for its continuance to the southern States. One might acknowledge a danger of a difference of habits arising under the slave policy, that would induce a dangerous difference in character, were it not for the fact, that this state of things has existed so long, and that the people of the north and the people of the south are rather assimilating than becoming more widely distinct in their habits and opinions.

Next comes local interest. This, after all, is the only point worthy of much consideration. It is a branch of the subject that presents two or three different aspects. That of employment, that of geographical inducements to divide, and that of minute separate interests. It is plain that the people of a country in which there is so great a diversity of soil and of climate, must pursue different employments. But is not this fact rather a motive of harmony than of dissension? They can supply each other's wants, without incurring the danger of rivalry. The northern man will exercise his ingenuity, and will be the mariner; the man of the middle States will grow the primary necessaries of life; and the southern man will supply both with luxuries. The manufacturer will buy wheat, and tobacco, and wine, and fifty other necessaries, of the Virginian, Marylander, &c. and cotton, and sugar, and olives, and fruits, of the southern man. They are necessary to each other; and it is therefore plain their interests are united.

As to the geographical inducements to separate, it

is impossible (when distance is admitted to be con-
quered) to discover more than one. There might,
under certain circumstances, be a reason why countries that lie on the tributaries of the Mississippi, for
instance, should wish to be under one government.
But they *are* under one government already, and by
what process can they be more so than they are at
this moment? The Kentuckian, and Tennessean,
and Ohiese, and Indianian, might lose some advantages, in the way of geographical inducements, by
separating from New-York to cling to Louisiana, or
vice versa; but what could he possibly gain? There
might have been a danger of such a separation, when
the outlet of the Mississippi was the property of another nation; but the outlet of the Mississippi is now
the property of the republicans themselves. The
citizen of New-Orleans has just as much influence in
the general government as the citizen of New-York
or Boston. Independently of these facts, which, I
think, contain an unanswerable argument, each day
is so ramifying and connecting interests throughout
the whole of this Union, as to render it difficult to
the States, which might be thought to be the most
exposed to what I have called geographical inducements, to make a selection, even in circumstances
that should compel a choice.

The control of minute interests might easily lead
to dissensions, in a free country. But the natural
and exceedingly happy constitution of American society leaves the States the control of all matters that
do not require concentrated action; it leaves even
the counties and towns, also, the right of controlling
their more minute interests.

Now, where are we to seek a rational argument
for believing that this confederation will dissolve?
Its plan of government leaves as few matters of contention as possible; while the interests, the habits,
the feelings, and the history, of the people, are the

same. Moral and physical causes unite to keep them together, while nothing indicates that they must divide, but sage and incredulous shakings of the head! I make no doubt, that if Cœur de Lion had been told his brother would be forced to grant a charter to his barons, his head would have been shaken too; and that Queen Elizabeth would not have believed that the royal *veto* could ever slumber for a century; or that Isabel might have entertained rational doubts of her American provinces becoming more important dominions than her own Aragon—and yet all these things have come to pass! Are we to believe for ever only what we wish? We are told that China contains a hundred and fifty millions of people, in one empire; and why are we to believe that semi-barbarians have more wisdom than a nation that has shown itself as shrewd, as firm, and as constant as the Americans?

Let us give one moment's attention to the political history of this republic since its establishment.

Between the years 1775 and 1789, a confederation existed, which, though it imperfectly answered the objects of the war, partook of that flimsiness of texture which has proved the bane and weakness of so many previous political unions. The Americans, instead of becoming impatient and restive under acknowledged difficulties, deliberately went to work to remedy the evil. The present constitution was formed. Its chief merit consists in its yielding to unavoidable evils, its consulting natural objects, and its profiting by those advantages which had endured the test of time. This is a broad foundation on which to repose the fabric of government.

Until near the end of Washington's administration, the Americans were scarcely treated with the courtesy that was due to a nation. The character of that illustrious man lent a dignity to his government, which adventitious circumstances would have refused. England boldly held military posts within the undeniable limits of the country ; and a thousand indignities, and numberless acts of injustice, disgraced the history of that period. Commanders of vessels of war exercised a lawless authority on the coasts of the republic ; and there is an instance on record of a captain of a sloop of war, openly and insolently refusing to obey the civil authorities of the country, because he knew that he commanded a greater nautical force than that of the whole republic united. At that day, Europeans generally believed these people black and barbarous ; and they listened to accounts of their proceedings, as we listen to the events of farther India.

Then followed the general war, with its abuses. The vast commerce of America grew, but it became a prey to all the belligerents. Acts, that would disgrace any man of the smallest pretension to character, were committed by boastful nations, under the pitiful plea of power ; and the complaints of a remote people, were despised and ridiculed, for no other reason than that they were a nation weak and dispersed. But a mighty spirit was in the land. The statesmen were wary, firm in their principles, yielding to events while they protested against injustice, and watchful to let no opportunity of regaining their rights pass without improvement. At this period, an immense region, which possessed countless positive advantages, which offered a foothold to rivals, and which was a constant temptation to division among themselves, was peaceably acquired. The purchase of Louisiana was the greatest masterstroke of policy that has been done in our times. All the wars, and conquests, and cessions of Europe, for the last hundred years, sink into insignificance, compared with the political consequences that are dependent on this increase of territory. Spain had been accessory to the wrongs, and Spain too was quietly made to contribute to the peace and security of the republic, by a cession of the Floridas.

A new era is now about to dawn on this nation. It has ceased to creep; it begins to walk erect among the powers of the earth. All these things have occurred within the life of man. Europeans may be reluctant to admit the claims of a competitor, that they knew so lately a pillaged, a wronged, and a feeble people; but Nature will have her laws obeyed, and the fulfilment of things must come. The spirit of greatness is in this nation: its means are within their grasp; and it is as vain as it is weak to attempt to deny results that every year is rendering more plain, more important, and more irresistible.

NOTES.

NOTE A.—*Pages* 89 and 205.

Soon after the writer arrived in England, he read an article in the LXXIII. number of the Quarterly Review, which created some surprise, as it imparted very different opinions on the subject of the United States' navy, from those which he had communicated to his friends. The article to which he alludes, professes to review the " Personal Narrative of Travels," &c. " with Remarks on the present State of the American Navy, by Lieutenant the Honourable Frederick Fitzgerald de Roos, Royal Navy," and another book on the same country, to which it is not necessary to refer. Anxious to know whether it was possible that he himself could have fallen into so many gross errors on the subject of the American marine, he took the following plan of arriving, as near as circumstances would allow, to the truth. He sent the Review and Travels to an American naval officer, now in Europe, with a request that he would read them, and favour him with his written opinion of the professional facts contained in both. The answer is below.

" I shall comply with your request quite cheerfully. You are at liberty to make such use of the little information I shall impart, as you may think proper: though I have some delicacy in placing my name before the world as an author, which, as you very well know, implies a pursuit but little in accordance with the education and habits of a sailor.

" I presume you do not intend that I shall touch on any matters contained in either of the works you have sent me, but those which are strictly professional. Were any one disposed to enter into a critical examination of the Review, or of the ' Travels,' I think very many points would present themselves for critical examination. The reviewer, for instance, might be asked on what authority he pronounced that ' ten thousand of the men that fought at Waterloo, would have marched through North America,' when it is matter of history, that twelve or fourteen thousand of the same men, went to the right about, after penetrating the State of New,

York some forty or fifty miles, for fear of the militia of his diaffected New-England, which was flocking across Champlain to oppose them in thousands, and who, forty years before, had led the precise number he has named (10,000) captives to Boston! I had thought the battles of Chippewa, Niagara, and the two affairs of fort Erie, to say nothing of Bunker's Hill, New-Orleans, Plattsburgh, Saratoga, and a multitude of other places and events, might have spared us, in 1828, the vapourings that were so much in fashion in 1775. I incline to the opinion that the reviewer is no better soldier than I am myself: and I think it will be in my power to show that he has not the utmost possible familiarity with naval subjects. Mr. de Roos might also be asked on what authority he says 'that most of the respectable inhabitants of New-York are seen in turn' in the bar-room of the City Hotel. If it be the same authority which induced him to say that 'New-York is situated on the *Peninsula* which separates the Hudson and the East River,' I beg to assure him, that it is not entitled to the smallest credit. But we will quit these general subjects, for those on which I am more particularly at home.

"The reviewer commences his nautical career by saying, 'It is not for us to decide on the policy of the American government, with regard to the increase of its naval force.' I take this to be the least exceptionable declaration in the whole article. I shall pass over every point that requires argument to support it, for it is my intention to deal as much as possible with facts. The reviewer says, 'it will require a long time, &c. before America can deal single-handed with the navy of any of the maritime powers of Europe.' Now, I think, the facts would show that, England and France excepted, there is not another navy in the world as strong as that of the United States. 'Viewing it in its greatest extent,' &c. says the reviewer, 'it (the American navy) may be considered to consist of twelve sail of the line, twelve frigates, nine sloops, and a few barges, &c.' The navy of the United States consists of twelve sail of the line, one sixty, twelve forty-fours, three thirty-sixes, sixteen corvettes and sloops, with a few smaller cruizers. These vessels are all on the ocean. There is (as you say by an error of the press) an omission of several frigates in your own letter, page 76 of Vol. II., of the sheets you have obligingly permitted me to read. Your total amount of our marine is correct, but the omission has been made in the detail. Considering the size and condition of these vessels, what other marine, except those named, is as strong? The reviewer says, that 'the order of Congress for building these ships (of the line) limited their size to that of seventy-fours,' &c. Now it happens that the limitation was just the other way, the law saying that they should not be *less* than of seventy-four guns. I do not understand what the reviewer means, when he says a ship is not intended to be launched, '*being* built under sheds.' Does he believe the Americans build ships to look at? Next comes a minute division of an erroneous account of our force. (See Review, page 273, near the bottom.) One instance of its mistakes shall suffice. ' Of the twelve frigates, five have been built,' &c. The United States, the Liberator, the Guerrier, the Java, the Macedonian, the Constitution, the Congress, the Brandywine, and the Potomac, are all afloat, and most of them have been used. In this detailed account the reviewer rightly gives two ships rating twenty-four guns, ' but which,' he continues, ' can mount many more.' One word on this subject in passing. The John Adams, twenty-four, is an American-built ship. She is pierced for twenty-four guns, and mounts twenty-four guns, and is rated twenty-four guns. The Cyane, the other vessel in question, was captured from the English. She mounts thirty-two guns, mounted thirty-two, if not thirty-four, when taken, was put down at that time, in Steele's list, at *twenty* guns, and is now rated by us at twenty-four guns. I mention these circumstances, in order that they may be proved to be wrong if I am mistaken. Your remarks on the subject of the rating of vessels, I believe to be correct. It is worthy of observation, that the reviewer, in his enumeration of our total force, (page 273,) omits these two twenty-fours, though he introduces them in the close of the same paragraph.

" I am well content that the reviewer should believe the Caledonia more than a match for the Pennsylvania; but, I must say, I think it would have been more prudent not to hazard any prophetic opinions on the subject. Ships of one hundred and thirty guns seldom lower their flags to opinions and it would have been well to have had the result of an experiment, before so much theoretical confidence was manifested. I have not the smallest doubt that there are many brave men in the British navy, (in command of the Caledonia) who would seek a conflict with the Pennsylvania, in the event of so great a calamity as a war; but I am quite sure that any man among them who is likely to be successful in so serious a struggle, would be conscious of all its hazards. I shall say nothing on the subject of the reasoning of the reviewer in relation to the size of ships and the weight of metal. I am old enough to remember very similar doctrines much in fashion in relation to frigates, but as I am very certain that each nation will pursue its own policy in the construction and armament of its vessels, there is no use in making it a matter of argument. If there be any thing connected with my profession for which I have an especial aversion, it is whipping a ship on paper.

" The reviewer is just as confident, that in all the naval battles of the late war, the Americans had a decided superiority of force, as he is now, that even against this superiority of force, the Caledonia could capture the Pennsylvania. I am content that he should think so, though I am by no means disposed to give implicit credit to the erudite authority he quotes (Mr. James) in support of this opinion.

" There is a remarkable declaration of the reviewer (page 278) to which I desire to call your attention. He says that the United States, *being an agricultural and commercial nation,* ' it is their obvious policy to avoid war as much as possible, consistent with national honour.' If I were not a sailor and a Yankee, and he a reviewer and an Englishman, I should venture to say, that I presume he means ' *consistently* with national honour.' I give you this little grammatical flourish much in the same humour that the reviewer gives us his professional knowledge, and, perhaps, quite as ignorantly. But, retreating to my deck, I would ask if the reviewer means to imply that England goes to war for other objects?

" The next fact that I shall allude to, is the complement of the North Carolina. The reviewer states, that it is ' considerably more than 1,100 persons.' I am compelled to say he has been grossly deceived. If he will look at page 236 letter B [1] of the documents of the Secretary of the Navy for the present year, he will see the detail of the complement of the Delaware, (a sister ship of the Carolina) including every person on board, from the commodore to the boys, exclusively of the marines. The total is 720 souls. At page 257, No. I. [1] he will find the estimate for her marine, viz. 117, including the staff of a squadron. The two sums together make 837 souls, which, I can assure the reviewer, is the full war complement of the ship, with a flag officer, band marine staff, &c. &c. though liable as in all ships, to be di minished by service, or temporarily increased by a few super numeraries, particularly by an officer or two, now and then

" You have sufficiently exposed, in your own note, the mis take of the reviewer on the subject of the cost of maintaining our navy.

" Perhaps the most singular assertion in the whole article is the following: ' *The American timber is so bad,* that three of the line-of-battle ships are already in a state of decay.' *All good* American ships are built of *live oak* and *locust;* I should be glad to know where better timber is to be found. It is true, that during the war, we were compelled to construct several vessels in a hurry, and that a little other timber was admitted, rather than not get the ships in time, and that such timber has been found decayed. I write with a detailed report of the Commissioners of the Navy for the year 1827, before me. It mentions the particular condition of every vessel in the service. I extract the following: ' Ohio, seventy-four: outside plank much decayed, from the rail to the ways, and some spots of decay inside, in the plank across the stern, in the ceiling, and gun-deck clamps.' ' Washington, seventy-four: will require considerable repairs in her planking, top-timbers, beams and floor-timbers: the copper should be examined before she goes to sea.' ' Franklin, seventy-four: will require planking from near water's edge to the rail, and an examination of her copper.' As these three ships are in much the worst condition of any of the twelve, I presume they are the vessels alluded to. The foregoing is the official statement of those who are best informed in the matter. The Washington has been built fourteen years, the Independence thirteen, and the Ohio ten. If the reviewer thinks that British ships do not often want planking above water, I presume he is mistaken. But the Washington is, confessedly, defective in many of her timbers. The Washington was built in the war, and, I believe, of mixed timber. I have also heard, though I will not vouch for its truth, that she was, in part, built of captured timber, which had been intended for the British navy. A sufficient evidence of the quality of our timber is, however, contained in the fact, that we have never been obliged to break up a ship that was built expressly for a cruizer, larger than a sloop of war, since the regular establishment of our navy in 1797. The Java was thought to be the worst ship, of her size, we ever had; but, on examination, it was found that she would very well bear repairs. But what interest has the reviewer in proving we have rotten ships? did he ever know an American officer apologize for a defeat on account of a rotten ship?

" The next topic worthy of notice, is the dry docks. The reviewer proves, to his own satisfaction, that a dry dock in England costs 15,000*l.* less than one in America. In other words, ten of these dry docks, which would be sufficient for the largest navy in the world, would cost, in America, an excess of 150,000*l.* I do not see that the point is worthy of a discussion, since they are not perishable things.

"I had forgotten to comment on the opinion of the reviewer, that England possesses 'coal and iron in greater quantities than any other country of the world.' The assumption is a little gratuitous, and I think an intelligent examination of the facts would convince him of his error.

"There is a strange perversion of the frank and manly exposition of certain acknowledged defects in our dock-yards and naval system, which it is the duty of the secretary of the navy to make to Congress, and which, I presume, he will continue to make annually until they are amended. One is tempted to believe such ministerial candour is unusual, or the reviewer could not mistake its motive. A wise man would be induced to believe it a proof of a desire for reformation; but the reviewer appears to think it infers a confession of imbecility. Perhaps, however, something should be allowed for the course of policy pursued by the two nations in executive matters.

"In page 284, there is another gauntlet thrown (by the reviewer) from the Barham of *fifty guns*, to any American *sixty gun frigate*. 'She (the Barham) being in all respects a much finer ship.' I shall not dispute the prowess nor the perfection of the Barham, though I must still doubt the prudence of saying so much about them. There is a renowned dramatic hero who destroyed a whole army very much in the same way. I cheerfully acquit every British naval *officer* of the indiscretion.

"I shall venture again to step beyond my proper limits. What does the reviewer mean by stating that 'Diplomatic Treaties, &c. cost the United States 5,140,099 dollars?' (See Review, page 285.) He foots up the 'civil department of the state' at 7,155,307 dollars. This is a good deal worse than the Barham! The official statements of the whole expenditure of the United States' government for the year 1826, are now before me. The whole amount of the 'civil, *miscellaneous*, and diplomatic' expenses for that year, are 2,600,177 dollars 79 cents. (See Document, page 35, [4] Treasurer's Report, 1826.) I follow your example, and extract items. 'Light-house establishment, 188,849;' 'Marine-hospital establishment, 54,336;' 'Public buildings in Washington, 91,271;' '*Stock in the Chesapeake and Delaware Canal Company*, 107,500;' '*Stock in the Dismal Swamp Company*, 150,000;' '*Stock in the Louisville and Portland Canal Company*, 30,000;' 'Payment of claims for buildings destroyed, per act of March, 1825, 208,311;' '*Diplomatic department*, 152,476 40 cents;' '*Mission to the Congress of Panama*, 9000;' '*Contingent expenses of foreign intercourse*, 18,627

&c. &c. *All* the expenses that can *by possibility* be construed to belong to ' Diplomatic Treaties,' &c. are footed up separately, and, together, they make the sum of 232,719 8 cents!! The *miscellaneous* charges are also footed separately, and make 1,110,713 23 cents; and the *civil* make 1,256,745 48 cents. I do not wonder that a writer who sees figures through such a medium should say immediately afterwards, ' it is the obvious policy of the governing powers of a country like that we have been describing to cultivate peace and amity with all the world.' I am quite of his mind, though seemingly for very different reasons. It is lucky for this writer that he has not fallen into the hands of one of our regular quill-drivers, or he would be beaten out and out, notwithstanding his singular felicity in deciding combats on paper.

" Let us look at one more of his weak points. In page 279 he says we expended (he refers to the year 1826) 4,222,952 dollars to *support* our navy. He is silent as to the expense of *building* ships, though we had several frigates and ships of the line on the stocks that year, and had just commenced building ten sloops of war, three of which were actually launched before the month of June. Of the army he says nothing for that year, though he tells us, that in 1824 it cost 5,270,254 dollars. Why he selected the year 1824, it is impossible for me to say, when the reports of 1826 were just as clear, and probably they were before him. But we will take his own premises. *His* American ' civil department of state' cost 7,155,307 dollars; *his support* of the American navy cost 4,222,952 dollars; and *his* army for the year 1824 cost 5,270,254 dollars. (It actually happened, including fortifications, Indian department, road surveys, &c. &c. that the expenditure belonging to the war department, for 1826, was upwards of 6,000,000.) Now all these sums make 16,648,513 dollars, to say nothing of the expenses of building ships and forts. On the same page the reviewer puts the net revenue of the country at 20,385,430 dollars, which leaves an excess of 3,636,817 dollars for the other expenses of the government. Immediately after, he says, ' the public debt on the 1st of October, 1825, was 80,985,537.' This, at five per cent. about a fair average, would require 4,049,276 dollars to pay the interest. But he admits that the debt had been diminished nearly 10,000,000 of dollars in the years 1824 and '25. The Secretary of the Treasury says, page 6 of his last report, that in the years 1825 and 1826, 21,297,210 dollars were paid on the *principal* of the public debt. I should like to know where the money came from, since, by the reviewer's showing, the whole expense of the government exceeded the whole receipt 1,412,359 dollars. If he believes his own premises, he will at least allow us the credit of having a very clever financier somewhere about the Treasury. But I must stop, or he will be apt to think that I belong to that class of Americans whom he accuses of indulging in a ' cold, *calculating* tone of argumentation.'

" If, as he says, the government of the United States is ' ostentatious,' it must be the ostentation of this cold tone of argumentation, for every body knows they get very little money to figure with. I shall not animadvert on the close of his sentence. If any American minister at the English court has failed in ' courtesy and civility,' let it be proclaimed in a manly manner to the world, or spare us inuendos. You cannot expect that I should go any further with this writer. I know nothing of boundary lines : all I hope is, that they may be peaceably settled.

" As to the German, or pretended German author, reviewed, I have nothing to say to him. He either knows a vast deal more of my country than I know myself, or he knows nothing at all about it. Mr. de Roos being a professional man, and coming out under his own name, is entitled to more respect.

" I think it unfortunate that this gentleman did not give himself sufficient time to make his observations.

" Mr. de Roos is hasty in his inferences. He thinks a dock-yard was placed at Philadelphia because the people were ' unwilling to be behind-hand with her neighbours in the possession of such an advantage.' It appears to me a sufficient reason, that Philadelphia was one of the largest, and, what has hitherto been an object with us, one of the safest sea-ports in the country. Baltimore is as large a town now as Philadelphia was when the yard was established, and yet Baltimore has no dock-yard, while Portsmouth, Gosport, and Mobile (all three quite small places) have dock-yards.

" At Washington, Mr. de Roos entered the navy-yard. He saw the house of the commissioner, (captain of the yard ;) but ' could observe no other residence belonging to officers.' I take this acknowledgment to be another proof of his haste, as the master-commandant has a very neat and commodious dwelling within a few rods of the other house, and nearly in its front. I think, too, he must have passed the extensive quarters of the officers of the marine corps, which are very near the gate, and before which there are always sentinels. Mr. de Roos is mistaken in calling the inclined plane Commodore Porter's : it was built under the inspection of Commodore Rodgers. He is also unfortunate in his opinion of the fate of the Potomac (on that plane,) for she was launched without difficulty, shortly after he saw her. (See page 17.) ' The shed, or rather houses, under which they build their ships, are not of an approved construction.' By whom?—by Mr. de Roos? Mr. de Roos says, ' It has been the fashion of travellers to accuse the Americans of a habitual violation of veracity in conversation;' but then he thinks this accusation is without foundation. I am happy that he found reason to think so.

" In New York, Mr. de Roos describes a peculiarity in the construction of the *Boston* sloop of war, on board of which vessel he unquestionably believed he had paid a visit. I can assure him that the Boston sailed for the coast of Brazil some months before he visited New-York, and she had not returned as late as March, 1828. Mr. de Roos says that ' only one vessel (a sixty gun frigate) was building' at New-York. He is again mistaken: there were two frigates (the Sabine and the Savannah) on the stocks there the whole of the year 1826. The Lexington and Vincennes sloops were launched in March and May of the same year.

" Mr. de Roos next describes the Ohio, 74, which he terms a splendid ship. I am glad to hear that a professional gentleman has reason to be pleased with any of our vessels; but I think he labours under some error when he adds, ' I afterwards learned that this vessel (the Ohio) was an instance of the *cunning*, I will not call it wisdom, which frequently actuates the policy of the Americans.' The substance of his charge is, that we fit out fine ships, and send them abroad to create a false idea of our power. Not being in the secret of the commissioners of the navy, who select all the vessels used, I shall not venture an opinion on the matter; but it is clear the Ohio has never been used in this manner, since, so far from ever having been at sea at all, she has never even been entirely finished. It is also some presumption that he has been led into an error, that the Franklin and Washington, the former of which looked ' quite small, after seeing the Ohio,' have both been much in actual service.

" Mr. de Roos is wrong when he says we pay *bounties* for seamen. I presume his error arises from the *advance* which is always paid to a sailor in America, whether it be for a vessel of war, or for a merchant-ship. I do not well see how he can be right in supposing that the recruiting officer made his report while he (Mr. de Roos) was in the yard, since that officer makes his report only to the department at Washington. How does Mr. de Roos reconcile ' the raw recruits from the inland States,' page 66, with ' the war complement of their choicest seamen,' page 63?

" If Mr. de Roos is of the same mind as Mr. Halliburton, (whom he quotes,) in believing that all circumstances go to show the difficulties of our having a navy, I hope he will be disposed to give us the more credit, should the result differ from his expectations.

" Mr. de Roos is entirely mistaken in what he says about Boston. Nearly, if not quite half of the whole naval force that has sailed from the United States since 1812, has sailed from that port. He is also wrong in calling the Natchez a 74, when she is a sloop of war. As these are most of the naval facts touched upon by Mr. de Roos in his brief account, I shall now turn my attention to your own statement.

" I have already noted the error in the detailed account of our force, and which you state to be an omission of the press. Your estimate of the number of men necessary to man our present ships is sufficiently correct, though you have not certainly allowed officers enough. The ships of the line alone would require near 800 officers, including all those who are commissioned, or have warrants. The frigates would need as many more, and the sloops and smaller vessels quite half as many more. Two thousand officers would be employed, at least, if all our ships were manned. This is a little more than twice our present number; but it is intended to increase the lists, I believe. At all events, we could at any moment create the necessary number by promoting qualified midshipmen.

" I presume, when you say that the United States must be admitted to possess 30,000 seamen, you mean what are technically called *able* seamen. The estimate is, I think. sufficiently low.

" I shall close this note by adverting to a part of the review that had escaped me in running my eye rapidly over its contents. I am sorry to see the reviewer treating the subject of impressment in so cavalier a manner. Of course, I allude to the impressment of American seamen into the British service. This is a grave question, and plain dealing in time of peace will be very likely to prevent trouble here after. Though the reviewer takes it as part of his premises, there is no more unsafe calculation than to believe ' the past will speak for the future' in relation to America. We do not dispute the right of England to make her own municipal laws; but we do dispute her right to exercise them in any way that shall make it unsafe for an American to navigate the ocean. I admire the coolness with which the reviewer says, 'If they (the Americans) have any plan to offer, by which American seamen may be *protected against serving in our fleets*, and British seamen from *entering* theirs, Great Britain will undoubtedly be ready to *discuss* it.' We *have a plan* for the *protection of our seamen*. The Pennsylvania, and her five noble sisters, whose frames are now providing, the Alabama, the Delaware, the Ohio, the New-York, the Vermont, the North Carolina, &c. &c. &c., furnish a hint of its outline.

" I intend to part in good humour with my unknown friend, the reviewer; and, in order to let him see it, I shall give him a piece of perfectly disinterested advice. If England wishes to *discuss* any question connected with a right to impress men out of American ships, the sooner she does it the better; for, in a very few more years, it will not do even to *talk about.*"

THE END.

NC